WATER DEFICITS
AND PLANT GROWTH

VOLUME I
Development, Control, and Measurement

CONTRIBUTORS TO THIS VOLUME

H. D. Barrs   T. T. Kozlowski

I. R. Cowan   F. L. Milthorpe

A. S. Crafts   Johnson Parker

W. R. Gardner   C. B. Tanner

S. A. Taylor

WATER DEFICITS
AND PLANT GROWTH

EDITED BY

T. T. KOZLOWSKI

DEPARTMENT OF FORESTRY
UNIVERSITY OF WISCONSIN
MADISON, WISCONSIN

VOLUME I

Development, Control, and Measurement

1968

ACADEMIC PRESS New York and London

ACADEMIC PRESS INC.
111 Fifth Avenue, New York, New York 10003

United Kingdom Edition published by
ACADEMIC PRESS INC. (LONDON) LTD.
Berkeley Square House, London W.1

LIBRARY OF CONGRESS CATALOG CARD NUMBER: 68-14658

255266

PRINTED IN THE UNITED STATES OF AMERICA

LIST OF CONTRIBUTORS

Numbers in parentheses indicate the pages on which the authors' contributions begin.

H. D. BARRS (235), C.S.I.R.O. Division of Irrigation Research, Griffith, N.S.W., Australia

I. R. COWAN* (137), University of Nottingham School of Agriculture, Sutton Bonington, Loughborough, England

A. S. CRAFTS (23), Department of Botany, University of California, Davis, California

W. R. GARDNER (107), Department of Soils, University of Wisconsin, Madison, Wisconsin

T. T. KOZLOWSKI (1), Department of Forestry, University of Wisconsin, Madison, Wisconsin

F. L. MILTHORPE** (137), University of Nottingham School of Agriculture, Sutton Bonington, Loughborough, England

JOHNSON PARKER (195), Northeastern Forest Experiment Station, U.S. Forest Service, U.S.D.A., Hamden, Connecticut

C. B. TANNER (73), Department of Soils, University of Wisconsin, Madison, Wisconsin

S. A. TAYLOR† (49), Department of Soils and Meteorology, Utah State University, Logan, Utah

* Present address: Research School of Biological Sciences, The Australian National University, Canberra City, A.C.T., Australia.
** Present address: School of Biological Sciences, Maquarie University, Eastwood, N.S.W., Australia.
† Deceased.

PREFACE

The rapidly proliferating interest in water resources and accelerated research activity on effects of drought on plants indicated the need for this two-volume treatise. Its purpose is to present a comprehensive work on the physical basis of development and control of internal water deficits in plants, the valid measurement of such deficits, and the characterization of various physiological and growth responses of both herbaceous and woody plants to water deficits. The primary concern throughout is with water-stressed plants rather than general water relations of plants which are not undergoing water stress. The treatise is purposely interdisciplinary and should therefore be particularly useful as a text or reference for investigators and students in such fields as plant physiology, soil science, physics, meteorology, plant pathology, horticulture, forestry, agronomy, and hydrology.

An effort was made to standardize terminology throughout the treatise. Because of the large number of different terms used, however, in a few chapters the same symbol is used for different quantities. To avoid difficulties with terminology each author has defined the terms used in his chapter. Special emphasis was given to selection of reference material in an effort to make the volume authoritative, well documented, and up-to-date.

In planning this treatise invitations to prepare chapters were extended to a distinguished group of scientists in universities and government laboratories in the United States and abroad. I wish to express my sincere gratitude to each of these eminent contributors for his scholarly contribution and patient cooperation in revising chapters.

The counsel of Dr. J. E. Kuntz and Dr. R. D. Durbin of the University of Wisconsin in reviewing one of the contributions is acknowledged with appreciation.

T. T. Kozlowski

Madison, Wisconsin
March, 1968

CONTENTS

CONTENTS OF VOLUME II

PLANT WATER CONSUMPTION AND RESPONSE

WATER DEFICITS
AND PLANT GROWTH

VOLUME I
Development, Control, and Measurement

CHAPTER 1

INTRODUCTION

T. T. Kozlowski

DEPARTMENT OF FORESTRY, UNIVERSITY OF WISCONSIN, MADISON, WISCONSIN

I. IMPORTANCE OF WATER TO PLANTS

The worldwide interest in water relations of plants is accentuated by increasing sensitivity to the seriousness of dwindling water supplies in many regions. A need to increase crop production exists in the face of mounting food shortages, and water conservation is an important factor in overcoming food deficiences.

Wherever plants grow, their development is limited to some degree by either too little or too much water, but mostly the former. The importance of water to plants is dramatized by the fact that many deserts and grasslands could support luxuriant plant growth if only an adequate supply of water were available. Deserts flourish, at least for a time, when water is supplied.

It cannot be emphasized too strongly that, although plants grow best in regions of high and recurrent rainfall, all land plants periodically undergo internal water stress even if soil is maintained near field capacity. Furthermore, in most regions soil moisture supplies are at optimal levels only rarely during the growing season. Hence, tremendous losses in plant growth occur annually because of recurrent and periodic or sustained internal water deficits in plants. The amounts of such losses are staggering and usually are not realized because data for many areas are not available to indicate how much more growth would occur if plants had favorable water supplies throughout the growing season. By altering the chemical and physical composition of tissues,

1

water deficits also modify various aspects of plant quality such as the taste of fruits and the density of wood. Much evidence has accumulated showing that the metabolism and growth of plants in drying soil are influenced by even mild water deficits in plant tissues and that such deficits usually occur long before drying soil approaches the permanent wilting percentage (Kozlowski, 1958, 1964). Growth limitations because of internal water deficits in plants frequently are overlooked in situations in which there are other deleterious agents such as plant competition, disease, or insect pests. Stunting and killing of desirable plants by "weed competition" commonly involve competition for water leading to a desiccation effect. Root diseases and insect injury to roots often interfere with absorption of water and thereby cause desiccation of shoots. In some vascular wilt diseases, the desiccation of tops following vascular plugging often plays a major role in foliage wilt and the ultimate death of infected plants (Kozlowski *et al.*, 1962). Water deficits also play an important role in predisposing host plants to attacks by certain fungus pathogens and insects.

Leaf desiccation causes considerable winter injury to gymnosperms (Figs.

FIG. 1. "Needle droop" resulting from desiccation of current season's shoots on the top portion of a *Pinus resinosa* tree. From Patton and Riker (1954).

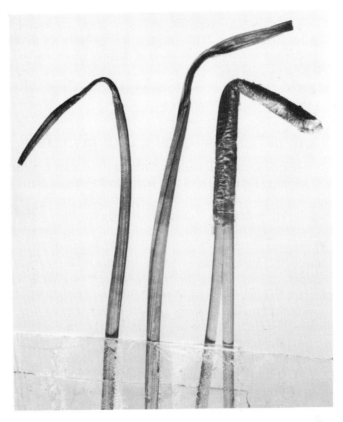

Fig. 2. Typically bent *Pinus resinosa* needles affected by "needle droop." From Patton and Riker (1954).

1 and 2). During some warm winter or spring days transpiration is appreciable, but water cannot be absorbed rapidly by evergreens from cold or frozen soil and leaves consequently dry out (Kozlowski, 1958, 1964; Kramer and Kozlowski, 1960). Such injury, which has been widely reported, has been variously referred to as "red belt," "parch blight" (Boyce, 1961), and "needle droop" (Patton and Riker, 1954). Curry and Church (1952) described desiccation injury in New York State and found that entire mountainsides were covered with discolored evergreen trees.

Physiological changes in trees that reflect decreasing vigor often are a prerequisite to attack by certain insects. Copious exudation of oleoresins in gymnosperms and the flow of sap or gum in angiosperms are correlated with resistance to bark beetle attacks (Vité and Wood, 1960). Vité (1961) showed that the success of bark beetle attack was closely correlated with low oleoresin exudation pressure. Whereas initial attack occurred at random, only beetles in trees with low oleoresin exudation pressures made successful invasions that led to mass attacks later. Differences in susceptibility as a result of site and stand conditions were related to rates of flow of oleoresin, and these, in turn, were related to stem hydration. Oleoresin exudation pressures decreased as internal water deficits in trees increased, indicating that drought often predisposed trees to attack by bark beetles.

II. DEVELOPMENT OF WATER DEFICITS

Internal water deficits in plants are controlled by relative rates of water uptake by absorption through roots and water loss by transpiration. During the day transpiration exceeds absorption. The resulting internal water deficits in plants usually are reduced or even eliminated during the night, when both absorption and transpiration are low, but the rate of the former process is greater.

As Kramer (1962) stated, internal water deficits can be the result of excessive transpiration or slow absorption from dry, cold, or poorly aerated soil or more commonly a combination of both. Even established plants on well-watered soils routinely undergo water stresses during the day because transpiration exceeds absorption. These two processes, which are partly controlled by different sets of factors, usually are out of phase. Transpiration, e.g., is largely controlled by the aerial environment (solar radiation, temperature, humidity, wind, etc.) as well as by leaf structure and stomatal opening. Absorption is controlled by the rate of transpiration, but it is also regulated by the size and distribution of the root system and several soil factors (temperature, soil moisture tension, concentration of the soil solution, aeration, etc.). Recurrent temporary wilting of leaves in the afternoon because of excessive transpiration is not serious in well-watered soils because leaves usually recover turgidity at night. However, wilting becomes serious when soils begin to dry out because leaves are increasingly less likely to recover turgidity at night and permanent wilting often results.

Transplants often undergo massive physiological shocks because root injuries invariably result in excess transpiration over absorption of water. Hence, desiccation of aerial parts commonly occurs. Even when soil moisture of transplanted trees was maintained close to field capacity, transpirational losses exceeded absorption rates, illustrating the deleterious effects of disrupting the soil–plant–air continuum during transplanting (Kozlowski, 1967; 1968b). Some idea of the effect of transplanting on internal water relations of plants may be gained from the work in Japan by Watanabe (1958a,b,c) with 1-year-old *Cinnamomum camphora* seedlings. Many transplants wilted and the water content of their leaves dropped to 30% of that of plants which survived transplanting.

Even in well-watered soils, regular diurnal development of internal water stresses in plants is shown by afternoon decreases in moisture content, relative turgidity, and water potential of plant tissues as well as by shrinkage of various plant parts (Fig. 3). Wilson *et al.* (1953) followed diurnal fluctuations in the moisture contents of various parts of *Helianthus* and *Amaranthus* plants. The moisture contents of leaves, stems, and roots reached a minimum during the afternoon and attained a maximum during the night. In gladiolus the moisture content of leaves decreased during the day and remained at low levels until sunset. Thereafter the stomata closed, transpiration ceased, and leaf water content rose rapidly to a maximum at about 8 PM (Halevy, 1960). Weatherley (1950) observed that relative turgidity (RT) of cotton leaves fell to a minimum value in the late afternoon, after which it rose steeply. Even when soil moisture was relatively abundant, potato leaves underwent marked diurnal changes in relative turgidity. As the evaporating power of the air increased in the morning the RT of leaves decreased at a constantly diminishing rate. Finally, in the late afternoon and early evening the RT values increased at a lower rate than they had decreased in the morning (Werner, 1954).

Both diurnal and seasonal shrinkage and expansion of plants because of hydration changes have been reported for many different species of plants (Anderson and Kerr, 1943; Wilson, 1948; Wilson *et al.*, 1953; Kozlowski, 1958, 1963, 1964, 1965; Kozlowski and Winget, 1964). Most data show marked shrinkages in diameters of plant stems in the afternoon and expansions at night. Wilson (1948) also showed a marked shrinkage in the length of tomato stems below the first node during the day and an equal elongation during the night. However, growth of the stem above the first node was at approximately the same rate during both day and night. Meidner (1952) recorded maximum diurnal leaf shrinkage during the day of 8–13 % of total thickness in *Zizyphus mucronata*, *Heteromorpha involucrata*, *Gymnospora buxifolia*, and *Xymalos monospora*. Changes in leaf thickness were primarily the result of changes in the volumes of water-storage tissues. Changes in leaf water content and leaf thickness were highly correlated.

There is also considerable evidence of shrinkage of reproductive tissues of plants during the day and expansion at night because of hydration changes (Kozlowski, 1961, 1962, 1964, 1965). High transpirational losses from leaves in the afternoon apparently set up free energy gradients which result in the extraction of water from fruits. At night the fruits refill with water. The amount of daily fruit shrinkage often varies with the stage of fruit development, soil moisture availability, weather, and degree of internal water stress in the plant (Kozlowski, 1968a).

The response of young, enlarging cotton bolls to internal water stress was different from that of full-sized bolls. As long as bolls increased in size and

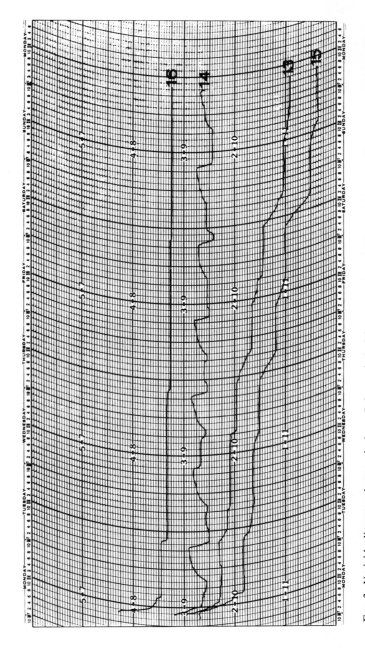

FIG. 3. Variable diameter changes during a 7-day period of four transplanted *Pinus resinosa* seedlings. From Kozlowski (1967). Copyright by the University of Chicago.

primary wall formation occurred in fiber cells, an increase in boll diameter continued during the day and night (Anderson and Kerr, 1943). Enlargement during the day exceeded that during the night, suggesting that high midday temperatures had a more significant effect on growth than the more favorable water relations during the night. As soon as the bolls reached full size and secondary walls began to form in the fibers, diurnal variations in boll diameter occurred, with shrinkage apparent during the day followed by expansion during the night. During a period of drought the amount of shrinkage increased by day while recovery at night was slow. When permanent wilting occurred during severe droughts there was practically no recovery of the bolls at night. When plants were fully turgid a short period of sunlight during the day induced some shrinkage in mature cotton bolls. In contrast, severe wilting of plants was required to induce boll shrinkage under conditions of low soil moisture availability. Anderson and Kerr (1943) studied cotton plants that differed by 2 weeks in age and were growing in adjacent rows. The older plants had few enlarging bolls, whereas the young plants had many. Leaves of the young plants wilted earlier during the day than those on older plants. This difference apparently occurred because bolls of the older plants served as reservoirs from which the leaves extracted water. In contrast, the enlarging bolls of the young plants continued to remove water from vegetative tissues and promoted early wilting. Kozlowski (1968a) noted that daily shrinkage of cherry fruits in a midstage of development greatly exceeded that at an early stage of growth (Fig. 4).

III. STATUS OF SOME IMPORTANT PROBLEMS

Fundamental knowledge about internal water deficits in plants has accumulated slowly. One reason for this is that it is difficult to invade plants without altering the hydrostatic plant system. Water is rapidly redistributed in plants as free-energy changes occur in various parts of the system because of injury, evaporative losses, and conversion of insoluble to soluble compounds and their utilization (Kozlowski, 1964). As Weatherley (1964) summarized, definitive findings on internal water relations of plants have been few, not because plant physiologists failed to ask appropriate questions but because adequate techniques were not available to find unequivocal answers. Nevertheless, in modern times there has been an impressive upsurge in fundamental work on plant–soil–water relations as attested by the accelerated production of research papers, reviews, and books, including those of Kramer (1949), Crafts et al. (1949), Marshall (1959), Steward (1959), Kramer and Kozlowski (1960), Sutcliffe (1962), Kozlowski (1962, 1964), Rutter and Whitehead (1963), Slavik (1965b), Salter and Goode (1967), and Slatyer (1967). Several monographs of the Agronomy Society of America, UNESCO volumes

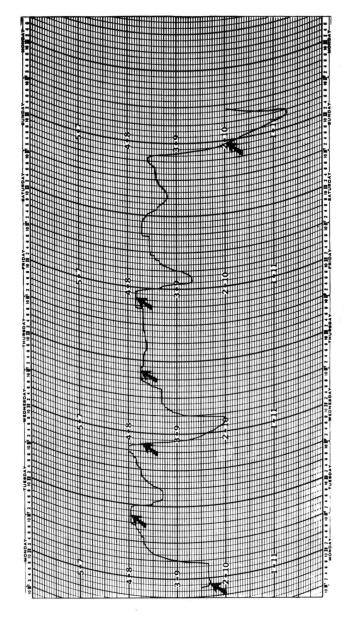

Fɪɢ. 4. Diameter changes during 1 week of Montmorency cherry fruit which showed marked diurnal expansion and contraction during the midphase of fruit growth. The arrows indicate the time of irrigation. From Kozlowski (1968a).

on arid zone research, and the first three volumes of the "Encyclopedia of Plant Physiology" also deal with fundamental aspects of water deficits in controlling plant growth. The present section briefly introduces a few of the major plant problems. These will be expanded and others discussed in detail in various chapters of this treatise.

A. CHARACTERIZATION AND MEASUREMENT OF WATER DEFICITS

In appraising the hydrodynamic system of plants, various interrelationships of a complicated soil–plant–air continuum are involved. Water transport within plants occurs by viscous flow in the liquid phase and molecular diffusion in the gaseous phase. In moist soils liquid phase transfer is the dominant process, but as soil dries vapor transfer becomes increasingly important. In very dry soils surface migration may be important (Philip, 1966). The complicated interactions of flow in the various phases require a terminology which is understandable and useful to soil scientists, plant physiologists, and meteorologists. Although certain parts of the soil–plant–air continuum can be isolated and analyzed for some processes, an understanding of mechanisms of creation of water deficits in plants requires dealing with water transport through all parts of the soil–plant–air continuum rather than with isolated parts of it. Unfortunately, the various disciplines involved and their terminologies developed independently. Among terms widely used to express water availability in soil were field capacity (FC), permanent wilting percentage (PWP), moisture tension, diffusion pressure deficit (DPD), moisture equivalent, water supplying power, pF, total soil moisture stress (TSMS), capillary capacity, and water potential. Water deficits in plant tissues have been characterized over the years in terms of moisture content, DPD (synonyms for DPD include suction force, suction tension, water absorbing power, and net osmotic pressure), and water potential (ψ) (Kozlowski, 1964). In modern times there has been much effort to develop a standard and meaningful terminology for soil–plant–air–water relations. Many problems are involved in characterizing water balance of plant tissues, and these are further discussed in Chapters 3 and 8. An appreciation of a few of the difficulties may be gained from considering one commonly used measure of water deficit: moisture content of tissues. It has been customary to express moisture content of plant tissues as a percentage of the oven dry weight of the tissue. Since dry weight changes often are not proportional to changes in the actual amount of water in tissues, variations in moisture content do not necessarily reflect changes in protoplasmic hydration. Photosynthesis, respiration, and translocation can produce significant and rapid changes in tissue dry weight (Kramer and Kozlowski, 1960; Kozlowski, 1964). Over long periods, progressive cell wall thickening usually causes significant dry-weight increase. Hence, changes in the percentage of water content of different tissues under various conditions may reflect changes in actual water alone, in dry weight alone, or in both of these. When changes occur in the actual amount of water in tissues as well as in the dry weight, the changes in the latter often are considerably greater.

Kozlowski and Clausen (1965) showed that seasonal increases in the percentage of moisture of buds of several species of angiosperms and gymnosperms were traceable to rapid translocation of moisture into the buds. During the same period the buds also increased in dry weight, but at a lower rate than that at which water moved into them. In contrast to the pattern in buds, the percentage of moisture in angiosperm leaves decreased rapidly in the early part of the growing season and slowly after midsummer. These decreases were traceable to the relatively greater increase in dry weight rather than to a decrease in actual water content. Results of a greenhouse experiment (Table I)

TABLE I

VARIATION WITH TIME IN LEAF MOISTURE CONTENT, WEIGHT OF WATER, AND DRY WEIGHT PER LEAF OF GREENHOUSE-GROWN SEEDLINGS OF *Quercus ellipsoidalis*[a]

Days	Moisture content (% oven-dry wt)	Water (gm)	Dry wt (gm)
0	262 ± 7.21[b]	0.115 ± 0.005	0.044 ± 0.003
2	218 ± 14.19	0.096 ± 0.001	0.046 ± 0.006
4	240 ± 8.78	0.110 ± 0.009	0.046 ± 0.004
6	194 ± 8.68	0.116 ± 0.006	0.058 ± 0.004
10	203 ± 8.60	0.117 ± 0.008	0.059 ± 0.005
14	168 ± 2.63	0.106 ± 0.006	0.068 ± 0.004
18	163 ± 2.84	0.113 ± 0.008	0.063 ± 0.004
22	163 ± 4.42	0.100 ± 0.009	0.061 ± 0.004
26	144 ± 4.40	0.104 ± 0.011	0.073 ± 0.009

[a] From Kozlowski and Clausen (1965).
[b] Mean and standard error, ten plants per sampling date.

showed that the moisture content of leaves (as a percentage of their dry weight) decreased with time whereas dry weight increased. In contrast, no significant differences in the actual amount of water per leaf occurred with time. Over the 26-day period of the experiment the leaf dry weight increased on the average by 66%.

The seasonal trend in moisture content of gymnosperm foliage varied with needle age (Kozlowski and Clausen, 1965). Moisture content (percentage of dry weight) of needles produced in the current year declined seasonally, whereas in 1-year-old needles the percentage of moisture increased first and then showed little change. These differences in moisture patterns within different-aged needles were caused largely by changes in dry weight resulting from carbohydrate translocation from the old needles into the new rapidly growing needles.

Several investigators have identified various reasons for changes in the moisture contents of reproductive tissues of plants. For example, whereas the moisture content of the placenta and pericarp of tomato fruits more than 15 days old never dropped below 94%, the seeds dehydrated to approximately 50% as they developed and matured. Although there was an accumulation of dry matter during development, the main factor causing the decrease in percentage of moisture was actual loss of water from the seeds. Mechanisms within the seed as well as within the whole fruit participated in the dehydration system (McIlraith et al., 1963).

Seasonal changes in moisture contents of Picea glauca and Larix laricina cones were studied by Clausen and Kozlowski (1965b). An initial increase in the percentage moisture content of cones between late May and early June was the result of an increase in actual water content that exceeded the dry weight increase for the same period. Thereafter, the percentage of moisture decreased markedly even though actual moisture content remained the same or even increased. Decrease in the percentage of moisture, although actual moisture content remained high, was traceable to a greater proportional increase in dry weight. After the beginning of August, by which time the seasonal increase in cone dry weight was completed, the cones began to dehydrate. These experiments demonstrated that the percentage of moisture of different tissues fluctuates because of water translocation into or out of tissues, changes in dry weight, or both. Furthermore, one type of change may predominate in altering the percentage of moisture early in the development of certain tissues, whereas at a later stage the percentage of moisture of the same tissues may change for different reasons. Hence, there are rather obvious limitations in the use of changes in percentage of moisture, at least when used by itself, as an indication of water stress in some plant tissues.

That dry weight changes can significantly influence moisture contents of plant tissues within a matter of hours was shown by Halevy and Monselise (1963). They demonstrated that maximum water percentages of herbaceous and woody plants usually were reached at midnight and were followed by a decrease and then a second increase toward morning. The decrease in moisture content after midnight was caused primarily by increased dry-matter content rather than by reduced water content per leaf. The situation was further complicated by variations in dry weight changes of leaves of different ages. For example, in young leaves of gladiolus, depletion of both water and dry matter occurred during the night. In older leaves, however, the fluctuations were more complicated and involved transport of water and dry matter into leaves as well as out of them (Fig. 5). The decrease in moisture content of leaves after midnight observed in *Helianthus*, *Amaranthus* (Wilson *et al.*, 1953), and *Parthenocissus* (Stanescu, 1936) plants may have been the result of solute translocation.

Although it is well known that protoplasmic hydration profoundly influences physiological activity and plant growth, many investigators observed that certain plant processes were active over a fairly wide range of moisture contents of tissues. This further points up the inadequacy, in many instances, of using moisture content as a reliable measure of internal water stress. Ackley (1954) found little correlation between water deficit and water content

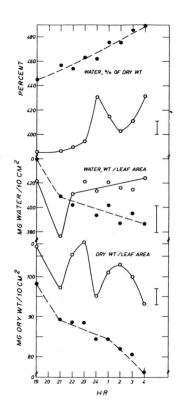

FIG. 5. Water content as a percentage of dry weight, water, and dry weight on a leaf area basis of second (solid circle) and fifth (open circle) leaves of gladiolus at different times during the night. Vertical lines at night represent standard errors for adjacent curves. From Halevy and Monselise (1963). Copyright by the University of Chicago.

of pear leaves at various times during the growing season, and Clausen and Kozlowski (1965a) showed that water content and relative turgidity of *Pinus resinosa* needles of different ages often were not correlated.

There is much support for the conclusion of Kramer (1963) that young plant tissues have high moisture contents, but as cells mature their walls thicken and the amount of dry matter increases so that the percentage of water decreases. Therefore, a decrease in moisture content (percentage of oven dry weight) can occur, and often does, without appreciable change in actual water content. Full turgor may occur in leaves of one species at a moisture content that is found in severely wilted leaves in another species or in leaves of different ages on the same plant. For these reasons better methods of expressing internal water stress are needed.

There has been a trend toward abandonment of discussion about hydraulic terminology and toward development of a unified thermodynamic terminology for plant and soil water relations. Water potential (ψ), the difference between free energy of water in a system and of pure free water, the reference state at the same temperature, appears to be the most useful and widely accepted term in such a system. In soil the water is held by various forces and cannot do as much work as pure free water, so ψ is negative. The negative sign often is avoided by considering ψ in terms of additional work necessary to remove soil water. Weatherley (1964) suggested that water potential depression (ΔW) was also a very useful term for assessing the state of water in plant tissues.

B. Water Transport in Plants

Although much is known about the tissues in which water moves in plants, several important aspects of water transport as they impinge on internal water deficits are unsolved.

Slavik (1965a) considers the path of water from the root to the leaf surface to consist of three sections. The first leads from the root epidermis across the cortex and the endodermis and finally into the vessels of the root. The second stage leads chiefly through xylem elements. Finally, the third section leads from the vessels in leaf veins through the mesophyll cells into intercellular and epidermal cells.

The actual pattern of water transport in xylem elements through plants varies greatly among species. In herbaceous plants upward water transport occurs in xylem in vascular bundles which may be scattered throughout the stem or distributed in definite patterns (Kozlowski, 1964; Dimond, 1966). In woody plants water moves in a cylinder of the outer sapwood, but the specific pattern varies among species. In stems of ring-porous trees the upward movement is largely confined to a thin cylinder of the outer sapwood, whereas in mature diffuse-porous angiosperms and gymnosperms the path of ascent

14   **T. T. Kozlowski**

involves a much greater portion of the sapwood (Kozlowski, 1961). In gymnosperm seedlings the outer xylem ring may conduct less water than the other rings (Kozlowski *et al.* 1966).

Internal resistance to water movement may occur in various tissues of herbaceous plants, as discussed in Chapter 6 and by Jensen *et al.* (1961). There is considerable resistance to water movement within woody plants, e.g., in the heartwood or in some parts of annual xylem rings. Contributing to resistance of water transport through the heartwood of gymnosperms are sealing of pit-pairs through aspiration, occlusion with extractives, incrustations of pits with ligno-complex substances, and combinations of these (Harris, 1954; Krahmer and Coté, 1963). In the heartwood of angiosperms,

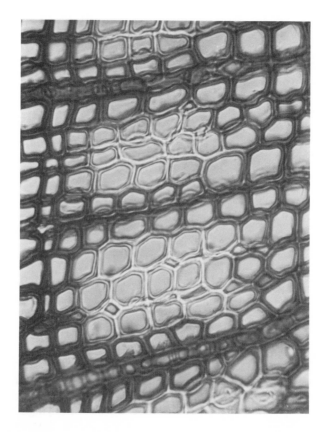

Fig. 6. Lateral transport of dye along several rays through the nonconducting latewood tracheids of a *Pinus sylvestris* seedling. The dye has moved laterally from the rays into one adjacent and parallel file of tracheids on each side of the rays. From Kozlowski *et al.* (1966).

barriers to water transport appear to be provided by tyloses in vessels, incrustations, and various extractives (Chattaway, 1949).

Within individual annual rings of gymnosperms, a preferential path of upward water movement has been identified in large-diameter elements (Fig. 6). In pines, e.g., most water moved in large-diameter, earlywood tracheids. Medium-sized tracheids generally conducted less water than the first-formed large ones. The smallest tracheids within a ring, whether elements of a false ring or the last-formed elements of a normal ring, often transported no water (Kozlowski et al., 1966). There appear to be marked differences in the distribution and structure of bordered pits of earlywood and latewood that account for the observed variations in water transport. Lundegardh (1954) also found a preferential path of water movement in parts of annual rings of several species of woody angiosperms and concluded that small xylem elements exerted a high transport resistance because of high capillary "friction." Whatever the specific nature of the resistance in various tissues of woody plants, it appears that water tends to follow a path of least resistance in its ascent.

Lateral Transport

Water ascends in stems by way of conducting elements in a path similar to the arrangement of the elements. It often is assumed that the conducting elements are essentially vertically arranged. However, experiments with injected dyes in tall trees show that water often spirals in its ascent, indicating that the plant axis is twisted and that spiral grain is more common than straight grain. Large differences in spiral grain exist among species, among trees within a species, in different annual rings within a tree, and at different stem heights. In fact, strictly vertical movement of water in trees appears to be somewhat uncommon (Kozlowski and Winget, 1963; Kozlowski et al., 1966, 1967).

Variations in the paths of water ascent in stems of different species of woody plants have received much attention partly because of their significance to insect and disease control. Many systemic chemicals move upward in tree stems along the path of water ascent in xylem tissues. Hence, the distribution of water and injected chemotherapeutants into the crown varies greatly with specific patterns of water uptake. This was demonstrated by Rudinsky and Vité (1959), who found the most complete distribution of water into tree crowns by a system of spiral ascent and the least effective distribution by vertical ascent.

Much research is needed on the extent to which the xylem rays supply water to the cambium. In gymnosperms water moves horizontally along xylem rays across zones of latewood tracheids that do not appear to conduct water upward (Kozlowski et al., 1966), but whether enough water is supplied to the cambium in this way is not clear at present. Ziegler (1959, 1964) suggested that it may not be necessary for the xylem rays to supply water to the cambium, since the phloem may supply adequate moisture. There is some evidence that in wounded plants the cambium and even xylary derivatives obtain water from the phloem. For example, Brown and Sax (1962) lifted longitudinal bark strips of *Populus trichocarpa* and *Pinus strobus* away from the bole and enclosed them with plastic to prevent desiccation. The cells exposed on the inner surface of the strips were mainly xylem mother cells capable of further cell division. These exposed cells proliferated rapidly and apparently were capable of deriving water from the phloem. The phloem, however, might not be the source of water in unwounded plants. Ziegler (1964) also stated that tracheid cells at the margin of xylem rays of certain gymnosperms are not continued in the bark, further emphasizing the lack of dependency of the cambium on xylem rays for water supply. There is little specific evidence, however, on how effectively the cambium can obtain water from either the phloem or xylem during prolonged droughts.

C. CONTROL OF INTERNAL WATER BALANCE IN PLANTS

Plants have three basic means for controlling internal water deficits: absorption, transpiration, and internal redistribution of water. Plant control of water loss primarily by stomatal regulation is discussed in detail in Chapter 6. Loss of water by cuticular transpiration is prevented in many plants by waxy coatings. Stems, fruits, petals, and leaves may all be covered by waxy materials. The cuticle, a layer of cross-linked hydroxy fatty acids, usually is bounded by a layer of wax. The amount of surface wax varies greatly among species but in some may represent up to 15% of leaf dry weight. Surface waxes of plants represent a wide range of organic compounds. Those examined in detail are complex mixtures of long-chain alkanes, alcohols, ketones, aldehydes, acetals, esters, and acids (Eglinton and Hamilton, 1967).

Maintaining low internal water stress in plants constitutes a practical problem of paramount importance. For several decades attention has been given to maintaining favorable internal water balance of tree nursery stock by suppressing transpiration with various leaf coatings. Such compounds have included oils, plastic films, wax emulsions, and metabolic inhibitors. There has been little agreement, however, on the usefulness of antitranspirants. Leaf coatings reduced transpiration effectively in some cases but not in others. Effects on survival of transplants have been beneficial in some cases but useless in others. Many leaf coatings, which control transpiration chiefly by physically blocking the stomates, have proved especially disappointing. Although they often reduced transpiration, they also inhibited photosynthesis and eventually killed outplanted trees (Goren *et al.*, 1962; Slatyer and Bierhuizen, 1964; Angus and Bielorai, 1965; Kozlowski, 1968b), e.g., plastic-film-type antitranspirants were more permeable to water vapor than to CO_2. Photosynthesis in treated plants was reduced as much or more than transpiration, except under conditions of stress, when photosynthesis was greater than in the controls (Gale and Poljakoff-Mayber, 1967).

A completely different approach to control of water loss involves the use of antitranspirants that operate as metabolic inhibitors. Work by Zelitch and co-workers (1964) with herbaceous plants showed that stomatal movement resulted from different metabolic activities in guard cells and other cells as well. A variety of metabolic inhibitors prevent stomatal opening in the light and induce closure of already open stomates. These include such compounds as α-hydroxysulfonates, respiratory inhibitors such as azide, inhibitors of reactions related to photosynthesis, chelating compounds, and some growth regulators (Zelitch, 1961, 1964; Zelitch and Waggoner, 1962a,b). Zelitch (1961) observed that hydroxysulfonates effectively inhibited the enzyme glycolic oxidase and caused rapid changes in products formed during photosynthesis. When slightly wilted plants were supplied with such an inhibitor of glycolic oxidase, transpiration decreased and leaves regained turgidity faster than leaves of control plants. The inhibitor appeared to influence the osmotic pressure of guard cells and thus controlled stomatal aperture. Zelitch and Waggoner (1962a,b) noted that phenylmercuric acetate sprayed on leaves at concentrations of 10^{-4} M closed stomates for at least 14 days. Furthermore, such induced stomatal closure reduced transpiration more than it inhibited photosynthesis.

Alkenylsuccinic acids (ASA) and certain of their derivatives were very effective agents for the control of stomatal aperture (Zelitch, 1964). Marked reduction of transpiration with lesser reduction of photosynthesis followed treatment. These long-chain, unsaturated dibasic fatty acids appeared to act as inhibitors of stomatal opening through effects on lipid layers of guard cells membranes. They appeared to penetrate guard cells more rapidly than other epidermal cells.

The alkenylsuccinic acids also have been reported to increase the permeability of cell membranes of roots to water. Kuiper (1964), e.g., noted that when decenylsuccinic acid penetrated into the lipid layer of root membranes it increased water permeability 8 times. This suggested a strong possibility that some transpiration suppressants may be more effective if applied to the roots rather than to the foliage.

The early experiments with metabolic antitranspirants appeared to be overoptimistic with respect to their practical uses in inducing drought hardiness. Kozlowski and Clausen (1967) did not find significant improvement of the internal water balance of several species of woody plants after they were sprayed with alkenyl or decenylsuccinic acid (DSA). Toxicity often followed treatment. Dye penetration tests of leaves showed that the efficiency of the cutinized layer in preventing water loss was decreased by DSA.

The increased permeability of roots following treatment with metabolic inhibitors often appears to be traceable to root injury. Kozlowski and Clausen (1967) found no strong evidence of increased root permeability of pine seedlings following root immersion in alkenylsuccinic acid at 1×10^{-2} M, except when roots were injured. Newman and Kramer (1966) noted that roots of intact bean plants were killed by 1-hour immersion in 10^{-3} M DSA.

Despite some disappointing results with metabolic antitranspirants, enough success has been achieved with some herbaceous plants to warrant expansion of work with these compounds. Even if growth should be inhibited by stomatal closure during the crucial period following outplanting, the possibility of saving transplants by maintaining favorable internal water balance is far more important than is temporary growth inhibition. Longer retention and greater specificity are needed for antitranspirants that promote stomatal closure, and greater selectivity to gases and vapors is needed for film-forming types (Gale and Hagan, 1966).

D. Nature of the Effect of Water Deficit on Plant Growth

Characterization of the mechanism of inhibition of various aspects of plant growth by water deficits constitutes a problem of major interest and importance. As will be shown in subsequent chapters, internal moisture stress in plants influences many physiological processes adversely, and this results in growth inhibition in herbaceous plants (Woodhams and Kozlowski, 1954; Kramer, 1963) and in woody plants (Kozlowski, 1964). For example, voluminous data are available showing that water stress affects water uptake, root pressure, seed germination, stomatal closure, transpiration, photosynthesis, enzymatic activity, mineral relations, nitrogen metabolism, flow of oleoresin and latex, and other processes (Kramer, 1949; Army and Kozlowski, 1951; Kozlowski, 1964). The exact manner by which internal water stress affects various aspects of growth has been a subject of vigorous debate. There is evidence that internal water stress affects growth by both direct and indirect mechanisms, with the latter operating by variously altering food, hormone, and mineral relations. The mechanism of growth inhibition as a result of water deficit often is very different between annual and perennial or herbaceous and woody plants. For example, in perennial woody plants, lag effects of water stress on growth often occur, with the plant often responding during the subsequent year. These variations in growth control of herbaceous plants and trees are discussed in detail in Chapters 4 and 5 of Vol. II.

REFERENCES

Ackley, W. B. (1954). Seasonal and diurnal changes in the water content and water deficits of Bartlett pear leaves. *Plant Physiol.* **29**, 445.

Anderson, D. B., and Kerr, T. (1943). A note on the growth behavior of cotton bolls. *Plant Physiol.* **18**, 261.

Angus, D. E., and Bielorai, H. (1965). Transpiration reduction by surface films. *Australian J. Agr. Res.* **16**, 107.

Army, T. J., and Kozlowski, T. T. (1951). Availability of soil moisture for active absorption in drying soil. *Plant Physiol.* **26**, 353.

Boyce, J. S. (1961). "Forest Pathology." McGraw-Hill, New York.

Brown, C. L., and Sax, K. (1962). The influence of pressure on the differentiation of secondary tissues. *Am. J. Botany* **49**, 683.

Chattaway, M. M. (1949). The development of tyloses and reaction of gum in heartwood formation. *Australian J. Sci. Res. Ser. B* **2**, 227.

Clausen, J. J., and Kozlowski, T. T. (1965a). Use of the relative turgidity technique for measurement of water stresses in gymnosperm leaves. *Can. J. Botany* **43**, 305.

Clausen, J. J., and Kozlowski, T. T. (1965b). Seasonal changes in moisture contents of gymnosperm cones. *Nature* **206**, 112.

Crafts, A. S., Currier, H. B., and Stocking, C. R. (1949). "Water in the Physiology of Plants." Ronald Press, New York.

Curry, J. R., and Church, T. W. (1952). Observations on winter drying of conifers in the Adirondacks. *J. Forestry* **50**, 114.

Dimond, A. E. (1966). Pressure and flow relations in vascular bundles of the tomato plant. *Plant Physiol.* **41**, 119.

Eglinton, G. and Hamilton, R. J. (1967). Leaf epicuticular waxes. *Science* **156**, 1322.

Gale, J., and Hagan, R. M. (1966). Plant antitranspirants. *Ann. Rev. Plant Physiol.* **17**, 269.

Gale, J., and Poljakoff-Mayber, A. (1967). Plastic films on plants as antitranspirants. *Science* **156**, 650.

Goren, J., Mendel, K., and Monselise, S. P. (1962). Effect of polyvinyl coating on survival of transplanted nursery stock under experimental and commercial conditions. *Proc. Am. Soc. Hort. Sci.* **81**, 231.

Halevy, A. H. (1960). Diurnal fluctuations in water balance factors of gladiolus leaves. *Bull. Res. Council Israel Sect. D* **8**, 239.

Halevy, A. H., and Monselise, S. P. (1963). Meaning of apparent midnight decrease in water content of leaves. *Botan. Gaz.* **124**, 343.

Harris, J. M. (1954). Heartwood formation in *Pinus radiata* (D. Don.) *New Phytologist* **53**, 517.

Jensen, R. D., Taylor, S. A., and Wiebe, H. H. (1961). Negative transport and resistance to water flow through plants. *Plant Physiol.* **36**, 633.

Kozlowski, T. T. (1958). Water relations and growth of trees. *J. Forestry* **56**, 498.

Kozlowski, T. T. (1961). The movement of water in trees. *Forest Sci.* **7**, 177.

Kozlowski, T. T. (ed.) (1962). "Tree Growth." Ronald Press, New York.

Kozlowski, T. T. (1963). Growth characteristics of forest trees. *J. Forestry* **61**, 655.

Kozlowski, T. T. (1964). "Water Metabolism in Plants." Harper, New York.

Kozlowski, T. T. (1965). Expansion and contraction of plants. *Advan. Frontiers Plant Sci.* **10**, 63.

Kozlowski, T. T. (1967). Diurnal variations in stem diameters of small trees. *Botan. Gaz.* **128**, 60.

Kozlowski, T. T. (1968a). Diurnal changes in diameters of fruits and stems of Montmorency cherry. *J. Hort. Sci.* **43**, 1-15.

Kozlowski, T. T. (1968b). Physiological implications in afforestation. *Proc. 6th World Forestry Conf. Madrid, 1966.* F. A. O. Rome.

Kozlowski, T. T., and Clausen, J. J. (1965). Changes in moisture contents and dry weights of buds and leaves of forest trees. *Botan. Gaz.* **126**, 20.

Kozlowski, T. T., and Clausen, J. J. (1967). Effects of alkenylsuccinic acids on moisture content of woody plants. *Plant Physiol.* **42**, (Suppl), 17.

Kozlowski, T. T., and Winget, C. H. (1963). Patterns of water movement in forest trees. *Botan. Gaz.* **124**, 301.

Kozlowski, T. T., and Winget, C. H. (1964). Diurnal and seasonal variation in radii of tree stems. *Ecology* **45**, 149.

Kozlowski, T. T., Kuntz, J. E., and Winget, C. H. (1962). Effect of oak wilt on cambial activity. *J. Forestry* **60**, 558.

Kozlowski, T. T., Hughes, J. F., and Leyton, L. (1966). Patterns of water movement in dormant gymnosperm seedlings. *Biorheology* **3**, 77.

Kozlowski, T. T., Hughes, J. F., and Leyton, L. (1967). Movement of injected dyes in gymnosperm stems in relation to tracheid alignment. *Forestry* **40**, 207.

Krahmer, R. L., and Coté, W. A., Jr. (1963). Changes in coniferous wood cells associated with heartwood formation. *Tappi* **46**, 42.

Kramer, P. J. (1949). " Plant and Soil Water Relationships." McGraw-Hill, New York.

Kramer, P. J. (1962). The role of water in tree growth. *In* " Tree Growth " (T. T. Kozlowski, ed.), pp. 171–182. Ronald Press, New York.

Kramer, P. J. (1963). Water stress and plant growth. *Agron. J.* **55**, 31.

Kramer, P. J. (1964). The role of water in wood formation. *In* " The Formation of Wood in Forest Trees " (M. H. Zimmermann, ed.), pp. 519–532. Academic Press, New York.

Kramer, P. J., and Kozlowski, T. T. (1960). " Physiology of Trees." McGraw-Hill, New York.

Kuiper, P. J. C. (1964). The effect of decenylsuccinic acid on frost or drought resistance in plants. *Science* **146**, 544.

Lundegardh, H. (1954). The transport of water in wood. *Arkiv. Botan.* [2] 3 (6), 89.

McIlraith, W. J., Abrol, Y. P., and Heiligman, F. (1963). Dehydration of seeds in intact tomato plants. *Science* **142**, 1681.

Marshall, T. J. (1959). Relations between water and soil. *Commonwealth Bur. Soil Sci. (Gt. Brit.) Tech. Commun.* **50**.

Meidner, H. (1952). An instrument for the continuous determination of leaf thickness changes in the field. *J. Exptl. Botany* **3**, 319.

Newman, E. I., and Kramer, P. J. (1966). Effects of decenylsuccinic acid on the permeability and growth of bean roots. *Plant Physiol.* **41**, 606.

Patton, R. F., and Riker, A. J. (1954). Needle droop and needle blight of red pine. *J. Forestry* **52**, 412.

Philip, J. R. (1966). Plant water relations: some physical aspects. *Ann. Rev. Plant Physiol.* **17**, 245.

Rudinsky, J. A., and Vité, J. P. (1959). Certain ecological and phylogenetic aspects of the pattern of water conduction in conifers. *Forest Sci.* **5**, 259.

Rutter, A. J., and Whitehead, F. H., (eds.) (1963). " The Water Relations of Plants." Blackwell, Oxford.

Salter, P. J., and Goode, J. E. (1967). Crop responses to water at different stages of growth. *Commonwealth Bur. Hort. Plantation Crops (Gt. Brit.) Resources Res.* **2**.

Slatyer, R. O. (1967). " Plant-Water Relationships." Academic Press, New York.

Slatyer, R. O., and Bierhuizen, J. F. (1964). The influence of several transpiration suppressants on transpiration, photosynthesis, and water use efficiency of cotton leaves. *Australian J. Biol. Sci.* **17**, 131.

Slavik, B. (1965a). Supply of water to plants. *Meteorol. Monographs* **6**, 149.

Slavik, B. (ed.) (1965b). "Water Stress in Plants," Proc. Symp. Prague, 1963, Junk, The Hague.

Stanescu, P. P. (1936). Daily variations in products of photosynthesis, water content, and acidity of leaves toward the end of the vegetative period. *Am. J. Botany* **23**, 374.

Steward, F. C. (ed.) (1959). "Plant Physiology," Vol. II. Academic Press, New York.

Sutcliffe, J. F. (1962). "Mineral Salts Absorption in Plants." Pergamon, Oxford.

Vité, J. P. (1961). The influence of water supply on oleoresin exudation pressure and its resistance to bark beetle attack in *Pinus ponderosa*. *Contrib. Boyce Thompson Inst.* **21**, 37.

Vité, J. P., and Wood, D. L. (1960). A study on the applicability of the measurement of oleoresin exudation pressure in determining susceptibility of second growth ponderosa pine to bark beetle infestation. *Contrib. Boyce Thompson Inst.* **21**, 67.

Watanabe, S. (1958a). Silvicultural studies on Kusu (*Cinnamomum camphora* Sieb.) V. Transpiration and survival of seedlings during some period after transplanting. *Tokyo Daigaku Nogakubu Enshurin Hokoku (Bull. Tokyo Univ. Forests)* **54**, 19.

Wantanabe, S. (1958b). Silvicultural studies on Kusu (*Cinnamomum camphora* Sieb.) IX. The relationship between dying and survival of seedlings of Kusu. *Tokyo Daigaku Nogakubu Enshurin Hokoku (Bull. Tokyo Univ. Forests)* **54**, 43.

Watanabe, S. (1958c). Silvicultural studies of Kusu (*Cinnamomum camphora* Sieb.) X. Influence of soil drying on growth of seedlings of Kusu. *Tokyo Daigaku Nogakubu Enshurin Hokoku (Bull. Tokyo Univ. Forests)* **54**, 57.

Weatherley, P. E. (1950). Studies in the water relations of the cotton plant. II. Diurnal and seasonal variations in relative turgidity and environmental factors. *New Phytologist* **50**, 36.

Weatherley, P. E. (1964). The state and movement of water in the leaf. *Symp. Soc. Exptl. Biol.* **19**, 157.

Werner, H. O. (1954). Influence of atmospheric and soil moisture conditions on diurnal variations in relative turgidity of potato leaves. *Nebraska Univ. Agr. Expt. Sta. Res. Bull.* **176**.

Wilson, C. C. (1948). Diurnal fluctuations of growth in length of tomato stem. *Plant Physiol.* **23**, 156.

Wilson, C. C., Boggess, W. R., and Kramer, P. J. (1953). Diurnal fluctuations in the moisture content of some herbaceous plants. *Am. J. Botany* **40**, 97.

Woodhams, D. H., and Kozlowski, T. T. (1954). Effects of soil moisture stress on carbohydrate development and growth in plants. *Am. J. Botany* **41**, 316.

Zelitch, I. (1961). Biochemical control of stomatal opening in leaves. *Proc. Natl. Acad. Sci. (U.S.)* **47**, 1423.

Zelitch, I. (1964). Reduction of transpiration of leaves through stomatal closure induced by alkenysuccinic acids. *Science* **143**, 692.

Zelitch, I., and Waggoner, P. E. (1962a). Effect of chemical control of stomata on transpiration and photosynthesis. *Proc. Natl. Acad. Sci. (U.S.)* **48**, 1101.

Zelitch, I., and Waggoner, P. E. (1962b). Effect of chemical control of stomata on transpiration of intact plants. *Proc. Natl. Acad. Sci. (U.S.)* **48**, 1297.

Ziegler, H. (1959). Our knowledge of translocation in rays. *Proc. 9th Intern. Botan. Congr., Montreal* **2**, 441. Univ. of Toronto Press, Toronto.

Ziegler, H. (1964). Storage, mobilization and distribution of reserve material in trees. *In* The Formation of Wood in Forest Trees" (M. H. Zimmermann, ed.), pp. 303–320. Academic Press, New York.

CHAPTER 2

WATER STRUCTURE AND WATER IN THE PLANT BODY

A. S. Crafts

DEPARTMENT OF BOTANY, UNIVERSITY OF CALIFORNIA, DAVIS, CALIFORNIA

I. INTRODUCTION

In order to appreciate the unique function of water and the effects of water stress in the physiology of plants, one must recognize the nature of water as a liquid, as a solvent, and as a substrate. It has long been postulated that liquid water consists of more than one molecular species. Ice is recognized as made up of polar molecules, coordinately arranged in a latticelike framework and bound together by strong intermolecular forces consisting largely of hydrogen bonds.

Liquid water forms a continuum with sufficient order to display X-ray diffraction patterns; the existence of any one molecular configuration, however, is only of statistical significance because the total mass is in continual flux. There are several theories concerning the structure of liquid water; most of these propose the existence of at least two distinct states for water molecules; none accounts for all of the properties of water. Némethy (1965) groups these theories into two main categories (1) theories which emphasize models in which most molecules maintain a regular hydrogen-bonded structure, such as ice (tridymite), or some crystalline form, such as that found in gas hydrates (in these models some water molecules are displaced from the lattice sites and enter vacant spaces in the hydrogen-bonded lattice); and (2) theories which emphasize the limited spacial extent of the hydrogen-bonded networks in the liquid. These networks are treated as clusters with irregular regions of nonhydrogen-bonded water molecules between them. This model, based on the theory of Frank and Wen (1957), has been elaborated in the "flickering cluster" theory of Némethy and Scheraga (1962a). Although these theories account for many of the properties of water, the detailed structure of liquid water is still unsettled.

A. WATER MODELS

Kavanau (1964) suggests four different models of water structure. Of these, the "vacant-lattice-point" model of Forslind (1952, 1954), the "water-hydrate" model supported by the work of Claussen (1951a,b) and Pauling and Marsh (1952), and the "distorted bond" model of Pople (1951) fit category (1) of Némethy; the "flickering cluster" model, category (2) (Némethy, 1965).

In Forslind's (1952, 1954) model, the liquid phase of water is considered to be essentially a crystalline system of very open structure such that the interstitial spaces between the groups of molecules have tetrahedral coordination sufficiently large to accommodate unbonded molecules without disturbing the structural order. As ice melts the thermal amplitudes of vibration become sufficient for some molecules to pass through the faces of the surrounding tetrahedrons and assume interstitial positions. The resultant defects, each consisting of one vacant lattice point and one interstitial non-associated molecule, increase the disordering of the lattice and enhance further breakdown. There are opportunities for molecules to change places, for lone molecules to pass through the faces of surrounding tetrahedrons and assume interstitial positions, and for these lattice defects to move through the overall lattice and work their way to interfacial boundaries. Here the lattice is destroyed and lone interstitial molecules congregate. This accounts for volume decrease and density increase which maximize at 4°C. In liquid water at 0°C, 9% of the lattice points are computed to be vacant, and interstitial molecules constitute 16% of the total number of molecules in the system.

Hydrates of nonpolar gases have been known for a long time, but only within recent years has it been postulated that a "water-hydrate" model might account for many of the unusual properties of water. Buswell and Rodebush (1956) described two unusual manifestations of hydrate formation in nature. One was the frosting of corn at 40°F, well above freezing; the second was formation of slushy snow in natural gas pipelines at temperatures as high as 68°F. Claussen (1951a,b) and Pauling and Marsh (1952) described structures formed around solutes that, although retaining the bond angles and intermolecular distances characteristic of ice, are looser than ice and contain large cavities. Pauling (1959, 1960) suggested that liquid water possesses labile structures similar to gas and salt hydrates. Methane, e.g., though very slightly soluble in water and failing to ionize or accept hydrogen bonds, does form a hydrate in which several water molecules are associated with each methane molecule. This solution reaction liberates 10 times as much heat as the solution of methane in hexane, and the methane molecule occupies more than twice the volume of a water molecule. A refinement of the water-hydrate model was proposed by Danforth and Levy (1962). In this model, water consists of an icelike framework in which each oxygen atom is enclosed tetrahedrally by 4 other oxygen atoms forming layers of 6-membered, puckered rings. Two adjacent layers, related by mirror symmetry, form polyhedral cavities with 12 vertices; some of the cavities are occupied by lone interstitial water molecules. The ratio of framework molecules to interstitial molecules is 4.0, corresponding to 50% occupation of the framework cavities.

In the "distorted bond" model Lennard-Jones and Pople (1951) proposed that few hydrogen bonds are broken in liquid water near the melting point. Pople (1951) has suggested that these bonds are bent or distorted rather than broken, which destroys the regular repeating ice lattice shown by X-ray diffraction. This produces an irregular arrangement having increasing numbers of molecules in first- and second-neighbor shells around a given molecule.

In contrast to the above three models, the "flickering cluster" model proposes that liquid water consists of two distinct phases in a continuous mixture. In 1954, Grjotheim and Krogh-Moe visualized liquid water as consisting of a mixture of an icelike molecular species, with all 4 hydrogen bonds intact around each molecule and having density identical with that of ice, combined with a nonhydrogen-bonded close-packed species with a density extrapolated from water at high temperature. Haggis *et al.* (1952), from a similar model having 4 molecular types of 4, 3, 2, and 1 hydrogen bonds for the bonded clusters plus the unbonded species, calculated values for the dielectric constant of water that approximate experimental values. Frank and Wen (1957) have focused attention on the partially covalent nature of the hydrogen bond. Besides dipole-interaction energies, hydrogen bond formation involves a contribution from delocalization energy brought about by dipole overlap. Large deviations from colinearity of the O—H and H $\cdots$ O directions (distortions) are not possible. Frank and Wen postulate that formation of hydrogen bonds in water is a cooperative phenomenon; bonds are not made and broken singly but several at a time; formation of 1 hydrogen bond promotes the formation of others by the same water molecule, thus bringing about "chain" propagation. The breaking of 1 hydrogen bond in a cluster induces the breaking of adjacent hydrogen bonds. Thus, short-lived clusters of highly hydrogen-bonded regions imbedded in a matrix of non-hydrogen-bonded molecules are produced. This "flickering cluster" model accounts for a number of experimentally derived quantities such as density values, relaxation times, and structural features. To one who has watched Brownian movement of very fine colloidal particles in a dark field, certainly, from the standpoints of frequency and amplitude, such a model seems more logical than a rigid icelike structure.

Némethy and Scheraga (1962a) and Frank (1965) favor the "flickering cluster" model, and they present a detailed analysis of the problems involved in water structure. One inherent difficulty is the lack of reliable values for the energy of breaking of the O—H $\cdots$ O hydrogen bond. Estimates ranging from 1.38 kcal (Grjotheim and Krogh-Moe, 1954) to 6.8 kcal (Verwey, 1941) have been made, and the value of 4.5 kcal proposed by Pauling (1940) is quoted commonly. Starting with the assumption that, in ice, hydrogen bonding results in a coordination number of 4, Némethy and Scheraga (1962a) calculated the energy levels of molecules which have 3, 2, 1, and 0 hydrogen bonds. The latter represents the unbonded matrix; the 3, 2, and 1 hydrogen-bonded molecules represent the water molecules on the surface of the clusters; the tetra-bonded species are those in the interior of the clusters. The non-bonded molecules have dipole–dipole and London forces acting between them, and their coordination number is greater than 4.

Némethy and Scheraga (1962a) arrive at a value for the hydrogen bond of 1.32 kcal which they use in calculating values for free energy, enthalpy, entropy, and heat capacity. They obtain close correlation with experimental values for the first 3 properties above and fair correlation for the heat capacity. Figure 1 shows the schematic representation of their model. Calculations on cluster sizes range from 90.6 at 0°C to 57.0 at 20°C to 21.0 at 100°C. Mole fractions of nonhydrogen-bonded molecules in liquid water vary from 0.2435 at 0°C to 0.4373 at 100°C.

B. HYDROPHOBIC BONDS

In a second paper Némethy and Scheraga (1962b) attack the problem of water structure and hydrophobic bonding in proteins. Starting with aqueous solutions of simple hydrocarbons they conclude that the net intermolecular interaction energies of the solute with nonhydrogen-bonded water differ from interaction energies with the water molecules of hydrogen-bonded clusters, resulting in a change in the coordination number of hydrogen-bonded water molecules near the solute. Hydrogen bonding is increased, and

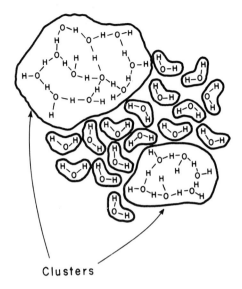

Clusters

FIG. 1. Schematic representation of liquid water, showing hydrogen-bonded clusters and unbonded molecules. The molecules in the interior of the clusters are tetracoordinated, but not drawn as such in this two-dimensional diagram. From Némethy and Scheraga (1962a).

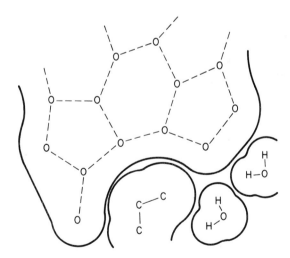

FIG. 2. Schematic cross section of a hydrogen-bonded water cluster near a hydrocarbon solute molecule, indicating the formation of a partial cage around the solute. The O—H⋯O hydrogen bonds are represented by broken lines. The heavy outlines correspond to the surfaces defined by the van der Waals contact radii of the molecules involved. From Némethy and Scheraga (1962c).

the hydrogen-bonded clusters extend around part of the solute molecule, giving rise to a partial cagelike structure. Figure 2 shows their diagram of this situation.

A water molecule having 4 hydrogen-bonded neighbors can also have a solute neighbor, and the van der Waals interaction between the solute and water lowers their energies. Since these forces are proportional to the inverse sixth power of distance, interaction between solute and water beyond the first layer of water is negligible. Changes in energy levels in the process of solution cause a lowering of energy which corresponds to an increase in icelikeness and thus an increase in the net number of water molecules in clusters near the solute surface. Cages so formed do not exist as separate entities but always as partial clusters extending beyond the first shell around the solute molecule. Large solute molecules may adjoin two or more cages which are parts of different neighboring water clusters.

C. Water in Biological Systems

The fact that, in living systems, the nonpolar side chains of a protein may be implicated in the formation of hydrates with intervening water molecules indicates one reason for the importance of water structure in understanding physiological processes. The interactions of hydrocarbons in aqueous solution result in hydrophobic bonds, and Scheraga (1965) has given a clear presentation of this subject in relation to protein structure. Although it was early considered that the interaction of hydrocarbons in aqueous solution arose simply from van der Waals forces between the hydrocarbon molecules, it has been shown that the contribution from this interaction is only about 45% of the total free energy of a hydrophobic bond at 25°C. Two nonpolar side chains of a protein in water are surrounded by partial cages of tetra-bonded water molecules. If the two groups approach each other until they touch, there will be a decrease in the amount of water around them; this constitutes a reversal of the solution process. Thus, formation of a hydrophobic bond is accompanied by melting of the icelike structures. The thermodynamic parameters for hydrophobic bond formation have opposite signs from those for solution; hydrophobic bond formation also involves van der Waals interaction between the nonpolar side chains.

Némethy and Scheraga (1962b) have calculated values for free energy changes, enthalpy, and entropy for formation of hydrophobic bonds between all possible pairs of side chains which normally occur in proteins and also for situations involving three and more side chains. Study of the interaction between nonpolar parts of carboxylic acids and polystyrene resins, for dimerization of carboxylic acids in water and for the lowering of the transition temperature for thermal denaturation of ribonuclease by alcohols of varying chain length, gave results which tended to substantiate the calculations (Scheraga, 1965). Work on hydrophobic bonding in the α-helix, on nucleic acids, on polar–nonpolar side-chain relations, and on association of proteins with large molecules has been described; incomplete work on properties of water in solutions of electrolytes has been carried out (Scheraga, 1965).

Two notable features of water molecules are their small size, enabling them to fit into small interstices in proteins, and their ability to both give and receive hydrogen bonds. Hydrogen bonding is inevitable wherever peptide links are present; this is particularly prominent in the unfolded state of proteins. Four molecules of water may be found by each peptide group, but mutual hydrogen bonding is predominant in the interior of globular proteins.

Jacobson (1953) speculated that if a helical section of water were to be removed, the Watson–Crick DNA double helix might fit well into the cavity. Results of Hearst and Vinograd (1961) indicate that T4 bacteriophage Cs DNA molecules at 25°C may have about 50 water molecules per nucleotide residue at water activity around unity. Berendsen (1960, 1962) suggests that a similar mechanism may explain the relation between collagen and water.

Structuring of water in regions of membranes having un-ionized polar groups incapable of hydrogen bonding may result from weak dipole–dipole interactions.

Forslind (1952, 1954) has shown that coupling between water and clay crystals may induce increasing order and rigidity to the water lattice which may extend for a distance of 300 Å. Coupling between water and an interface may have specificity, depending upon the structural similarity between the water lattice and the stabilizing interface. Forslind further proposed that gel formation and the existence of long-range interactions in gel-forming systems depend upon specific adsorption of water at the interface with the colloid. Kavanau (1964) questions the thickness of water films on interfaces of biological membranes with water, but he agrees that the degree of polarization and deformation of the water lattice depends upon specific binding interactions. These may vary as widely as do the chemical and physical properties of the macromolecular substances themselves.

D. WATER IN LIVING SYSTEMS

Ling (1962, 1965) conducted studies on the physical state of water in both living and nonliving systems and proposed the "association-induction" hypothesis which seems to reconcile many of the differences between the older "sieve" theories of membrane function and modern work with sophisticated methods. Recognizing the great importance of proteins in living systems, Ling (1965) states that the sequences of amino acid residues underlie biological specificity to the extent that a difference of a single amino acid residue in a protein containing hundreds may produce profound differences in the behavior of the entire tissue. However, as important as protein specificity is to living systems, there can be no life without water. Thus, proteins, whether in the contractile form or as functioning enzymes in the living cell, are associated with water, and water usually makes up 75–85% of living tissues on a fresh weight basis. The unique behavior of such tissues and cells reflects not only the behavior of the proteins per se, but that of the protein–water system.

Water in living systems does not function merely as a solvent; water molecules in association with proteins and other macromolecules apparently exist in a state different from that of normal water. Views on the state of such water vary; in early theories the asymmetry in distribution of solutes was attributed to critical pore size on the cell membrane (sieve theory) or to a continual pumping (i.e., sodium pump, permease). The association–induction theory of Ling (1962, 1965) proposes that cell water has different solubility properties than normal water for nonelectrolytes, amino acids, and ions. Such properties are based on restricted rotation of polyatomic nonelectrolytes and polyatomic hydrated ions and on differences in hydrogen-bond formation in the protoplasm. It also stresses that the living protoplasm, and hence protoplasmic water, does not exist in a single physical state but in several metastable cooperative states in the course of its normal physiological activity. Ling visualizes such water as existing in polarized multilayers oriented on the surfaces of all proteins. One cannot demonstrate this by a direct physical approach on an *in vitro* system because, in living cells, the protein–water systems are metastable; removal of water causes irreversible changes.

Ling uses a three-point attack on the problem of water structure in living systems: (1) He establishes multilayer adsorption of polarized water in one or more nonliving stable model systems; (2) he chooses properties exhibited by water in living cells in the resting state that differ from those of ordinary water and yet can be studied without serious injury; (3) he establishes that this same property also is shown by the water in a nonliving model system. Using equilibrium distribution of nonelectrolytes and ions, Ling employs strong electrolyte solutions, copper ferrocyanide gels, and a particular collagen from carp's swim bladder and sheep's wool as models.

By measuring water vapor sorption in collagen and sheep's wool, Ling finds that water molecules exist in the form of multilayers in these materials. Studying equilibrium sucrose distribution in an aqueous suspension of copper ferrocyanide gel, McMahon *et al.* (1940) found a much higher concentration of sucrose in the supernatant than if all of the sucrose had been evenly distributed in the total water of the system. They found that each molecule of copper ferrocyanide renders 10.6 water molecules nonsolvent, a volume that cannot be accommodated in the crystal lattice nor on the surface of the ferrocyanide. McMahon *et al.* (1940) termed this "imbibed" water. Ling considers it to be adsorbed in multilayers.

Salting out is another example of selective exclusion, a phenomenon owing its origin to polarization of water molecules around ions; this is not limited to strong electrolytes; sucrose can salt out nonelectrolytes such as ethyl acetate. Ling used ion exchange resins to show selective exclusion of several electrolytes; urea on Amberlite IR-200 accumulated to a concentration 20 times higher than in the external medium; alcohols and sugars showed similar phenomena. Ling cites work on three types of living tissue showing exclusion of nonassimilated sugars by intracellular water which he considers to be polarized and oriented.

Studying Na, Ca, and Mg ions in frog muscle, Ling found, contrary to classic theory, that all three will permeate the living system, but that a mechanism of exclusion is present. To explain these various exclusion phenomena, Ling proposes that the entire living cell constitutes a bulk-phase fixed-charge system in which ionic sites on proteins selectively adsorb ions and nonelectrolytes so that distribution is usually lower within than in the extracellular water. This results from restricted rotational and translational motions. Thus, in the living state, water structure seems different than in the physical systems used in so many physicochemical studies.

Whereas Kavanau (1964) concludes that much evidence is against gross, long-range immobilization of water into thick icelike hydration crusts around macromolecules, Scheraga (1965) visualizes a layer of water around a nonpolar solute having a greater degree of hydrogen bonding and more ordering—a "partial cage" of icelike properties. Ling proposes that water in living systems is multilayered and exists reversibly in several metastable cooperative states. He explains many of the properties of living cells by his association–induction hypothesis.

Frank (1965) points out that water has been viewed as a mixture since the time of Röntgen in the last century. Röntgen's reasons for considering water to be a mixture were the phenomenon of maximum density, the fact that the temperature of maximum density is lowered when pressure is increased, and that the viscosity of cold water is decreased by the application of pressure. Röntgen explained these phenomena by assuming that water consists of two molecular species, one bulky and one dense.

Of the many models for water structure proposed since Röntgen's time, the "flickering cluster" concept of Némethy and Scheraga (1962a) seems to reconcile the many observations that have been made. From the standpoint of physics it seems best able to account for the phenomenon of maximum density, the high viscosity and dielectric properties, and the enthalpy and entropy characteristics unique to water. As mentioned, the nature of Brownian movement seems to demand the presence of structured particles of some mass (i.e., clusters) in a continuous fluid rather than the regular hydrogen-bonded or extended crystalline structure of Némethy's class 1, discussed earlier. Many biological phenomena seem compatible with a model composed of bulky clusters of strongly bonded molecules in a matrix of dense unbonded molecules having highly fluid properties. The high permeability of many membranes to water is logical if the actual passage may take place in the fluid, unbonded form; movement through membranes of continuous structured water is hard to visualize. Since hydrogen bonding is a cooperative process in constant flux, it seems possible that clusters on one side of a membrane may "melt down," reforming on the other side, because pressure is a structure-destroying force, whereas tension is a structure-forming one. The high viscosity, tensile strength, solvent, and dielectric properties of a substance which at the same time is fluid seem compatible only with a model which is simultaneously structured and yet not rigid as is a crystal.

With the "flickering cluster" model in mind it is of interest to list the influences that bring about formation and breakdown of structure, that is, factors that shift the equilibrium from bulky to dense and vice versa (Table I).

TABLE I

FACTORS THAT MAKE OR BREAK STRUCTURING OF WATER

Structure-making factors	Structure-breaking factors
Low temperature	High temperature
Low pressure	High pressure
Chemically inert solutes (hydrocarbons, rare gases, alkyl halides, etc.)	Ionic solutes, $(Na^+, Cl^-, etc.)$
Polyfunctional solutes (amino acids, proteins, surfactants)	Urea

E. WATER STRESS AND WATER STRUCTURE

From the above considerations it should be evident that pressure is an important parameter determining the physical state of water. Pressure causes ice to melt and forces the equilibrium in liquid water away from structured toward the nonhydrogen-bonded dense state, reducing viscosity, surface tension, and dielectric constant. Tension brings about the opposite effects; reduced pressure increases viscosity, surface tension, and dielectric constant. Probably the most prominent effects upon biological systems are the increased structuring bringing about thickening of multilayers at interfaces, increased frictional resistance to movement resulting from increased viscosity, and strengthening of menisci and other surface films as a result of increased surface tension. All of these factors tend to slow down water movement and water loss, and thus protect the plant against dehydration. Hence, these effects of stress on water structure have been at least partially effective in plant survival in regions where stress is a common property of the water body in the plant.

II. WATER IN THE PLANT BODY

Water is required for germination of seeds, and it functions in the early hydration of cells and tissues. As soon as growth starts water serves as a carrier in the distribution of mineral nutrients and plant foods. With leaf expansion water enters the process of photosynthesis. And all processes of metabolism, conditioned as they are by protein synthesis and enzyme function, require an aqueous environment. Throughout this gamut of activities the role of water is very closely related to its structure. The "flickering cluster" theory of water structure (Némethy and Scheraga, 1962a) seems most compatible with the many observations on water function in plants. The presence of relatively free nonhydrogen bonded molecules as a constant constituent of liquid water explains the ready flow of water through cell walls and protoplasmic membranes. It must be in this form that single water molecules escape from the menisci within the intermicellar spaces of mesophyll cell walls in the process of transpiration. Free molecules of this sort probably serve in the many reactions catalyzed by enzymes, and water in multilayers may account for the great quantities associated with biocolloids as "bound" water in tissues.

Before taking up the relations of water stress to other processes in which water plays important roles, it seems appropriate to give some consideration to the nature of water in the plant body, its function as solvent and carrier, its relation to other plant components on a molecular basis, and its importance as a plant constituent. Plants cannot exist in the absence of water; they do not grow when it is not available in sufficient quantity.

A. THE PLANT BODY: SYMPLAST, APOPLAST

Münch in 1930 introduced two concepts that have proved of great value in considerations of plant physiology. These are *symplast*, a term indicating that the sum total of living stuff in a plant is an interconnected, integrated continuum, and *apoplast*, a term used to describe the total nonliving cell wall continuum that surrounds and contains the symplast. According to these concepts all substances absorbed by plants move in via the apoplast, and all solutes within the symplast may move throughout this system without having

to pass permeability barriers. Crafts (1961) proposed that the mature functioning sieve tubes of the phloem be considered as a special phase of the
symplast and that the nonliving xylem conduits be included in the apoplast.

B. Water as Continuum

The body of water within a living plant is commonly recognized to be a
continuum (Crafts, 1961; Vaadia et al., 1961). While Philip (1958) and
Bonner (1959) propose that under low soil moisture conditions a vapor gap
may surround roots, Vaadia et al. suggested that the water continuum of the
plant extends without interruption into the soil. Certainly, under most
conditions of plant growth this must be true (see also Gardner and Ehlig,
1962).

The continuum of water in the plant–soil complex is, within the plant
body, a liquid mass enclosed within a film or interface made up of a myriad
of menisci at the surface of, or embedded within, the apoplast. Whereas the
air–water interface in soils resides within both the macrocapillaries between
soil particles, and microcapillaries within the colloidal phases, in the plant
the interface resides principally within the cell walls. When water is under
stress these are of molecular dimensions and hence capable of generating
tensions into the hundreds of atmospheres (Briggs, 1950; Ursprung, 1915).

Movement of water into and through the plant body follows a source–sink
pattern, with the soil as the ultimate source and the atmosphere as largely the
ultimate sink. Water used in organic synthesis is a small portion of the total
volume utilized by the plant. The large bulk moving through the plant to
provide the transpirational needs finds its sink in the stomatal chambers of
leaves; a small amount is lost through lenticels, the cuticle of stems and
leaves, and the intercellular space system.

Since most of the plant water is liquid and in constant flux, it must be
made up of a mixture of hydrogen-bonded molecules with varying amounts
of unbonded molecules associated by dipole–dipole bonds and London forces
as pictured by physical theories of water structure (Némethy and Scheraga,
1962a,b,c, Frank, 1965). Immobilization of water in multilayers or partial
cages probably occurs within the interstices of the pectic and cellulosic
constituents of the cell wall. Within the cuticle, in suberin of bark, and all
through the protein and lipid phases of the cytoplasm, hydrophobic bonding
must be prevalent.

Two physical factors, temperature and pressure, predominate in their
influences on the structural properties of plant water. Low temperatures
promote the coordinated icelike character of water; increasing temperatures
through thermal agitation break up the lattice structures and promote
fluidity. High pressures crush or smear out the crystal lattice of coordinated

water and promote fluidity; reduced pressure acts like cooling, enhancing the hydrogen-bonded lattice and increasing viscosity. These are probably the primary influences of water stress in the physiology of plant processes. The icelikeness of water is greatly enhanced by pressure lowering, and in the many colloidal phases of plants—e.g., cell walls and cytoplasm—where hydrogen-bonding inherently promotes immobilization, pressure reduction reinforces this tendency. Not only will fluidity be reduced and frictional resistance to flow increased; pressure lowering will hold molecules more tenaciously to menisci from which evaporation is occurring. Also, as menisci recede into microcapillaries, free diffusion as occurs from the open ends of capillaries is blocked, and the deeper the capillary cavities the more the blocking. All these influences will reduce transpiration and conserve water. However, in the limiting case of permanent wilting, this is accomplished at the sacrifice of growth and dry weight production.

C. Water as Solvent

Water is recognized as a common solvent for polar compounds, and it serves in the plant body as a solvent for such compounds as sugars, organic nitrogen compounds, O_2, and a host of other constitutents. As a polar solvent its high dielectric constant indicates its strong ability to saturate force fields between ions and its short relaxation time of 10^{-11} seconds, its highly fluid properties. In the soil, water serves as solvent for plant nutrients and as a carrier to present these nutrients to absorbing surfaces of roots. Within the plant, water is the solvent for mineral nutrients that move from roots to foliage through the apoplast system, and within the symplast water makes up the body of the assimilate stream and the vacuolar contents. It is the medium within which the multitude of metabolic reactions takes place.

Since water is a continuum in the plant, with high surface tension and tensile strength, the pressure status is in dynamic equilibrium, and stress in the soil or the atmosphere or both is reflected throughout the plant body; water potential tends to equalize within the total liquid mass so that deficiency in one part is quickly transmitted to all parts. Xylem conductors have internal strengthening so that they can withstand tensions of many bars. The phloem conduits, on the other hand, make up an elastic system inflated by turgor pressure, and when water is in stress, some is withdrawn from the phloem and sap concentration increases. The same is true of vacuolated cells of mesophyll, cortex, and pith. Such concentration of sap may have profound effects on metabolic processes within these cells.

Finally, the water continuum, extending as it does through every living structure of the plant, must sustain stress throughout the living protoplasm. Thus, chloroplasts, mitochondria, nuclei, and all cytoplasm must be affected by stress within the plant body. Stress, reflected in reduced hydrostatic pressure, makes for structuring, increased viscosity, dielectric constant, surface tension, and colligative properties. In fact, stress alters every physical and chemical property of the solvent water and changes every process in the plant. The only water not affected is that which is already so tightly bound as multilayers on, or structured in, colloid and nonpolar surfaces as to be already rendered nonsolvent for chemical reactions.

D. Water in Membranes

Because water makes up approximately 80% of all living matter on a fresh weight basis, the state and structure of water in the living cell are of major importance in cell physiology. Long known to be critical in questions of solute uptake, movement, and storage, the membrane system of the cell as revealed by the electron microscope and biochemical studies is complex and diverse in structure. Membrane systems are known now to be composed of a profusion of components involving not only the surface but the interior of the cell as well. All of the organelles characteristic of plant cells, including nuclei, mitochondria, golgi apparatus, plastids, quantosomes, etc., are bounded by membranes. The membranes at the cell surface are found to be tortuously infolded into the cell interior. Extending throughout the cytoplasm contacting all of the above inclusions, and passing from cell to cell through the plasmodesmata is the endoplasmic reticulum, a paired membrane system that must be highly active and in constant flux in the living state (Hechter, 1965).

From structural as well as functional aspects of cell physiology, it is presently clear that there must be many distinctive types of aqueous regions in cells where water molecules occur in different environments and hence may be differently structured. It is questionable whether the water in the fluid hyaloplasm has the same structure as that in the various organelles and in the membrane system. Water between paired membrane systems, within tubules (Ledbetter and Porter, 1964), mitochondria, or bound within the loculi of the grana or the fret channels in the chloroplast, must be subject to different forces than that in streaming cytoplasm. The point here is that water intimately associated with membrane systems and other fixed macromolecular structures should be differentiated from that of the mobile, fluid portion of the cell.

Membrane systems vary in their forms and volumes; in bacterial cells they may make up 10% of the cell mass; in some organs of higher plants they may make up from 50 to 60% of the cell; in meristems and highly active secretory cells they may constitute an even higher proportion. Davson and Danielli (1952) reviewed membrane structure in relation to permeability phenomena. Their model consisted of one or more bimolecular leaflets of lipid with a monolayer of protein covering each; the hydrocarbon chains of the lipids were arranged radially. Electron microscopy has indicated that the characteristic features of such a membrane consist of two dense narrow lines separated by a band of lesser density, the thickness of the trilaminar unit being about 75 Å.

Further studies have substantiated the general nature of this trilaminar model, and Robertson (1964) used the term "unit membrane" to embrace this structure. This concept proposes that all biological membranes are constructed on a single fundamental design, with the basic organization consisting of two lipid monolayers (the light middle portion) sandwiched between two continuous monolayers of nonlipids (the two dark layers). Most workers propose that these two outer layers consist of or involve largely proteins. Figure 3 shows this concept as presented by Hechter (1965) and Green and Perdue (1966).

Water is a bulk component of membrane systems making up from 30 to 50% of a total system. In an ordered lamellar membrane system water in the membrane somehow must be structured in relation to the ordered polar groups of proteins and phospholipids. It has been proposed (Fernández-Morán, 1962) that water in a membrane may be organized in icelike or crystal-hydrate lattices as an integral component serving an essential role for various membrane functions. Localized reversible phase changes in structured water might condition conformational changes in protein layers and concurrently modify the arrangement of the polar lipids from an ordered bimolecular leaflet to a less tightly packed micellar form. Selective permeability might be thought of in terms of molecular sieves lined with ordered water; marked permeability changes could result from melting of water structures in local regions. By constituting a continuous hydrogen-bonding medium, ordered water structures could take part in fast proton charge transport mechanisms

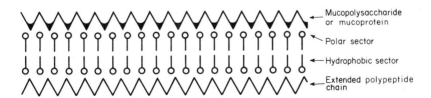

FIG. 3. A representation of the unit-membrane concept. The asymmetrical nonlipid layers, presumably protein in nature but of unknown composition and structure, are represented as continuous structures. The mixed lipid bilayer consists primarily of phospholipids; the hydrophilic portion of the lipid molecules are represented by the circles, and the extended hydrocarbon chains are represented by the attached tails. Modified from Hechter (1965) and Green and Perdue (1966).

or in electron transport via hydrogen-free-radicals or hydride-ion flow (Hechter, 1965).

In developing a theory for the design of the protein coat of a membrane Hechter proposes that, in aqueous media, the nonpolar groups of a polypeptide have such a great aversion to water that a polypeptide or protein tends to fold so that a maximum number of hydrophobic ends are shielded from the water by close-packing mutual interactions. Interactions of the polar side chains with water at the aqueous surface, and with each other secondarily, contribute to stability. Depending upon the character of the amino acid sequences involved, the minimal energy state of a protein may be achieved with a total or a partial helical arrangement. If a large preponderance of nonpolar amino acid side chains exist in a protein, a minimal energy state may be achieved by polymerization because nonpolar regions of the monomer react with each other. Such an arrangement may lead to a hexagonal arrangement, and Warner (1964) proposes that such hexagonal subunits may be packed into a hexameric A-protein unit and that these may be cemented together at hydrophilic surfaces by two water layers to form a protein coat. Warner postulates that in this model the two water layers that play a structural role are highly ordered and arranged hexagonally as in an icelike lattice.

In this A-protein model made up of hexameric units cemented together by water, the overlap pattern leaves a central channel where the hexagonal discs do not overlap. The amino acid residues at the edges of this passage comprise a total of 12 carboxyl groups and 24 hydroxyl groups quite uniformly distributed around the edge; this channel is thus lined with COO^- groups, and OH^- groups; the latter represent hydrogen-bonding sites occupied by water. Thus, Warner's hexameric model visualizes an aqueous channel within the protein of a membrane lined with hydrogen-bonded water, possessing COO^- sites for binding cations. Such a channel would be permaselective for cations, would exclude anions, and would provide for ready movement of water by exchange. With continued structuring of the hexagonal subunits, new channels emerge with side chains on the edges comprised of hydroxyl groups and basic groups of amino acids; this produces aqueous channels permaselective for anions.

These modern views of membrane structure, built up from atomic models and designed to fit thermodynamic requirements, emphasize the important role played by water. Figure 4 illustrates Hechter's ideas as noted above. In this, the individual hexagonal subunits are shown as interlocked through hydrophobic surfaces to form disc units held together by two layers of water in an icelike state. The aqueous channels in the protein layer possess fixed charge sites; most of this water in the aqueous channels has an icelike structure. The bilayer arrangement of the mixed lipids shown in Fig. 4, involving interdigitation of fatty acid tails, is assumed to depend on the icelike layers of

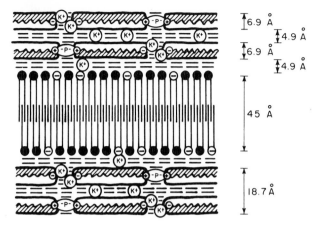

FIG. 4. Schematic representation of the resting membrane where the basic features of the unit-membrane concept are retained and the protein layers are represented as a system of interlocked hexagonal discs cemented together by water layers in an icelike arrangement to form a precisely ordered lattice system. From Hechter (1965).

water that fix the hydrophilic portion of lipid molecules in position in relation to the hydrophilic surfaces of the neighboring protein subunits. Potassium is shown to be the principal counterion for fixed negative sites in the resting membrane and phosphate as the counterion for fixed positive sites, but other ions possibly involved are not shown. In this model, selectivity for potassium over sodium depends upon the organization of the membrane units to form a precise lattice.

Green and Perdue (1966) question the unit membrane theory on several grounds. Studies on the phospholipid–protein complex of several membranes have indicated that binding is predominantly hydrophobic rather than electrostatic, implying deep penetration of the hydrophobic region of protein by the hydrocarbon tails of the phospholipid molecules. Electron transfer complexes of mitochondrial membranes lose their capacity for integrated electron transfer when lipid is removed and regain it when lipid is reintroduced.

When phospholipid is extracted from mitochondrial and other membrane systems the appearance of cristae and the dimensions of the layers cannot be distinguished from those of normal unextracted membranes. If the protein layers were held apart by lipid bilayers the structure should collapse when extracted; such collapse has not been observed. Thus, the basic structure of the membrane system must be protein; the clear space between the electron dense layers seen in so many electron microscope views of membranes must consist partly of protein and not alone of hydrocarbon chains.

Green and Perdue point out that much evidence now points to membrane structure as made up of repeating subunits of macromolecules of molecular weights from 0.5 to 1 million. They define membranes as vescicular or tubular systems, the continuum consisting of nesting, lipoprotein-repeating units. Although each membrane has characteristic repeating units that are complementary in form, these units may vary in composition. In the inner membrane of the mitochondrion there may be as many as 10 different species of elementary particles, each chemically and enzymatically unique.

Organelles are systems of membranes; the interrelations of the membranes within such a system are precise and unique to the organelle. A number of integrated metabolic sequences have been shown to be localized within the repeating units of membranes. Examples are the electron transfer chain, the enzyme system catalyzing the glycolytic sequence of reactions involved in the citric acid cycle, the mitochondrial system for elongation of fatty acids, and the microsomal system for synthesis of proteins (Green and Perdue, 1966).

Weier et al. (1966) visualize the chloroplast membrane system as made up of partitions, end granal membranes, marginal layers, and fret membranes, all enclosing an aqueous continuum of loculi and fret channels (Fig. 5a). Within the grana (partitions plus loculi) that carry the chlorophyll, the trapping of solar energy takes place. ATP, NADPH, and ferridoxin may move, and thus carry energy, from the hydrophilic loculi to the hydrophilic fret

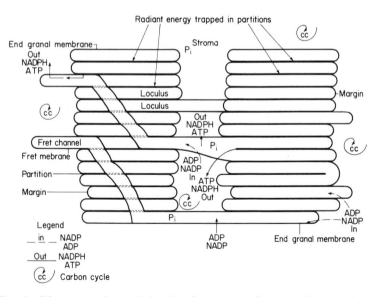

FIG. 5a. Diagram to show relationships between membranes and stroma in overall photosynthetic reactions. The carbon cycle is located in the stroma, and the light reactions occur in the grana, most probably in the partitions which are double-layered. From Weier et al. (1966).

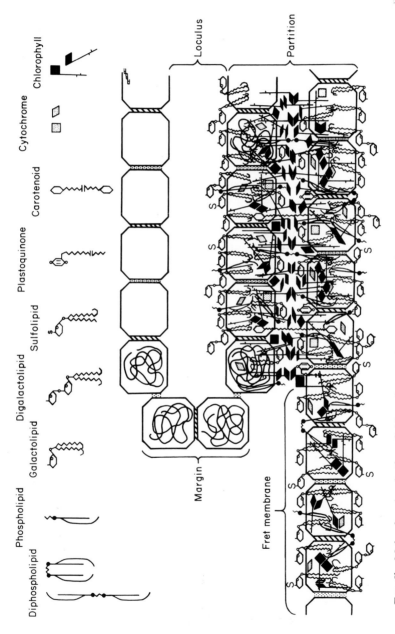

Fig. 5b. Molecular organization of chloroplast membranes as proposed by Benson and Weier. From Weier et al. (1966).

channels where a mechanism must exist to transfer them across the fret membranes to the stroma. Movement of the NADP and ADP must take place in the reverse direction back into the grana where the former is reduced and the latter is phosphorylated. The interconnection of the internal hydrophilic system facilitates energy equilibrium throughout the chloroplast. Weier *et al.* (1966) visualize the surfactant lipids as lining the surfaces of the membranes bordering the stroma, fret channels, and loculi, whereas the hydrophobic groupings are located within the partitions. Thus, the lipid moiety of the chloroplast membranes coats the inner components made up of protein subunits. This structure agrees well with that proposed above by Green and Perdue. Figures 5a,b from Weier *et al.* (1966) emphasize the complexity of the chloroplast membrane system.

The scheme of Hechter shown in Fig. 4 can be rationalized in terms of these latter theories if one visualizes the system of interlocked hexagonal discs as making up the repeating subunits of Green and Perdue and the lipoprotein subunits that constitute the double-layered partitions and single-layered granal membranes, marginal layers, and fret membranes of Weier *et al.* A further necessity is an interpenetration of the lipid bilayer with protein strands upon which the lipid is hydrophobically bound, this latter structure being less electron dense than the particulate subunits. A definite advantage of the models of Hechter and Weier *et al.* is the inclusion of definite aqueous components. When one realizes how sensitive photosynthesis and respiration are to water stress in plants (see Chapter 3, Vol. II), it is obvious that the aqueous components of cellular membranes are highly critical in their function.

Obviously there are many theories of membrane structure and function. The particular models described above seem to fit a great number of the current ideas; new theories compatible with future observational information will undoubtedly appear. Common to most theories is the picture of a multilayered structure of varying density bounded by two protein layers with water interspersed and serving as a major component. Most theories suggest that the water is highly structured, and Hechter's model explains the role of water in matters of permeability and selectivity; Weier and Benson's model, the function of aqueous phases in energy transfer.

The relation of pressure to structure and function of water in membranes has received little attention; the role of stress is not mentioned. Hence, any suggestions to be made here will be largely conjectural. Nevertheless, from our knowledge of water structure and membrane architecture, certain deductions seem justified. Since stress lowers water potential by decreasing free energy, it should have a structuring influence in somewhat the same way that solutes do. Thus, membranes in cells under stress should contain water more highly ordered than that in membranes at normal pressure.

Assuming the "flickering cluster" structure for water, in the cementing water layers of the hydrophilic portions of protein subunits, stress should make for even higher ordering; nonhydrogen-bonded molecules would be fewer; water mobility would be lowered. In the hydrophobic bonded lipo-protein and phospholipid regions, the normal squeezing out of water by the interaction of hydrocarbon tails would be accentuated; the lipoid moieties would become at least partly confluent; permeability to water and polar solutes would be lowered. At those interfaces where the flickering clusters would normally exist, withdrawal of water would tend to deplete the mobile, nonhydrogen-bonded molecules; clusters would grow and become confluent into multilayers, and movement of water and water-soluble solutes would be restricted.

Although these general functions of membranes probably would undergo alteration as described, permaselectivity for various ions probably would be less altered; general activity of cells would be lowered, but those specific functions essential to cell life probably would be carried on with little change until protoplasmic breakdown occurred and life ceased. Thus, again, in terms of membrane function water stress would lower activity and favor survival by prolonging life. It would bring growth to a halt and hence reduce production.

E. WATER AND ENZYMES

Since most life processes are catalyzed by enzymes, the relation of water to enzyme structure and function is important. All enzymes are of protein structure, and the role of water in such structures has been described above. Since the specificity of enzymes is related to structure, any change in structure caused by a change in water content should be critical. Hechter (1965) described the effect of a disturbance in the outer protein layer of a membrane that should apply equally to an enzyme. Whether the disturbance involves the opening of a sulfide bond, the introduction of electrons enabling the sulfide–sulfhydril reaction to take place, or the addition of a molecular species producing a conformational change that modifies the water structure of an aqueous chan-nel, the initiating disturbance produces a local change in associated water structures. If the structured arrangement of the water layers contributes to the conformational stability of the peptide units, as water structures are changed locally, configurational changes would occur in neighboring units so that a local perturbation is enabled to spread through the protein layers and bring about extensive alterations. Such changes should alter the geometry of the surfaces that determine enzyme specificity; changes in those reactions unique to the enzyme would undoubtedly occur.

In a review of the causes of injury in frozen and thawed cells, Mazur (1965) points to three effects of freezing: (1) temperature lowering, (2) ice formation, and (3) removal of water, raising the solute concentration in the cell. Mazur concludes that thermal shock resulting from cooling is not a major contributor to freezing injury. The formation of ice crystals may or may not be a cause of injury; slow thawing allowing recrystallization into large crystals is injurious; fast thawing has less serious effects.

Solute concentration by dehydration may prove very injurious to cells, and this is true in stress as well as in freezing. High concentrations of electrolytes can cause changes in the secondary and tertiary structure of macromolecules; they may remove lipids from membranes; and they can cause changes in pH as various species of solutes become saturated and precipitate out. Increasing concentration of cellular reactants may increase the velocity of some chemical reactions; conversely, by reducing water potential and lowering the number of nonhydrogen-bonded molecules, it might reduce the velocity of others. Thus, enzymes, through the effects of water upon their structure and through the effects of water as solvent and reaction medium, may be very definitely affected by water stress. Although the lowered water potential of water-stressed plants in general would lower mobility of water and ions, slow reaction rates, and alter synthetic processes, in the case of enzymatically controlled reactions this may not be universally true; certain reactions could be accelerated as water is removed from the cell.

F. Water as a Plant Constituent

A living plant is never completely devoid of water. Even dry seeds have a certain low moisture content; H and O are contained chemically in all carbohydrates, and water is released in their metabolism; bound water is present in cell walls and protoplasm. In fact, it may be difficult to drive all bound water from plant materials by heating because, as temperature is raised and the last bound water is leaving, caramelization and other processes start so that organic substrates are broken down chemically with a release of water; there is no clear-cut boundary between these processes.

So long as a plant lives and metabolism goes on, metabolic water comes out of the process. Such water may become bound to new metabolites; it may be recombined in synthetic processes, but traces are ultimately lost, even from seeds. In fact, seed-eating insects may derive their total supply of water from their metabolic processes, which involve oxidation of carbohydrates (Wigglesworth, 1939).

Photosynthesis goes on in an aquatic environment; the oxygen released comes from water; Clayton (1963) suggests that water is involved in electron conduction or may be directly utilized in the primary photochemical process. Thus, every product of carbohydrate metabolism carries hydrogen or oxygen derived from water. Most of the constituents of cell walls and protoplasm have these elements combined in their makeup and, hence, ultimately involve water in their synthesis. The hydrocarbon residues of cutin, plant fats, terpenes, and such components probably are the only ones not involving water of constitution. In the living plant, water of hydration and imbibition, water held osmotically in vacuoles and in phloem conduits, and water under different hydrostatic conditions in the xylem all enter into life processes of plants. As shown by experiments with isotopic water, liquid flow, diffusion across membranes, and exchange between liquid–liquid and liquid–solid phases all enter into plant water relations. Because of the physical structure of water, making up the water continuum of the plant, involving as it does hydrogen and dipole–dipole bonding which gives water its high internal pressure and surface tension, water equilibria serve as important integrating forces in plant life.

REFERENCES

Berendsen, H. J. C. (1960). The structure of water in tissue as studied by nuclear magnetic resonance. *Biol. Bull.* **119**, 287.

Berendsen, H. J. C. (1962). Nuclear magnetic resonance study of collagen hydration. *J. Chem. Phys.* **36**, 3297.

Bonner, J. (1959). Water transport. *Science* **129**, 447.

Briggs, L. J. (1950). Limiting negative pressure of water. *J. Appl. Phys.* **21**, 721.

Buswell, A. M., and Rodebush, W. H. (1956). *Water Sci. Am.* **194**, 76.

Claussen, W. F. (1951a). Suggested structures of water in inert gas hydrates. *J. Chem. Phys.* **19**, 259.

Claussen, W. F. (1951b). A second water structure for inert gas hydrates. *J. Chem. Phys.* **19**, 1425.

Clayton, R. K. (1963). Photosynthesis: Primary physical and chemical processes. *Ann. Rev. Plant Physiol.* **14**, 159.

Crafts, A. S. (1961). "Translocation in Plants." Holt, New York.

Danforth, M. D., and Levy, H. A. (1962). The structure of water at room temperature. *J. Am. Chem. Soc.* **84**:3965.

Davson, H., and Danielli, J. (1952). "Permeability of Natural Membranes," 2nd ed. Cambridge Univ. Press, London and New York.

Fernández-Morán, H. (1962). Cell-membrane ultrastructure. *Circulation* **26**, 1039.

Forslind, E. (1952). A theory of water. *Acta Polytech.* **115**, 9.

Forslind, E. (1954). Water association and hydrogels. *Proc. 2nd Intern. Congr. Rheology. Oxford, 1953.* pp. 50–63. Butterworths, London.

Frank, H. S. (1965). The structure of water. *Federation Proc.* **24**, (2), Part III, Suppl. 15, S-1.

Frank, H. S., and Wen, W. Y. (1957). III. Ion-solvent interaction. Structural aspects of ion-solvent interaction in aqueous solutions: A suggested picture of water structure. *Discussions Faraday Soc.* **24**, 133.

Gardner, W. R., and Ehlig, C. F. (1962). Impedance to water movement in soil and plant. *Science* **138**, 522.

Green, D. E., and Perdue, J. F. (1966). Membranes as expressions of repeating units. *Proc. Natl. Acad. Sci. U.S.* **24**, (2), Part III, 1295–1302.

Grjotheim, K., and Krogh-Moe, J., (1954). Correlation between structure and some properties of water. *Acta Chem. Scand.* **8**, 1193.

Haggis, G. H., Hasted, J. B., and Buchanan, T. J. (1952). The dielectric properties of water in solutions. *J. Chem. Phys.* **20**, 1452.

Hearst, J. E., and Vinograd, J. (1961). The net hydration of deoxyribonucleic acid. *Proc. Natl. Acad. Sci. U.S.* **47**, 825.

Hechter, O., (1965). Role of water structure in the molecular organization of cell membranes. *Federation Proc.* **24**, (2), Part III, Suppl. 15, S-91.

Jacobson, B. (1953). Hydration structure of deoxyribonucleic acid and its physico-chemical properties. *Nature* **172**, 666.

Kavanau, J. L. (1964). "Water and Solute Interactions." Holden-Day, San Francisco, California.

Ledbetter, M. C., and Porter, K. R. (1964). Morphology of microtubules of plant cells. *Science* **144**, 872.

Lennard-Jones, J., and Pople, J. A. (1951). Molecular association in liquids. I. Molecular association due to lone-pair electrons. *Proc. Roy. Soc.* **A205**, 155.

Ling, G. N. (1962). "A Physical Theory of the Living State." Ginn (Blaisdell) Boston, Massachusetts.

Ling, G. N. (1965). Physiology and anatomy of the cell membrane: The physical state of water in the living cell. *Federation Proc.* **24**, (2), Part III, Suppl. 15, S-103.

McMahon, B. C., Hartung, E. J., and Walbran, W. J. (1940). Studies on membrane permeability. II. Adsorption of sucrose and two salts on cupric ferrocyanide. *Trans. Faraday Soc.* **36**, 515.

Mazur, P. (1965). Causes of injury in frozen and thawed cells. *Federation Proc.* **24**, (2), Part III, Suppl. 15, S-175.

Münch, E. (1930). "Die Stoffbewegungen in der Pflanze." Fischer, Jena.

Némethy, G. (1965). Comparison of models for water and aqueous solutions. *Federation Proc.* **24**, (2), Part III, Suppl. 15, S-38.

Némethy, G., and Scheraga, H. A. (1962a). Structure of water and hydrophobic bonding in proteins. I. A model for the thermodynamic properties of liquid water. *J. Chem. Phys.* **36**, 3382.

Némethy, G., and Scheraga, H. A. (1962b). The structure of water and hydrophobic bonding in proteins. III. The thermodynamic properties of hydrophobic bonds in proteins. *J. Phys. Chem.* **66**, 1773.

Nemethy, G., and Scheraga, H. A. (1962c). Structure of water and hydrophobic bonding in proteins. II. Model for the thermodynamic properties of aqueous solutions of hydrocarbons. *J. Chem. Phys.* **36**, 3401.

Pauling, L. (1940). "The Nature of the Chemical Bond." 2nd ed. p. 304. Cornell Univ. Press, Ithaca, New York.

Pauling, L. (1959). *In* "Hydrogen Bonding" (D. Hadzi and H. W. Thompson, eds.) p. 257. Pergamon, Oxford.

Pauling, L. (1960). "The Nature of the Chemical Bond," 3rd ed. p. 257. Cornell Univ. Press, Ithaca, New York.

Pauling, L., and Marsh, R. E. (1952). The structure of chlorine hydrate. *Proc. Natl. Acad. Sci. U.S.* **38**, 112.

Philip, J. R. (1958). The osmotic cell, solute diffusibility and the plant water economy. *Plant Physiol.* **33**, 264.

Pople, J. A. (1951). Molecular association in liquids. II. A theory of the structure of water. *Proc. Roy. Soc.* **A205**, 163.

Robertson, J. D. (1964). Unit membranes: A review with recent new studies of experimental alterations and a new subunit structure in synaptic membranes. *In* "Cellular Membranes in Development" (M. Locke, ed.) p. 1. Academic Press, New York.

Scheraga, H. A. (1965). The effect of solutes on the structure of water and its implications for protein structure. *Ann. N. Y. Acad. Sci.* **125**, Article 2, 253.

Ursprung, A. (1915). Über die Kohäsion des Wassers in Farnannulus. *Ber. Deut. Botan. Ges.* **33**, 153.

Vaadia, Y., Raney, F. C., and Hagan, R. M. (1961). Plant water deficits and physiological processes. *Ann. Rev. Plant Physiol.* **12**, 265.

Verwey, E. J. (1941). The charge distribution in the water molecule and the calculation of the intermolecular forces. *Rec. Trav. Chim.* **60**, 887.

Warner, D. T. (1964). Molecular models. IV. A suggested conformation for the protein subunit of tobacco mosaic virus. *J. Theoret. Biol.* **6**, 118.

Weier, T. E., Stocking, C. R., and Shumway, L. K. (1966). The photosynthetic apparatus in chloroplasts of higher plants. *Brookhaven Symp. Biol.* **19**.

Wigglesworth, V. B., (1939). "The Principles of Insect Physiology." Dutton, New York, New York.

CHAPTER 3

TERMINOLOGY IN PLANT
AND SOIL WATER RELATIONS

S. A. Taylor

DEPARTMENT OF SOILS AND METEOROLOGY, UTAH STATE UNIVERSITY, LOGAN, UTAH

I. THE TERMINOLOGY DILEMMA

The growth of any science is accompanied by a progressive change and the growth of terms and terminology used to describe the concepts and methods of that science. When new concepts are developed and new discoveries are made, terms are used to describe them. Sometimes these terms are adaptations or changes of existing words or names that describe another concept that the investigator or author thinks is similar or analogous to the situation he is trying to describe. Other investigators approaching the subject from another point of view, and based on a different set of background experiences, may use a different term to describe the same phenomenon. A to-each-his-own term may seem to be most fitting. As more is learned about the condition being described, it is not infrequent to learn that the original descriptions and terms are not exactly right, and so new terms are introduced. Thus, several terms, each with its own adherents, are used to describe observed processes. These multiple terms tend to confuse all who have occasion to come in contact with or use the concepts, but they are particularly confusing to the student or the occasional reader.

Such a multiplicity of terms has developed in the terminology used to describe concepts and conditions associated with the stress of water in plants. It is only by continually analyzing these terms in view of new knowledge and supposedly adapting those that are most descriptive and useful that science can continue to grow. The discussion of the concepts described by the terms in use is one of the better ways for students and interested scientists to gain a thorough understanding of a complex subject. Only in this way can concensus be reached, and until this is done, each writer and investigator will continue to use the terms he likes best.

This discussion of terminology is presented with the hope of increasing the understanding of students and investigators who deal with plant and soil water relations. Consequently, it is not intended to be a glossary or catalog of the many terms used and their equivalents. Rather, a penetrating appraisal of some of the concepts and the terms used to describe them has been undertaken. The terms suggested as most appropriate today may not continue to be best when knowledge of the concept they describe becomes more complete. At the same time, several terms that were formerly used seem to be no longer adequate to describe conditions as they are understood today. Nevertheless, an attempt is made to develop a set of meaningful and consistent terms to describe a number of related concepts. If this has been properly done, the terms will be useful and may gradually replace less carefully considered terms, many of which have already served their period of usefulness.

One of the most difficult terms is water stress. This term refers to the physiological condition of water in plants and is unrelated to the usual physical definition of stress that is associated with a deforming force. Whenever the conditions of water are unfavorable to optimum plant growth, the plant is said to be under water stress. This condition is not the same for all plant species and varieties and may be different within the same plant at different times or stages of growth. The previous growth history of a plant and the status of its immediate environment have a marked influence on the soil and plant water conditions that induce stress. Thus, at any given soil water condition the plant may show no symptoms of stress if either the atmospheric desiccating conditions are low (i.e., high humidity, moderate to low temperature, no wind) or if the internal solute concentration of the tissue is high (i.e., high salt concentration or high sugar content of the cells and tissues. The same plant growing in soil at the same soil moisture condition may show stress symptoms and growth retardation if either the atmospheric conditions or the internal water status is different.

The water stress produced in plants by the presence of salts in the soil seems to be quite different physiologically from that produced by simple soil water deficit or high evaporative (transpirational) demand. The nature of plant cells and tissues produced in the two cases is visibly different; frequently, the colorings of the plant tissue are different. When stress is produced by excessive salt, the cell walls are frequently thick and heavy and often the plants do not exhibit any visible symptoms of wilting. On the other hand, stress produced by water deficit or high evaporative demand may induce moderate to severe wilting symptoms in the same variety of plants that do not wilt from salt-induced stresses.

Because of these and similar variations that may induce water conditions in the plant that are unfavorable for growth, the term water stress should and does describe a broad general concept. No attempt should be made to associate numerical values or precisely defined physical concepts with this general term. Whenever precise or descriptive terms can be used, they should be associated with one or more of the terms that describe either the state or movement of water in the soil-plant-atmosphere system.

Water deficit (WD) implies that the water content or condition is less than some optimum value. For this to be truly meaningful, there must be a clearly defined frame of reference. The most frequently used reference is pure free water at the same location in space and at the same temperature as the water under consideration (cf. Section II,C,1). This reference gives a convenient standard, that has been quite useful. Thus, the term water deficit implies that the amount or condition of water is smaller than the corresponding amount or condition in pure free water. However, the term deficit is sometimes applied in a physiological sense. For example, a soil moisture deficit may refer to some ideal condition that is impossible of precise definition, such as field capacity or saturation. Likewise, plant water deficit may be measured with reference to a moisture content that is determined by floating plant tissue for some arbitrary length of time on water. This water content may vary with the physiological condition and growth stage of the plant, so that the reference and hence the term itself becomes a variable function of the condition it purports to describe. Because of these many uses, there should be clear understanding and communication of a reference state whenever the term is used.

In addition to the two kinds of terminology problems that are illustrated by the terms water stress and water deficit, i.e., the generalization of a term by overusing it to describe a multitude of conditions and the inaccurate or careless choice of a reference state, there is a major problem associated with plant and soil water relations. This has arisen because workers of different interests and backgrounds introduced terms that were most familiar and meaningful to them. Thus, the literature contains a multitude of terms that describe essentially the same condition or process. Sometimes, however, there is no exact counterpart of a given term in a related set of terminology, so that if they are to be literally transposed to another term, an approximation must be made.

The term water content is one example. In soil science water content most frequently means the amount of water lost from the soil upon drying at 105°C, expressed either as the weight of water per unit weight of dry soil or as the volume of water per unit volume of soil in bulk. Some plant scientists express water content as the amount of water per unit dry weight of tissue while others express it as the amount of water per unit moist or the wet weight of plant material. This latter term in thermodynamics is mole fraction, providing quantities are expressed in moles.

Some hydrologists, hydraulic engineers, and others associated with these disciplines are interested in the bulk flow of liquids or solutions. They often think of fluid systems as being homogeneous and continuous. It is customary for them to use mechanical or hydraulic terms such as pressure, head, and flow velocity to describe their systems.

Physiologists and plant scientists have generally been concerned with the flow of one component of the solution, such as water, in a multicomponent system. Thus, terminology that is related to diffusion and concentration has been introduced. Sooner or later movement across a membrane becomes involved, and the somewhat artificial concept of osmotic pressure is introduced. This is artificial in that truly semipermeable membranes probably do not exist in the case of living membranes, since some kind of solute will diffuse through or enter into most such systems. Whenever differentially permeable membranes are present, the resulting pressure that can be obtained is a combination of the solute concentration and permeability characteristics of the membrane. Since osmotic pressure in its true sense is determined by solute characteristics alone, the existence of the differentially permeable membrane desecrates the term and causes one to wonder what is really meant.

When physicists and meteorologists deal with these systems, there is a tendency to use energy terms and express them in units of energy per unit mass or per unit volume, depending upon the particular system. Energy per unit volume is the same as pressure, so that if one is dealing with a single component system (such as pure water), the terms are compatible with hydraulic terminology. However, in a multicomponent system there is frequently an advantage to use energy per mole or per unit mass if the molecular weights of the substances are unknown . The latter terminology is usually preferred by those who describe the condition of water in a multicomponent system by use of thermodynamic arguments.

II. DEVELOPMENT OF A CONSISTENT SET OF TERMS

The terms associated with water and plant growth can be divided arbitrarily into different categories. Although these categories are interdependent, there are some conceptual advantages in thinking of terms that relate to the condition of water in soil and plants differently than for those that relate to movement of water. Terms dealing with atmospheric phenomena that exercise influence on plant behavior represent still a third grouping.

A. Terms Relating to the State of Water

The state of water in soil or plants refers to its physiological condition. Water that is subjected to molecular restraints of any kind is less free to enter into physiological reactions within plants than is pure free water. Restraints may result from differences in pressure, salt concentration, adsorption at colloidal interfaces, confinement in capillaries, or inadequate water supply at a particular place. It is becoming increasingly recognized that the degree of restraints on water molecules is dependent upon the temperature of the system.

1. Some Desirable Characteristics of Good Terminology

A useful set of terms should possess the following desirable characteristics.

a. Have a Valid Theoretical Basis. The terms should adequately describe a number of properties of the system, such as the physical state of water, the forces that cause water movement, the factors that resist movement, the amount or concentration of water, and the dissolved components, or forces and factors that cause water retention.

b. Describe Conditions Accurately. It would be convenient if terms could be quantitatively expressed in units and ways that could be easily combined or related by some simple mathematical equation or formula.

c. Not Suggest Unreal Concepts. The system of terms would be more useful if it were capable of expanding to encompass new but related concepts as they develop. The system should have broad application to the soil, plant, and atmosphere.

d. Have Broad Application. The basis of the terms should have a sound theoretical basis that is preferably broad enough to encompass an expansion. To be most useful, the theory should be capable of expansion and development to accompany the growth and change of the basic concepts of soil–water–plant relations.

e. Be Readily Understood. There should be no misleading suggestions. The terms should not, because of their similarity to other commonly used concepts, imply the existence of any unreal conditions.

f. Be Simple and Clear. The set of terms should be simple and clear enough to be thoroughly understood by thoughtful students.

2. Thermodynamic Basis

Terminology based on thermodynamic reasoning has been suggested by a number of researchers in both soil science and plant science (Babcock and

Overstreet, 1955, 1957; Bolt and Frissell, 1960; Broyer, 1947, 1951a,b; Day, 1942; Edlefsen, 1941; Edlefsen and Anderson, 1943; Gardner and Chatelain, 1947; Gardner, *et al.* 1951; Schofield, 1935; Slatyer and Taylor, 1960; Taylor, 1958; Taylor and Slatyer, 1960; Kramer *et al.*, 1966). Thermodynamics appears to offer a greater possibility of providing a unified terminology to which workers in both soil and plant sciences can agree than a set of terms based on any other set of reasoning yet considered. For this reason, the thermodynamics set is considered here in considerable detail.

The Gibbs free energy per unit mass (or specific volume) of water in a uniform, multicomponent system composed of solids, solutions, and gases at a given location in space has proven to be the most useful term for expressing the condition of water in the soil and plant system at any given instant. In the atmosphere the relative water vapor pressure, temperature and barometric pressure have been used. From these three variables, one can calculate, the Gibbs free energy of water in the atmosphere. At constant temperature and overall pressure the relative vapor pressure is uniquely related to the Gibbs free energy. Relative humidity and relative vapor pressure mean exactly the same thing (see Section C,2).

The soil–plant–atmosphere system is a multicomponent system composed of inert solids, reactive solids, solutes, gases such as oxygen and nitrogen, and water. In such a system one may study any single chemical species and measure its Gibbs free energy. This may then be called the partial Gibbs free energy or the potential of the particular chemical species. Hence, it is called the chemical potential. The partial Gibbs free energy of water in such a system is then known as the chemical potential of water which is usually shortened to water potential (ψ). Some have preferred to retain the term free energy of water while dropping the term Gibbs, but this has been confused with the Helmholtz free energy and now appears to be falling into disuse in favor of the more widely used term water potential.

The water potential may be defined by the Gibbs equation, which considers temperature, pressure, and composition as independent variables. Thus,

$$d\left(\frac{\partial G}{\partial n_w}\right) = \frac{\partial}{\partial n_w}\left(\frac{\partial G}{\partial T}\right) dT + \frac{\partial}{\partial n_w}\left(\frac{\partial G}{\partial P}\right) dp + \frac{\partial}{\partial n_w}\left(\frac{\partial G}{\partial n_w}\right) dn_w + \sum_j \frac{\partial}{\partial n_w}\left(\frac{\partial G}{\partial n_j}\right) dn_j$$

$$(1)$$

where G is the Gibbs free energy of the system, T and P are Kelvin temperature and total pressure on the system, n_w and n_j are the concentration (mass or mole fraction) of water and chemical species j in the system, subscript w indicates water in a system composed of many components of which water is only one, and the parentheses indicate that all variables except the one under consideration are held constant. The water content of the system may be expressed as either weight fraction, weight of water per unit dry weight material, or volume fraction, volume of water per unit bulk volume of the system, if proper care is taken in interpreting the results.

From basic thermodynamic relations it is known that $(\partial G/\partial n_w) = \mu_w$ is the potential of the chemical species that in this case is water. $(dG/dT) = -S$ where S is the entropy of the entire system, but $(\partial S/\partial n_w) = S_w$, which is the partial specific entropy of water in the system.* Likewise, $(\partial/\partial n_w)(\partial G/\partial P) = V_w$, which is the partial specific volume of water in the system. In accordance with the above pattern we may define $(\partial/\partial n_w)(\partial G/\partial n_w) = \partial\mu_w/\partial n_w = \zeta_w'$ which is the partial specific chemical potential of water in the system. It is a function of the water content and is commonly known in the soil system as the moisture retention characteristic. In soil systems the reciprocal of this term is called differential water capacity, which is defined (Aslyng, 1963) as the absolute value of the rate of change of the water content with matric or soil water suction. However, in practice the water potential is often used in place of matric suction. In the plant system it is related to the relative turgidity and varies with the type and activity of colloid in the system. The total contribution of all dissolved species j in the system can be expressed as

$$\sum_j \frac{\partial}{\partial n_w}\left(\frac{\partial G}{\partial n_j}\right)\Delta n_j = \sum_j \pi_j \,\Delta n_j$$

It has been pointed out (Bolt and Frissell, 1960) that another term to account for the work done in expanding or swelling of the system may need to be included where the matrix of the system changes. This may prove to be of considerable significance, particularly in plant systems where expansion against the wall pressure is significant. However, the effect is generally combined with the ζ_w' term as it is used and measured. In view of these considerations, the basic Eq. (1) can be written

$$d\mu_w = -S_w \, dT + V_w \, dP + \zeta_w' \, dn_w + \sum_j \pi_j \, dn_j \tag{2}$$

We can apply Eq. (2) first to pure free water at some reference temperature and atmospheric pressure and then to some arbitrary condition in the soil–plant system that is also at the reference temperature. The difference between the final arbitrary state and the reference state may then be expressed as

$$\psi = \Delta\mu_w = V_w \, \Delta P + \zeta'_{w(n_w)} \, \Delta n_w + \sum \pi_{j(n_w)} \, \Delta n_j \tag{3}$$

where $\zeta'_{w(n_w)}$ and $\pi_{j(n_w)}$ are functions that are not uniquely known but must be

---

* Some authors use a bar over the symbol to indicate partial quantities such as $\bar{S}$; however, the notation used here is that of Guggenheim (1957), in which the subscript is used to designate the partial quantities, for which water is S_w.

measured experimentally. The terms in this form of the equation are readily identified with measurable quantities.

The difference in the chemical potential of water in the system and pure free water at the same temperature, $\Delta\mu_w$, is called the water potential or moisture potential and is given the symbol ψ. A number of other terms that have been used to mean the same thing as water potential are diffusion pressure deficit (DPD), moisture stress, total moisture stress, capillary pressure, capillary potential, and suction pressure. This term, regardless of its name, represents the sum of all contributing factors to the water potential under any given set of external conditions. It can be readily measured using the vapor pressure psychrometer in any system at constant temperature (Korven and Taylor, 1959; Richards and Ogata, 1958; Monteith and Owen, 1958; Campbell et al., 1965). Temperature has a rather complicated influence on water potential so that it is necessary to make the actual determination at the same temperature at which the calibration was made (Taylor and Kijne, 1965; Klute and Richards, 1962; Zollinger et al., 1966).

The term $V_w \Delta P$ expresses the effect of an overall pressure difference between the water in the system and pure free water and is called pressure potential with the symbol ψ_p. The pressure potential results from a net pressure difference such as occurs as a result of turgor pressure in plants or hydraulic pressure in saturated soil. It does not result from a curved air–water interface or adsorption to a solid wherein some of the components or phases in the system remain at atmospheric pressure, because in these cases there is no overall pressure difference and the effect is included as part of the matric* component discussed hereafter. In arriving at this term in its present simple form, it has been assumed that the partial specific volume of water V_w is constant and independent of the pressure on the system at all water contents of the system. There is some indication that the assumption of constant V_w may not always be exactly correct (Anderson and Low, 1958); hence, it may be necessary to consider the variation in making the integration of Eq. (2). This term means the same as turgor pressure and is the negative of wall pressure (WP). It means the same as hydraulic pressure or hydraulic head, but it is different from overburden pressure or confining pressure, which is usually applied only to the solid phase of soil (Box and Taylor, 1962).

The term $\zeta'_{w(n_w)} \Delta n_w$ is attributable to the more or less solid colloidal matrix of the soil or plant system; hence, it is called matric potential. There have been conditions where the dry soil rather than pure free water has been used as the reference (Taylor and Kijne, 1965). This has certain special applications, but the present practice of using pure free water as the reference appears to be more useful for the combined soil–water–plant–atmosphere system.

* Matric is the adjective form of the noun matrix.

The moisture retention characteristic $\zeta'_{w(n_w)}$ is generally not constant but varies with both moisture content and the water history of the system (hysteresis). Consequently, it is usually not possible to calculate the term $\zeta'_{w(n_w)} \Delta n_w$ from a measurement of the water content. At a given moisture content with constant temperature, pressure, and solute concentration, the water in the system may be brought into equilibrium across a matrix impermeable membrane according to the equation $\zeta'_{w(n_w)} \Delta n_w = V_w \Delta P$, where V_w is the specific volume of water and ΔP is the tensiometric pressure or matric suction ζ. Since these two terms are equivalent ways of expressing the attraction of the matrix for water, either of them ($\zeta'_{w(n_w)} \Delta n_w$ or $V_w' \Delta\zeta$) is called the matric potential (τ) and herein given the symbol ψ_m. The matric potential can be readily measured by use of pressure plate or pressure membrane equipment. In the case of soils it may also be measured with tensiometers (Taylor, 1958; Taylor, et al., 1961). Similar techniques have been used by Wiebe (1966) to measure the matric potential vs. water content relation in some colloids of plant origin. The matric potential means the same as soil moisture tension, soil suction, matric or soil water suction, and imbibitional pressure.

Since $\zeta'_{w(n_w)} \Delta n_w = V_w' \Delta\zeta$ when the system is at constant temperature, Eq. (3) may be expressed as

$$\psi = \Delta\mu_w = V_w \Delta P + V_w' \Delta\zeta + \sum \pi_{j(n_w)} \Delta n_j \qquad (4)$$

where V_w differs from V_w' in that V_w is the specific volume of pure water while V_w' is the specific volume of the adsorbed or matrix water.

The term $\pi_{j(n_w)} \Delta n_j$ expresses the combined effect of all solute species present. It could be calculated if both the mole fraction and the effect of all the separate species in solution were known. In the water–soil–plant system it is more appropriate to estimate these effects from special measurements. Since this term expresses the effect of all solutes on water potential, it is called solute potential and given the symbol ψ_π. The term could be measured in equivalent pressure units by equilibrating water across an ideal solute impermeable membrane at constant T, P, and n_w (or ζ) to get $\sum \pi_{j(n_w)} \Delta n_j = V_w \Delta\Pi$ where $\Delta\Pi$ is the solute (or osmotic) suction π. However, most membranes are not ideal and show some degree of permeability to solutes as well as to water, in which case the measurement is a function of the relative permeability of the membrane for solutes and water, as will be seen later. One membrane that is ideal is an air gap. Consequently, one may measure the water potential of a solution with a vapor pressure psychrometer (Korven and Taylor, 1959; Richards and Ogata, 1958; Monteith and Owen, 1958; Campbell et al., 1965). At constant T, P, and n_w this measurement gives the solute potential. The term solute potential expresses similar meaning to osmotic pressure, solute pressure, osmotic suction, and solute suction. As it has been generally used, the term "osmotic potential" (OP), however, refers to the combined solute and matric potentials when applied to plant materials. At the present time, it seems appropriate that this use of the term be continued. When applied to soil systems (Aslyng, 1963) this sum (osmotic suction plus matric suction) is called "total suction."

Measurement of the various components of the water potential requires that certain other variables be held constant. The total potential will include any and all factors that are present at the time the measurement is made. Thus, if the psychrometric method for measuring vapor pressure is used, the experimental conditions of the measurement will determine what components of the potential are being measured. The vapor pressure must be measured at some temperature which may be different from the temperature at which the sample was taken, but still all measurements are finally made at the same temperature. Hence, the temperature effect, if any, is eliminated, and the measurements made are comparable to all others made at the same temperature. Generally, the overall pressure on the system is constant, but the degree of turgor may change. Thus, if measurements are made in living plant tissue, a turgor pressure term will be included, but if they are made on unsaturated soil that is open to the atmosphere, there will be no pressure term. If the sample of living tissue is killed by freezing, e.g., and another measurement is made, there is no more turgor pressure component, so that the result is the combination of the matric and solute potentials. This term has been called the osmotic pressure and is the condition that is here called osmotic potential. When made on soil, this potential has sometimes been called total soil moisture stress, moisture stress, or total suction. In addition, if the system contains no solutes, the method measures the matric potential. On the other hand, if there is only solution and no solid portion, the method measures only the solute potential.

Measurements of matric potential require that temperature, reference pressure, and solute content be constant throughout. Normally, it is possible to get constant temperature, and atmospheric pressure is usually sufficiently constant to be used for pressure. For all except the most exacting measurements the tensiometer, pressure plate, and pressure membrane equipment meet the necessary criterion for constant solute content because the membranes are permeable to solutes and at equilibrium the activities of the solutes in the soil and in the reference solution are the same. The activity in this case is usually a satisfactory estimate of the concentration.

Freezing point methods do not meet this criterion, however, since there is an activity difference between ice, which freezes as pure water, and soil solution, which contains solutes. Likewise, vapor pressure methods have a solute difference between pure water vapor, which has no dissolved solutes, and the water solution. Hence, if freezing point or vapor pressure methods are used for measuring matric potential, some independent method must be used to measure the solute potential at constant pressure and temperature, which value must then be subtracted from the total potential to give the matric potential at the reference temperature and pressure.

The solute potential ψ_π is identified with osmotic pressure in both plant and soil literature. It can be estimated with varying degrees of accuracy by established methods for determining osmotic pressure in plant systems (Crafts *et al.*, 1949). In soil systems it can be established from the osmotic potential of the saturation extract by adjusting to the actual soil water content (Richards, 1954). It can also be obtained by subtracting the matric potential from the total potential measured in a homogeneous system at constant temperature and reference pressure.

a. Flexibility of the System. Thermodynamic terminology has a degree of flexibility in that new components of the total potential may be separated as they are identified. The terms may be applied to systems that are not at constant temperature using either of two or more approaches. One may define a standard temperature state, such as 25°C (Taylor, 1958), to which all potentials are referred. It is then necessary to add another term ψ_T to the total potential Eqs. (3) and (4). This temperature potential term is given by

$$\int_{T_0}^{T} - S_w \, dT$$

Temperature relations have been studied to some extent (Taylor, 1958; Taylor and Stewart, 1960; Taylor and Kijne, 1965), but considerably more elaboration is needed in both plant and soil systems.

A second approach is that suggested by recent application of irreversible thermodynamics to soil and plant systems (Taylor, 1965; Taylor and Cary, 1964; Prigogine, 1961). Temperature influences the flow of water in two distinct ways: by influencing the water potential as discussed above and by inducing water flow directly along the thermal gradient. It is possible to combine these two influences into one, called the thermal gradient or thermal potential, and to have the constant temperature water potential as an independent factor.

In order to distinguish these two factors, which are quite different yet basically involve temperature, the first may be called the "temperature potential" and the latter the "thermal potential."

b. Gravitational Influence. Whenever the water in a system under consideration is located at some point in space different from that of the established reference, another term must be added to account for the work that must be done against the force of gravity in moving from the reference location to that in question. Thus, a gravitational potential has been defined as " the amount of work that must be done per unit quantity of pure water in order to transport reversibly and isothermally an infinitesimal quantity of water from a pool containing a solution identical in composition to the soil water (or plant solution) at a specified elevation at atmospheric pressure, to a similar pool at the elevation of the point under consideration" (Aslyng, 1963). Thus, the gravitational potential ψ_g is

$$\psi_g = \rho_w gh \tag{5}$$

where ρ_w is the density of water, g is the acceleration of gravity, and h is the vertical distance between the reference and the point in question.

Gravity is normally the only external force field that is operating on water in the soil–plant system. Hence, the total water potential ψ_{total} is given by

$$\psi_{total} = \psi + \psi_g \tag{6}$$

However, if other external force fields are present, they must also be considered.

c. *Ease of Understanding the Terminology.* It can be argued that a set of terms based on thermodynamics is easier to grasp and understand than a set based on mechanics. This is because terms based on mechanics may be misleading and suggest concepts that are untrue when applied to colloidal systems. For example, the concept that water in porous systems high in colloids exists in capillaries in which there are curved air–water interfaces is frequently untrue and just as often as not the interfaces that are there may be so much influenced by the solid–liquid interface that the curved air–water interface does not control the pressure in the liquid. Under such conditions it is much better to consider the water in this system to have a reduced energy as suggested by the water potential concept. The final result is that the terms based on either mechanical and pressure concepts or thermodynamic and energy concepts are about equally understandable, and the reason students have difficulty appears to be that the concepts they represent are generally understood only vaguely. Once a clear understanding of the basic concepts is obtained, then either set of terms, if carefully used, expresses the desired meaning.

The mechanical concept is based on the idea that water in unsaturated soil or living plant tissue is generally under a tension or a pressure deficit, meaning that the pressure is less than it would be in pure free water at the same location in space. Since the pressure is less than that of pure free water the potential is negative, but workers have tried to avoid the negative sign by using the term suction, which is negative pressure, or the term water deficit, which is measured in a negative direction. Furthermore, there is a general concept that a difference in diffusion pressure deficit or suction causes water to flow from the region of low suction to that of higher suction, when in reality this difference represents only one of several possible forces. Whether flow actually occurs depends upon a number of factors, most important of which are the permeability of the system or resistance to flow and the continuity of the phases. Also, the concept applies quite well to flow in the liquid phase but does not easily apply to flow wherein one or more phase changes, either from the liquid to the solid, liquid to gas, or even free liquid to adsorbed liquid, is involved. In these cases, one must change his concept from that of fluid flow along a hydraulic gradient to that of diffusion flow. Such difficulties are not difficult to explain, but they do cause some confusion, particularly with the learner.

The thermodynamic and energy concept implies that water is held in the soil or plant system by certain forces that must be overcome if it is to be removed. The amount of work required to remove a unit mass of water from the system in the form of pure free water at the same location and temperature is exactly the water potential. Since work must be done on the system to remove water, the potential is negative. Although it has not been done generally, the negative sign could be eliminated by substituting affinity, which like suction is directed opposite to the energy potential. Then, in place of water potential, one would use the term water affinity; instead of matric potential, he would use matric affinity; for solute potential, he would use solute affinity; etc. At the present time it seems to be preferable to use the potential terminology with the negative sign, where applicable, to show that work must be done to remove water. The use of the positive sign with potential should be avoided since that implies that water contained in the system is able to do work on its surroundings during the removal process.

The use of the energy potential with the negative sign, then, has clear meaning and can be combined through irreversible thermodynamics with other driving forces such as thermal, electrical, or solute concentration gradients, any of which may cause water to flow in the system in the absence of a hydraulic gradient and even in opposition to a hydraulic gradient at times. Flow terms are discussed in more detail in Section II,B.

If one understands the energy concept of soil and plant water, he can readily relate the associated terms to the mechanical or pressure terminology, since energy per unit volume is expressed in pressure units. The equivalent pressure is thus the minimum pressure that must be applied to water in the system to raise it to the state of pure free water. This is equivalent in magnitude, but opposite in sign, to the work per unit volume that must be done to remove an infinitesimal amount of water from the system. With this concept clearly in mind, it makes little difference whether the potentials are expressed in units of pressure or units of work per unit mass so long as the density of the water in its adsorbed state in the soil–plant system is clearly known and so long as one does not try to combine potentials expressed in one way with other potentials expressed in different units.

All of the potential terms can be expressed in different units, and the general term as discussed to this point does not distinguish the physical dimensions. Sometimes it is desirable to distinguish the reference condition. This can be done readily by introducing the term specific if potential is expressed as energy per unit mass, molar if expressed as energy per mole, or volumetric if expressed as energy per unit volume. Thus, one may have specific, molar, or volumetric water potential. The same modifying words may be applied to any or all of the component potentials. The units of specific water potential are ergs per gram or joules per kilogram; of molar potential, ergs per mole or joules per mole; and of volumetric potential, bar (10^6 ergs/cm^3 or 10^2 joules/liter) or millibar (10^{-3} bars).

If one wishes to study the simultaneous movement of two things, such as heat and water, solutes and water, electricity and water, electricity and solutes, or of three things, such as heat, water, and solutes, he must be careful that all of the potentials are expressed in the same consistent set of units. It has been found that if one consistently uses the meter-kilogram-second (mks) or the centimeter-gram-second (cgs) systems the results of electrical, thermal, and material energy are compatible. One may also use a combination of the mks and the cgs systems, in which case he may need to multiply or divide some of his units by appropriate powers of ten to make them compatible with his other units. It is useful and convenient to express the potential in terms of joules (10^7 ergs) per kilogram (10^3 gm); see Table I.

TABLE I

EQUIVALENT UNITS

Term	cgs	mks
Length	Centimeter (cm)	Meter (m) $= 10^2$ cm
Mass	Gram (gm)	Kilogram (kg) $= 10^3$ gm
Time	Second (sec)	Second (sec)
Force	Dyne (gm cm sec^{-2})	Newton (kg m sec^{-2}) $= 10^5$ dynes
Pressure	Barye (dyne cm^{-2})	Newton m^{-2} $= 10$ barye
	Bar $= 10^6$ barye	Bar $= 10^5$ Newton m^{-2}
Energy	Erg (dyne-cm)	Joule (Newton $-$ m) $= 10^7$ ergs
Heat	Erg	Joule
Mechanical	Erg	Joule
Electrical	Watt sec	Kw$-$sec$= 10^3$ watt sec

The most frequently used unit of pressure is the standard atmosphere, which is the weight of a column of dry air at sea level under an arbitrary condition of temperature. It is equal to the pressure of a column of mercury 76 cm high. This unit is purely empirical and is not consistent with any system of units now in use. Such a unit may be used so long as it is compared only with other terms that are expressed in the same units. It becomes inconvenient when it is combined with other units because inexact conversion factors must be applied, as shown in Table II. Pressure is also expressed in terms of equiva-

TABLE II

Units of Water Potential or Affinity and their Equivalents at 25°C

Energy units		Equivalent tension or suction units if density of water is 1.000 gm/cm^3					
ergs/gm	joules/kg	bars	milli-bars	centi-bars	atm	cm of water	Activity at 25°C
1	0.0001	0.000001	0.001	0.0001	0.0000009870	0.001017	1.000000
10000	1	0.01	10	1	0.009870	10.17	0.999993
1000000	100	1	1000	100	0.9870	1017	0.999272
1000	0.1	0.001	1	0.1	0.0009870	1.017	0.999999
10000	1	0.01	10	1	0.009870	10.17	0.999993
1013000	101.3	1.013	1013	101.3	1	1030	0.999366
983.0	0.09833	0.0009833	0.9833	0.09833	0.0009703	1	0.999999
0	0	0	0	0	0	0	1 (exactly)

lent heights of a column of mercury or water such as 64 cm of mercury or 864 cm of water. The only justification for continuing to use these units is that they are traditional and hence familiar. Such a reason seems rather weak compared to the arguments in favor of a consistent set of units that may be combined and compared readily with other units that express similar concepts. These inconsistent pressure units should gradually be replaced with the consistent units of the bar (or millibar).

The use of the term calorie to express heat units is based entirely on the specific heat of water. Since this value is not the same at all temperatures, it has been necessary to define the temperature at which the measurement is made. Thus, the calorie is defined as the amount of heat required to raise 1 gm of water from 15 to 16°C. The unit defined in this way is, like the atmosphere, inconsistent with all existing systems of units. For the sake of consistency, this heat unit should gradually be replaced with the erg or the more practical unit of the joule.

B. Terms Relating to Flow in the Plant and Its Environment

Water and associated solutes move through the soil, plant, and atmosphere as a result of interacting factors. Any material, whether it be water, sugars, salts, or other solutes, moves through soil–plant–atmosphere systems as a result of forces acting upon the material in such a way as to impart to it a tendency for movement in a particular direction. The rate of flow, and in fact the occurrence of flow, depends not only upon the combined forces but also upon the resistance to flow offered by the medium.

1. Expressing Flow

In general, flow of any material through a particular cross section of medium J_i depends upon a combination of all of the forces X_j and resistances acting upon the system. It is convenient to think of the reciprocal of the resistances as conductivities L_{ij}. The general situation can be expressed by the equation (Taylor and Cary, 1964; Prigogine, 1961; DeGroot and Mazur, 1962)

$$J_i = \sum_j L_{ij} X_j \tag{7}$$

Thus, any flow J_i is a linear combination of the products of all forces X_j acting on the system by the corresponding conductivity L_{ij}. In the general case, any force can give rise to any flow. For instance, an electrical potential gradient and a thermal gradient as well as a water potential gradient may cause water flow. Equations of the type expressed by Eq. (7) are called general flow equations. The flows represented by J_i are called fluxes, flows, or currents. The transfer coefficients or conductivities represented by L_{ij} are called phenomenological coefficients; if $i = j$ they are direct transfer coefficients, and if $i \neq j$ they are called linked transfer coefficients. Sometimes the linked transfer coefficients are called interaction coefficients. The forces represented by X_j are generally potential gradients of one kind or another.

Under conditions wherein only one force is acting and the only flow that occurs is that of the material directly related to the force, the flow is said to be conjugate with the force. Thus, if the only force acting is a water potential gradient, then the conjugate flux is that of water. Under these conditions, the general flow equation reduces to Darcy's law, which is called a phenomenological equation, i.e.,

$$J_w = -L_{ww} \nabla\phi \qquad \text{or} \qquad Q = -K\nabla\phi \tag{8}$$

where J_w and Q represent the water flux, L_{ww} and K represent the hydraulic conductivity, and $\nabla\phi$ is the water potential gradient.

Other phenomenological equations are Fourier's law of heat transfer, Ohm's law for electrical flow, and Fick's law for diffusion.

a. *Interacting Flows.* Osmotic flow, electro-osmotic flow, and thermo-osmotic flow are examples of processes in which water flows through a membrane in response to a solute concentration gradient, an electrical potential gradient, or a temperature gradient, respectively. As an example, Eq. (7) for thermo-osmotic flow is

$$Q = J_w = -L_{wq} \nabla(1/T) \tag{9}$$

which expresses the flux of water Q or J_w that occurs in response to a temperature gradient ($\nabla 1/T$) and where L_{wq} is the linked transfer coefficient which expresses the tendency for heat to carry water with it as it moves through the particular system under consideration.

b. Fluxes. The terms J_i in Eq. (7) are called fluxes, flows, or currents and represent the amount of material flowing through a particular cross section in unit time. If materials are flowing and their quantity is measured in mass units, then the term is called mass flux; if it is expressed in volume units, it is called volume flux. The flux divided by the area of the cross section is called flux density. Frequently, the term flux is used synonymously with flux density so that one must be alert to the particular usage in order to know exactly what is meant.

When heat is flowing, the term is called heat flux or thermal flux. Electrical flux is generally called electrical current. A flow of salt may be called salt flux, while solute flux may be assigned to the flow of any dissolved material.

c. Velocities. When material flow is expressed as a volume flux the terms have the dimensions of velocity. However, if the material is a liquid flowing slowly through a channel, such as a capillary, a conducting vessel or a pore, the flow is generally laminar. The velocity of particle movement directly in contact with the walls of the channel is essentially zero, but it increases with distance from the walls to a maximum value in the center. This means that the flux, which is expressed as a velocity, represents some weighted mean or average value of the many velocities with which the particles are actually moving. Also, in porous materials the paths that particles of liquid must follow are seldom straight but are usually tortuous. Thus, any particle has further to go and hence would move faster than is suggested by the mean velocity. One must be careful when dealing with the term *velocity of flow* to distinguish between the mean velocity and the actual velocity of individual particles.

2. Driving Forces

The driving forces expressed in Eq. (7) are usually gradients or differences of some kind of potential. Thus, the conjugate driving force for water flow is the total water potential gradient or difference. A gradient of any one of the components of the water potential may cause flow in the absence of all other gradients. Hence, water may flow along a gravitational potential gradient, a pressure gradient, a matric potential gradient, or a solute potential gradient when only one of the gradients is operating. However, if two or more gradients, such as the gravitational potential and the matric potential, are present in the same system at the same time, water will flow along the gradient that results from combining the forces in a vectorial manner.

If thermal gradients or solute potential gradients occur in a system along with a matric, pressure, or gravitational potential gradient, the forces may not be vectorially combined but rather must be considered separately since the mechanism for water flow is different for water flowing in response to a thermal gradient, a solute potential gradient, and a matric potential gradient. This requires that the transfer coefficient for the various types of flow will be different; hence, the forces must be combined with the appropriate transfer coefficient according to Eq. (7) before they are combined to express the flux.

a. Affinities. Sometimes the forces causing flow are expressed as affinities rather than as potential gradients. In effect, affinities are simply differences in potentials for systems at constant temperature and in the absence of external force fields. The particular advantage of the use of affinities over potentials is that flow occurs in the direction of increasing affinity while it is generally in the direction of decreasing potential. Hence, a negative sign usually appears in the phenomenological equation for flow when forces are expressed in potential terms and is absent if expressed in terms of affinities. For example, a pressure difference may represent a potential difference while a suction difference may represent an affinity.

b. Interacting Forces. If the forces represented by X_j in Eq. (7) are properly chosen, the complimentary linked transfer coefficients are equal, i.e., $L_{ij} = L_{ji}$. This means that the transfer coefficient relating the flow of water in response to a solute concentration difference, e.g., is equal to the flow of solute in response to a water potential difference. Said in another way, the tendency for water to carry solutes through a system is equal to the tendency for solutes to carry water through the same system. Such relations are called reciprocal relations and are often called Onsager's reciprocal relations after the name of the man who first identified them (Onsager, 1931a,b).

There are a large number of possibilities for choosing the forces that will be used, but in order for the reciprocal relations to be valid, they must be written in terms of measurable parameters. Furthermore, they must be chosen in such a manner that the sum of the products of the forces by their conjugate fluxes must be equal to the time rate of increase of internal entropy of the system, i.e.,

$$\frac{d_i s}{dt} = \sum_j J_j X_j \tag{10}$$

Development of this equation for any given system thus specifies X_j in thermodynamic parameters. Generally, X_j assumes the form of a chemical potential of any given species divided by the absolute temperature, i.e., $X_j = -\Delta\mu_j/T$ for a given molecular species. For thermal gradients, $X_j = \Delta\, 1/T$ or $-\Delta T/T^2$.

3. Resistance to Flow–Transfer Coefficients

The transfer coefficients are in general determined by the properties of the medium through which flow occurs, i.e., size and shape of pores, voids, and passages in soil material and plant materials. They may also depend upon the mechanism of flow; thus, a coefficient for mass flow will be different than for film flow or gaseous diffusion through the same medium. In case two or more kinds of flow take place through a particular medium at the same time, it is desirable to identify the coefficients with the kind of flow that takes place. Thus, one may write vapor transfer coefficient when referring to the flow of water vapor through the medium, liquid transfer coefficient when referring to liquid flow, or film transfer coefficient when referring to film flow through the same medium.

a. Conductivities and Permeabilities. The direct transfer coefficients L_{ii} are sometimes called conductivities or permeabilities. The reciprocals of these values are called resistivities or resistances. It is desirable to distinguish the material that is flowing by modifying adjectives such as thermal conductivity for heat flow, hydraulic conductivity for water flow, electrical conductivity for electrical flow, etc.

It has become customary to refer to the transfer coefficient in Darcy's Eq. (8) as permeability and to give it the symbol K. This term strictly applies to the mass flow of a liquid through a porous material. However, it has been applied to gaseous flow through a porous body as well as to the diffusive flow of liquid. The term hydraulic conductivity has achieved preference for the transfer coefficient describing the viscous flow of water through soil, i.e., the flux of water per unit of hydraulic (water) potential. The transfer depends upon properties of both the porous body and the permeating liquid. In order to have a coefficient that depends only upon the properties of the porous medium, the viscosity and density of the fluid may be separated from the hydraulic conductivity, in which case the transfer coefficient is supposed to be independent of fluid properties. The resulting transfer coefficient is then called intrinsic permeability or simply permeability. This use of the term permeability differs from the general use of the term as described above so that a reader must be alert to know what is meant when the term is used.

When water moves in unsaturated porous systems such as soils, the water content usually changes as water moves into the system. Thus, it has become convenient to define soil water diffusivity as the hydraulic conductivity divided by the differential water capacity (care should be taken to be consistent with units) or the flux of water per unit gradient of moisture content in the absence of other force fields (Aslyng, 1963). This term is intended to be analogous to thermal diffusivity ,which is the thermal conductivity divided by the heat capacity. When referred to the diffusion of gases, vapors, or solutes the term diffusivity is generally synonymous with coefficient of diffusion and is simply related, usually by a dimensional conversion factor, to the appropriate direct transfer coefficients of Eq. (7).

b. Interaction Coefficients. The interaction coefficients L_{ij} and L_{ji} express the linked transfer coefficients of Eq. (7). They have been called by a number of names, depending upon the interaction being described. Thus, the hydrothermal coefficient refers to the transfer of water in response to a thermal gradient, L_{wT}. Conversely, the thermal hydrocoefficient refers to the transfer of heat in response to a water potential gradient. In a similar manner one may define a hydrosolute coefficient L_{ws}, a hydroelectric coefficient L_{we}, a thermoelectric coefficient, an electrosolute coefficient, etc.

In dealing with the simultaneous movement of solutes and water, the ratio of the hydrosolute coefficient to the direct water transfer coefficient L_{ws}/L_{ww} has been found to be useful. This ratio has been called the reflection coefficient because it expresses the deviation of the behavior of a real membrane from that of an ideal semipermeable membrane.

C. Terms Relating to Energy Balance in the Biosphere

The only type of radiation of concern in soil–water–plant relations is that emitted by a body by virtue of its temperature. This is called thermal radiation to distinguish it from other radiation such as X-rays, γ-rays, radio signals, microwave radar, etc. Thermal radiation from the sun is the only thermal energy input of significance for the earth and its atmosphere. At the same time, the earth and its atmosphere are radiating to space, but the wavelength of the outgoing radiation is longer than that of the incoming radiation. The wavelength of radiation depends upon the temperature of the radiating body; thus, incoming radiation from the sun covers a band from about 0.3 to 3.0 μ. This is called shortwave radiation. The much-cooler earth radiates in a broader band with wavelengths greater than 3 μ and a maximum near 10 μ. All thermal radiation with wavelengths greater than 3 μ is called longwave radiation.

The atmosphere tends to form a blanket allowing the shortwave radiation to pass through but retarding the outflow of long-wave radiation. This blanket modifies the heating and cooling effects that would occur when the earth is exposed to the sun during the day and to cold space during the night, thus reducing the magnitude of the diurnal temperature fluctuations. This modifying effect has considerable biological significance since without it the life processes as they occur on the Earth would be greatly modified, if they could occur at all. Nevertheless, the net outgoing radiation from the earth and its atmosphere as a whole is very near to the net incoming radiation. Otherwise, the earth would be heating or cooling faster than it is. Thus, we have an overall energy balance in the biosphere. Nevertheless, within any local area over a part of the year or for any day at the surface of the land (soil, plant cover, or water) there will be a difference between the total incoming and outgoing radiation. This difference is called net radiation or net radiation flux.

1. Radiation

Radiant flux, like the other fluxes defined in Section II,B in connection with Eq. (7), is the amount of radiant energy per unit time emitted, received, or transmitted across a particular area. The flux divided by the area across which it is transmitted is called radiant flux density. The radiant flux density emitted by a source is called the radiant emittance or emissive power.

In biological literature the term radiant intensity is often used loosely to be synonymous with radiant flux density. However, in a physical sense this is incorrect, and the term radiant intensity is defined as the radiant flux per unit solid angle in any particular direction. If the radiant flux I is the same in all directions, then the radiant flux density R is exactly $R = \pi I$ (π is used here in a mathematical sense). The fraction of the incident radiation intensity that is absorbed by a body is the absorption coefficient, also called absorptivity. The reflection coefficient or reflectivity is the fraction of the incident radiation intensity that is reflected, and the transmission coefficient or transmissivity is the fraction that is transmitted.

The average flux density of solar radiation at the outer edge of the earth's atmosphere is called the solar constant and has a value of 1.94 cal cm^{-2} min^{-1} (8.1 joules/cm^2/min or 1350 watts/m^2). As the radiation passes downward through the atmosphere, the intensity is reduced by several processes of interest. Some of the radiation is reflected from clouds. This reflection occurs in all directions; hence, it is called diffuse reflection. Some of the energy is absorbed in the atmosphere by the gases, vapors, and suspended solids that are present. Still another part of the shortwave radiation is scattered by the atmosphere. The downward scattered and reflected radiation is called sky radiation. The sum of the shortwave radiation coming directly from the sun and from sky radiation is called global radiation.

Horizontal air motion (wind) carries thermal energy and water vapor with it. If either of these properties is significantly different in the transported air than would normally exist in the air being displaced at a particular location, the difference is called advective flux and the process is called advection. Thus, one may have advective energy if extra heat is carried by wind or advective humidity if extra water vapor is carried by wind. Advection may be positive or negative, depending upon whether the meteorological property is moving into or out of a particular area. These processes are of importance in assessing the short-time energy balance of a particular plant cover or a specific location. This effect may have considerable influence on the evapotranspiration of an irrigated region surrounded by or adjacent to an extensive dry area.

2. Atmospheric Humidity

A small but biologically significant portion of the atmosphere is made up of water vapor. The balance of the atmosphere is composed of dry air and a small amount of impurities. The impurities are called pollutants. The pressure exerted by water vapor is essentially independent of the pressure exerted by other atmospheric gas; consequently, one refers to the partial pressure of water vapor or simply the vapor pressure of water. If equilibrium conditions exist, i.e., no evaporation or condensation is taking place in the volume under consideration, the behavior of water vapor can be closely approximated by the ideal gas laws. Under these conditions, the vapor pressure p is given by

$$p = \frac{\rho_v}{M_w} RT \tag{11}$$

where ρ_v is the density of water vapor, M_w is the molecular weight of water (18 gm mole^{-1}), R is the universal gas constant (8.31×10^7 ergs mole^{-1} deg^{-1}), and T is the Kelvin temperature of the water vapor (generally taken as the temperature of the air of which the water vapor is one component). The density of water vapor ρ_v in the air is referred to as the absolute humidity, with dimensions of gm cm^{-3} (since this is such a small quantity ρ_v is usually tabulated as gm m^{-3}).

When in equilibrium with a pure free water surface, the vapor pressure reaches a certain value that depends upon the temperature of the air (at equilibrium, air and water surface will be at the same temperature). This value is called the saturation vapor pressure. Under normal circumstances the saturation vapor pressure is a unique function of temperature and can be found in reference handbooks.

The vapor pressure of the atmosphere around plants and over the soil varies considerably, but except for special situations it is always equal to or less than the saturation vapor pressure. The difference between the saturation vapor pressure p_0 and the existing vapor pressure p at any given air temperature is called saturation deficit and is represented by $(p_0 - p)$. Relative humidity h_r is defined by the ratio p/p_0 and is always less than one. This fraction is commonly multiplied by 100 to give percent relative humidity (rh $= 100\, h_r = 100\, p/p_0$).

At any particular vapor density, there is a temperature at which condensation just begins to take place. This corresponds to the temperature to which the vapor must be reduced in order to become saturated and is called the dew-point temperature or simply the dew-point. The dew-point temperature and wet-bulb temperature are not the same since the evaporation from a wet thermometer both decreases the temperature of the air by withdrawing latent heat from it and at the same time increases the vapor pressure by evaporating water. Thus, the temperature of the wet bulb depends upon the rate of air flow as well as its vapor density. However, it has been found that if the air flows past the wet bulb at a sufficiently high rate (greater than about 2 m sec^{-1}) a steady lower temperature is reached that is insensitive to further increases in flow velocity. This steady lower temperature is called the wet-bulb temperature.

The ratio of the mass of water vapor m_v to the mass of dry air m_a with which the vapor is associated is called the mixing ratio. The ratio of the mass of water vapor to that of moist air is called the specific humidity. Thus, the mixing ratio is m_v/m_a, while the specific humidity is $m_v/(m_a + m_v)$. Since the mass of vapor m_v is small in comparison to m_a, these two ratios have nearly the same numerical values for normal atmospheric air.

REFERENCES

Anderson, D. M., and Low, P. F. (1958). The density of water adsorbed on lithium, sodium and potassium bentonite. *Soil Sci. Soc. Am. Proc.* **22**, 99.

Aslyng, H. C. (1963). Soil Physics Terminology, Report of Terminology Committee, Commission I (Soil Physics). *Intern. Soc. Soil Sci. Bull.* **22**, 5.

Babcock, K. L., and Overstreet, R. (1955). Thermodynamics of soil moisture: A new application. *Soil Sci.* **80**, 257.

Babcock, K. L., and Overstreet, R. (1957). A note on the "Buckingham" equation. *Soil Sci.* **84**, 341.

Bolt, G. H., and Frissell, M. J. (1960). Thermodynamics of soil moisture. *Netherlands J. Agr. Sci.* **8**, 57.

Box, J. E., and Taylor, S. A. (1962). Influence of soil bulk density on matric potential. *Soil Sci. Soc. Am. Proc.* **26**, 119.

Broyer, T. C. (1947). The movement of materials into plants. I. Osmosis and the movement of water into plants. *Botan. Rev.* **13**, 1.

Broyer, T. C. (1951a). An outline of energetics in relation to the movement of materials through a two-phased solution system. *Plant Physiol.* **26**, 598.

Broyer, T. C. (1951b). Further theoretical considerations of modes of expression and factors possibly concerned in the movement of materials through a two-phased solution system. *Plant Physiol.* **26**, 655.

Campbell, G. S., Zollinger, W. D., and Taylor, S. A. (1965). Sample changer for thermocouple psychrometer: Construction and some applications. *Agron. J.* **58**, 315.

Crafts, A. S., Currier, H. B., and Stocking, C. R. (1949). "Water in the Physiology of Plants." Chronica Botanica, Waltham, Massachusetts.

Day, P. R. (1942). The moisture potential of soils. *Soil Sci.* **54**, 391.

DeGroot, S. R., and Mazur, P. 1962. "Non Equilibrium Thermodynamics." North-Holland Publ., Amsterdam.

Edlefsen, N. E. (1941). Some thermodynamic aspects of the use of soil-moisture by plants. *Trans. Am. Geophys. Union* **22**, 917.

Edlefsen, N. E., and Anderson, A. B. C. (1953). Thermodynamics of soil moisture. *Hilgardia* **15**, 31.

Gardner, W., and Chatelain, J. (1947). Thermodynamics and soil moisture. *Soil Sci. Soc. Am. Proc.* **11**, 100.

Gardner, W. H., Gardner, W. H., and Gardner, W. (1951). Thermodynamics of soil moisture. *Soil Sci.* **72**, 101.

Guggenheim, E. A. (1957). "Thermodynamics," 3rd ed. North-Holland Publ., Amsterdam.

Klute, A., and Richards, L. A. (1962). Effect of temperature on relative vapor pressure of water in soil: Apparatus and preliminary measurements. *Soil Sci.* **93**, 391.

Korven, H. C., and Taylor, S. A. (1959). The Peltier effect and its use for determining relative activity of soil water. *Can. J. Soil Sci.* **39**, 76.

Kramer, P. J., Knipling, E. B., and Miller, L. H. (1966). Terminology of cell water relations. *Science* **153**, 889.

Monteith, J. L., and Owen, P. C. (1958). A thermocouple method for measuring relative humidity in the range 95–100%. *J. Sci. Instr.* **35**, 443.

Onsager, L. (1931a). Reciprocal relations in irreversible processes. I. *Phys. Rev.* **37**, 405.

Onsager, L. (1931b). Reciprocal relations in irreversible processes. II. *Phys. Rev.* **38**, 2265.

Prigogine, I. (1961). "Thermodynamics of Irreversible Processes." Wiley, New York.

Richards, L. A. (ed.) (1954). Diagnosis and improvement of saline and alkali soils. *U.S. Dept. Agr. Agr. Handbook* **60**.

Richards, L. A., and Ogata, G. (1958). Thermocouple for vapor pressure measurements in biological systems at high humidity. *Science* **128**, 1089.

Schofield, R. K. (1935). The pF of water in soil. *Trans. Intern. Congr. Soil Sci., 3rd, Oxford, 1935.* **2**, 37.

Slatyer, R. O., and Taylor, S. A. (1960). Terminology in soil-plant-water relations. *Nature* **187**, 922.

Taylor, S. A. (1958). The activity of water in soils. *Soil Sci.* **86**, 83.

Taylor, S. A. (1965). The influence of steady temperature gradients upon water transport in soil materials. *In* "Humidity and Moisture: Measurement and Control in Science and Industry" (A. Wexler, ed.), Vol. 3, p. 343. Reinhold, New York.

Taylor, S. A., and Cary, J. W. (1964). Linear equations for the simultaneous flow of matter and energy in a continuous soil system. *Soil Sci. Soc. Am. Proc.* **28**, 167.

Taylor, S. A., Evans, D. D., and Kemper, W. D. (1961). Evaluating soil water. *Utah State Univ. Agr. Expt. Sta. Bull.* **426**.

Taylor, S. A., and Kijne, J. W. (1965). Evaluating thermodynamic properties of soil water. *In* "Humidity and Moisture: Measurement and Control in Science and Industry" (A. Wexler, ed.), Vol. 3, p. 335. Reinhold, New York.

Taylor, S. A., and Slatyer, R. O. (1960). Water-soil-plant relations terminology. *Trans. Intern. Congr. Soil Sci., 7th Madison, Wisc., 1960* **1**, 395.

Taylor, S. A., and Stewart, G. L. (1960). Some thermodynamic properties of soil water. *Soil. Sci. Soc. Am. Proc.* **24**, 243.

Wiebe, H. H. (1966). Matric potential of several plant tissues and biocolloids. *Plant Physiol,* **41**, 1439.

Zollinger, W. D., Campbell, G. S., and Taylor, S. A. (1966). A comparison of water-potential measurements made using two types of thermocouple psychrometers. *Soil Sci.* **102**, 231.

CHAPTER 4

EVAPORATION OF WATER FROM PLANTS AND SOIL

C. B. Tanner

DEPARTMENT OF SOILS, UNIVERSITY OF WISCONSIN, MADISON, WISCONSIN

I. INTRODUCTION

This chapter discusses the basic principles of evaporation and provides a background of methodology. It is concerned primarily with the transport of water vapor from the source of vaporization into the atmosphere and not with the state of water and flow of water to the source. The discussion will be at a relatively general level, since more detailed discussions of the principles and methodology are readily available in the literature (Sellers, 1965; American Meteorological Society 1965; Hagan, *et al.*, 1967).

There are five general approaches to describing evaporation:

1. The hydrological or water balance approach, which includes such diverse methods as lysimeters and soil sampling.

2. The eddy correlation approach. Several types of equipment have been developed to use this method, but equipment complexity and sensor limitations have restricted widespread use.

3. The energy balance approach, which rests on the fact that an enormous amount of energy is required to change liquid water to vapor without a change in temperature. The energy balance measures the energy flow in the various pathways to the vapor source, and from this derives the energy used in vaporization. By knowing the latent heat of vaporization, the volume and mass flux density can be computed. This is a favored micrometeorological method at present, although the eddy correlation method would be preferred if the technology were improved.

4. The aerodynamic or profile method describes the vapor mass flux and requires an estimate of the turbulent diffusivity or transport coefficient and the vapor gradient. The transport coefficient and diffusivity are described in terms of the air speed past the surface. This method generally is less satisfactory than the energy balance when the latter is conveniently applicable.

5. The combination approach, which combines parts of each of the energy balance and mass transport concepts. Considerable attention will be given to this concept and on models deriving from it which help define potential evaporation and water " availability " for evaporation.

All of these methods are applicable to such small surfaces as atmometers and leaves and to the extended surfaces of large fields and forests. Application to plots 5–50 m in scale is much more troublesome, and application to transport within a plant canopy is much more complex than to individual leaves or to the canopy as a surface.

This chapter discusses each of the above five evaporation concepts, referring to pertinent literature for detailed discussion. A list of symbols used is given in Table I.

TABLE I

LIST OF SYMBOLS[a]

Symbol	Explanation	Units
A	Area (catchment)	cm^2
C	Constant	1
C_c	Heat capacity of canopy	joule $gm^{-3} C^{-1}$
C_z	Drag coefficient for V_z, defined by Eq. (16b)	1
D	Displacement parameter, $D = d + z_0$	cm
E^*	Evaporation, surface depth, depth rate	cm, cm sec^{-1}
	mass flux density	gm cm^{-2} sec^{-1}
E	Latent heat flux density, $E = \lambda E^*$	$w\ cm^{-2}$
E_a	Evaporation type term defined by Eq. (25).	$w\ cm^{-2}$
E_p	Potential evaporation	$w\ cm^{-2}$
G	Heat flux density into ground	$w\ cm^{-2}$
H	Heat flux density into air	$w\ cm^{-2}$
K_h	Eddy diffusivity for heat	$cm^2\ sec^{-1}$
K_m	Eddy diffusivity for momentum	$cm^2\ sec^{-1}$
K_v	Eddy diffusivity for vapor	$cm^2\ sec^{-1}$
L	Characteristic length, leaf diameter	cm
M	Miscellaneous heat flux densities	$w\ cm^{-2}$
Nu	Nusselt number for heat transfer, $Nu = h_h L/\alpha_h$	1
Nu_m	Nusselt number for mass transfer, $Nu_m = h_v L/\alpha_v$	1
P	Atmospheric pressure	mb
Pr	Prandtl number, $Pr = \nu/\alpha_h$	1
Q_i	Volume of intercepted water	cm^3
Q_L	Volume of leakage from catchment (not measured in Q_r)	cm^3
Q_r	Volume of surface and subsurface runoff from catchment	cm^3
ΔQ_s	Volume change in water stored above water table	cm^3
ΔQ_w	Volume change in ground water storage	cm^3
R_n	Net radiation flux density	$w\ cm^{-2}$
R_s	Solar radiation flux density	$w\ cm^{-2}$
R_t	Thermal radiation flux density	$w\ cm^{-2}$
Re	Reynolds number, $Re = VL/\nu$	1
Sc	Schmidt number (mass Prandtl number) $Sc = \nu/\alpha_v$	1
T	Temperature	$°C, °K$
T_c	Temperature of canopy	$°C, °K$
T_d	Dew-point temperature	$°C, °K$
T_w	Wet-bulb temperature	$°C, °K$
V	Horizontal wind velocity	cm sec^{-1}
V_*	Friction velocity, $V_*^2 = \tau/\rho$	cm sec^{-1}
W	Precipitation, surface depth, or depth rate	cm, cm sec^{-1}
Z	Vegetation height	cm
a_s	Absorbance for solar radiation	1
c_p	Specific heat at constant pressure	joule $gm^{-1} C^{-1}$
d	Zero plane displacement	cm
e	Vapor pressure	mb

TABLE I—*continued*

Symbol	Explanation	Units
e^*	Saturation vapor pressure	mb
e_w	Wet-bulb vapor pressure	mb
f	Relative humidity	1
g	Acceleration of gravity	cm sec^{-2}
k	Karman's constant	1
h	Transfer coefficient $h = h_v \approx h_h$	cm sec^{-1}
h_h	Transfer coefficient for heat	cm sec^{-1}
h_m	Transfer coefficient for momentum	cm sec^{-1}
h_v	Transfer coefficient for vapor	cm sec^{-1}
q	Specific humidity	1
r_a	Diffusion resistance of air layer $r_a = 1/h$	sec cm^{-1}
r_i	Internal diffusion resistance	sec cm^{-1}
s	Slope of saturation vapor pressure curve $s = de/dT$	mb C^{-1}
w	Vertical wind velocity	cm sec^{-1}
z	Height	cm
z_0	Roughness length	cm
α_h	Molecular diffusivity for heat	cm^2 sec^{-1}
α_v	Molecular diffusivity for vapor	cm^2 sec^{-1}
β	Bowen's ratio, $\beta = H/E$	1
γ	Psychrometer constant, $\gamma = c_p P/\lambda\varepsilon$	mb C^{-1}
δ	Wet-bulb depression	°C, °K
ε	Ratio molecular weight water vapor to air	1
λ	Latent heat of vaporization	joule gm^{-1}
ρ	Density of moist air	gm cm^{-3}
τ	Shearing stress	dyne cm^{-2}
ν	Kinematic viscosity	cm^2 sec^{-1}

Subscripts

0	property of atmosphere–surface interface
z	Property at height z
i	Property of an internal interface (Fig. 6)

Mathematical symbols

′	Primes indicate departures from an average value
$\langle \rangle$	Indicates averaging
↓↑	Incoming and outgoing
ln	Natural logarithm
Δ	Increment

[a] *Note:* Often, as with flux densities, meters rather than centimeters can be used advantageously; also the calorie is frequently used as an energy unit, although the joule = watt sec is a preferred international unit.

II. WATER BALANCE METHODS

The water balance methods include catchment hydrology, soil moisture depletion sampling, lysimeters, and potometers. These methods can be discussed from the water balance equation

$$E^* = W - (Q_r + Q_L + Q_i + \Delta Q_w + \Delta Q_s)/A \qquad (1)$$

A. CATCHMENT HYDROLOGY

Gardner (1965) may be referred to for a brief outline of problems of hydrology, including those of the unsaturated phase. Although the art of catchment hydrology fills books, only a few precautions to be observed will be considered here. When Eq. (1) is applied to large natural catchments and to drainage and irrigation districts, it is clear that W, Q_r, and A must be measured with the required precision, and it is usually assumed that $Q_L = 0$. The ΔQ_w, ΔQ_s, and Q_i terms must either be measured or the average evaporation must be computed over a sufficiently long period so they can be neglected in comparison to other terms. The largest uncertainty usually is in the $Q_L = 0$ assumption and in measuring A. Considerable judgment is required in selecting natural catchments without leakage so that Q_L is negligible, and the area must be defined by the ground water contours which must be measured with ground wells or piezometers and cannot be assumed equal to that defined by topography. Independent meteorological methods provide useful supporting information to the hydrological measurement.

B. SOIL MOISTURE DEPLETION

Depletion measurements also are based on the water balance Eq. (1) where ΔQ_s is measured and frequently an attempt is made to either measure or control Q_r. The ΔQ_w and Q_L terms express continued depletion of water from the sampling zone by drainage, and the error in evaporation is as large as this unmeasured drainage. The size of the drainage error can be substantial (King, 1910; Robins et al., 1954; Nixon and Lawless, 1960). In Wisconsin, and probably in most humid areas, measurement of soil moisture depletion rarely provides reliable E^* measurements because of frequent rains and resulting drainage. Serious error due to drainage usually results since there is no way to ensure that drainage will be negligible. particularly where frequent and/or heavy precipitation may occur.

Provided that drainage errors are acceptable, soil moisture depletion may be measured by any of the techniques discussed by Holmes et al. (1967). The neutron moisture meter usually is preferred over other measurements. Sampling known soil volumes with tubes is the second choice and is preferred to moisture weight determinations and separate bulk density determinations (Taylor *et al.*, 1961). The neutron meter has several advantages: first, moisture volume fractions are determined directly; second, a large volume of soil usually is sampled; and third, the same soil volume is measured repeatedly. Even with a neutron moisture meter, soil moisture depletion sampling cannot be used over periods much shorter than about 1 week with errors less than 10– 20% and usually is useful only over longer periods.

C. LYSIMETRY

Lysimetry in its various forms is the only hydrological method in which the experimenter has complete knowledge of all the terms in Eq. (1) and is of importance not only for gathering evaporation information but also as an independent check on the suitability of micrometeorological methods and for calibrating empirical formulas used for estimating evaporation. McIlroy and Angus (1963), Pelton (1961), and Tanner (1967) provide additional information on lysimeter construction and use.

A lysimeter is a device in which a volume of soil, which may be planted to vegetation, is located in a container to isolate it hydrologically from the surrounding soil. Lysimeters are constructed to make $Q_L = 0$ and either to permit measurement of Q_r or to make $Q_r = 0$. Although lysimeters are well defined hydrologically, they must be representative samples of the surrounds if they are to provide useful evaporation measurements. Representativeness of soil (thermal, moisture, and mechanical properties) and of the vegetation (height, density, physiological well-being) is necessary. The intended use of the lysimeter will dictate the design and operation necessary to obtain suitable representativeness. Major factors affecting design include: (1) whether measurements of potential evaporation (maximum possible under given micrometeorological conditions) or measurements of E^* under drought are needed; (2) the structure of the vegetation (grass, hay, row crops, density, etc.) and of the roots (deep, shallow, etc.); and (3) the period over which the evaporation is to be measured (hours, days, or months). These factors influence the design of the lysimeter with respect to depth and moisture control, area, and the method of measuring water loss from the lysimeter. Design and operation also are affected by other factors, as discussed by Tanner (1967).

The evaporation from single plants in pots may be found by weighing the pot, and the evaporation from leaves may be found either with potometers or by weighing cut leaves. These standard techniques are simplified lysimeters.

III. EDDY CORRELATION PRINCIPLES

The product of the vertical wind and the vapor concentration $w(\rho q)$ is the instantaneous mass flux of vapor in the w direction, either up or down. Eddy correlation methods make use of this information. The reader is referred to Webb (1965), Thornthwaite and Hare (1965), and Sellers (1965, p. 142) for detailed discussions.

A. Eddy Correlation Formulas

If measurements of w and q are made at height z and the product is integrated over time, the vapor flux at height z can be found:

$$E_z{}^* = \langle w(\rho q)\rangle = \rho\langle q\rangle\langle w\rangle + \rho\langle q'w'\rangle \tag{2a}$$

where the values within angle brackets are means. If vapor pressure is used,

$$E_z{}^* = \langle(\rho\varepsilon/P)ew\rangle = (\rho\varepsilon/P)[\langle e\rangle\langle w\rangle + \langle e'w'\rangle] \tag{2b}$$

The expression as latent heat flux is

$$E_z = \langle(\lambda\rho\varepsilon/P)ew\rangle = (\lambda\rho\varepsilon/P)[\langle e\rangle\langle w\rangle + \langle e'w'\rangle] \tag{2c}$$

The sensible heat flux similarly can be written

$$H_z = \langle(\rho c_p T)w\rangle = (\rho c_p)[\langle T\rangle\langle w\rangle + \langle T'w'\rangle] \tag{3}$$

It can be seen that as an impervious surface is approached ($z \to 0$), $\langle w\rangle$ approaches zero, and then

$$E^* = (\rho\varepsilon/P)\langle e'w'\rangle \tag{4}$$

$$E = (\lambda\rho\varepsilon/P)\langle e'w'\rangle \tag{5}$$

$$H = (\rho c_p)\langle T'w'\rangle \tag{6}$$

If measurements are made at height z above the surface, under circumstances when $\langle w\rangle \neq 0$, then $\langle w\rangle$, $\langle e\rangle$, and $\langle T\rangle$ must be measured. Usually the vapor and heat flux at the surface are needed. This is given by Eqs. (2) and (3), provided $\langle e'w'\rangle$ and $\langle T'w'\rangle$ when measured at z are the same as that when measurements approach the surface; this is assured only by sampling under conditions of small horizontal gradients, as discussed in Section IV, E.

B. Eddy Correlation Measurements

Several methods have been developed for measuring $\langle e'w'\rangle$ and $\langle T'w'\rangle$. The first and simplest method conceptually is to measure the vertical wind with a sensitive, fast-response, propeller anemometer (Thornthwaite et al., 1961; Holmes et al., 1964; Dyer et al., 1967) and at the same time measure e and/or T. The integral of the product can be formed in several ways. Another system that employs a special heat transfer anemometer and fast wet- and dry-bulb thermometers has been used for several years in the Australian CSIRO, Division of Meteorological Physics (Dyer and Maher,

1965) to measure the flux density of vapor and sensible heat. Finally, the sonic anemometer–thermometer can be used to measure sensible heat flux density (Kaimal and Businger, 1963). The eddy correlation devices developed to date must be used 3–5 m above the surface, either because of the large sampling volume or the slow response and, consequently, require large fetch. The vertical propeller anemometer approach is being investigated in several places and, in the opinion of the writer, is very promising for measurement of evaporation from forests. None of these methods are useful for determining vapor or heat losses from individual leaves.

IV. PROFILE AND ENERGY BALANCE METHODS

This section introduces the basic eddy diffusion equations, the concepts of transport coefficients and resistance, and the similarity equations. The use of these concepts in the energy balance and aerodynamic or profile methods is then discussed. Sellers (1965, pp. 141–155), Webb (1965), Thornthwaite and Hare (1965), and Tanner (1967) provide more complete reviews.

A. EDDY DIFFUSION EQUATIONS

Both the profile and energy balance methods depend upon the eddy diffusion Eqs. (7a)–(7c) to find the vertical component of the flux density of momentum, sensible heat, and vapor:

$$E = \lambda E^* = -\lambda K_v(\partial \rho q / /\partial z) = -(\lambda \rho \varepsilon / P) K_v(\partial e/\partial z) \tag{7a}$$

$$H_z = -K_h(\partial \rho c_p T/\partial z) = -\rho c_p K_h(\partial T/\partial z) \tag{7b}$$

$$\tau_z = K_m(\partial \rho V/\partial z) = \rho K_m(\partial V/\partial z) \tag{7c}$$

where ρV, $\rho c_p T$, $\rho q = \rho \varepsilon/P$, and $\lambda \rho \varepsilon e/P$ are the concentrations of momentum, sensible heat, water vapor, and latent heat, respectively. The eddy diffusivities K_m, K_h, and K_v, which are measures of the turbulent mixing, vary strongly with wind speed.

If either V, T, or e or their gradients or the flux densities are measured over a homogeneous surface and at the same height, but spaced horizontally, the instantaneous values of these parameters will not be the same, nor will the average over a short time interval; however, if the averaging period is long enough, the measurements at the two locations will stabilize, one upon the other. In the same way, a single, instantaneous picture of a turbulent field is essentially unrepeatable and cannot be represented by diffusion equations, but if the eddy diffusion equations employ appropriate time–averages of gradients and fluxes they can be used to represent a statistically stable diffusion. Experience and measurements of variance spectra indicate that a sampling period of about 15–60 minutes is desirable; the period should neither be less than 10 minutes nor much longer than 1 hour.

The diffusion Eqs. (7a)–(7c) apply over some small height increment dz at height z. Frequently, the transport from the surface $z = 0$ to some height z is needed. The transport Eqs. (8a)–(8c) for this instance are similar to those of Eq. (7):

$$E = \lambda E^* = -(\lambda \rho \varepsilon / P)h_v(e_z - e_0) \tag{8a}$$

$$H = -\rho c_p h_h(T_z - T_0) \tag{8b}$$

$$\tau = \rho h_m V_z = \rho C_z V_z^2 \tag{8c}$$

The drag coefficient $C_z = h_m/V_z$ is a more frequently used expression than the transport coefficient h_m. Also, $C_z = f/2$, where f is the friction factor used in many texts on transport phenomena. There is some convenience in using diffusion resistances $r_v = 1/h_v$ and $r_h = 1/h_h$, as seen in Section V,D.

B. SIMILARITY RELATIONS

The similarity relations derive from the eddy diffusion equations. The similarity Eqs. (9a) and (9b) relating sensible heat flux density and latent heat flux density are used in the energy balance method. They are the ratio either of Eqs. (7b) and (7a) or of Eqs. (8b) and (8a) expressed in finite form, where $\Delta T = T_2 - T_1$ and $\Delta e = e_2 - e_1$ are measured over $\Delta z = z_2 - z_1$. This ratio, $\beta = H/E$, is called Bowen's ratio.

$$H/E = \beta = (c_p P/\varepsilon \lambda)(K_h/K_v)(\Delta T/\Delta e) = \gamma(K_h/K_v)(\Delta T/\Delta e) \tag{9a}$$

$$H/E = \beta = \gamma(h_h/h_v)[(T_z - T_0)/(e_z - e_0)] \tag{9b}$$

Relation (9) can be used to predict H if an independent measurement of E is available, such as with lysimeters, provided ΔT, Δe, and (K_h/K_v) are known. Similarly, if H is found from Eq. (6), E can be predicted.

In order to use the similarity relations (9a) and (9b) it is assumed that the ratio of the eddy diffusivities is constant and usually that $K_h = K_v$. These equations are for one-dimensional (vertical) flux, which means that there are no horizontal gradients. The assumption of one-dimensional flux is met experimentally only by assuring sufficient fetch, as discussed later.

The transport coefficients of vapor and heat from leaves and other such surfaces with laminar boundary layers are in the ratio $(h_h/h_v) = (\alpha_h/\alpha_v)^{2/3}$ or $(h_h/h_v) \approx 0.9$ at $300K$. This is close to unity and generally is taken to be so.

Also implicit in the similarity relations is the homogeneity of vapor and heat sources and sinks. If the size scale of the inhomogeneity of sources and sinks at the surface approaches the height of the measurement, it is clear that the above equations may not apply. For example, if the heat source and moisture source are separated, warm, dry parcels of air are separated from cool, wet parcels, and rise more rapidly, thus creating a difference between K_h and K_v. In addition, inhomogeneities of this nature cause serious sampling problems. Since the gradient measurements are affected largely by the local conditions, the heat and moisture may not be weighted correctly by a sensor close to an inhomogeneous surface. For this reason, the energy balance and profile methods which use similarity cannot be assumed *a priori* to be suitable for row crops or patchy surfaces unless they have been tested.

The similarity relations that are used in the profile methods and the combination method are derived from Eqs. (7) and (8), as given in Eq. (10) and (11).

$$E/\tau = -(\lambda\varepsilon/P)(K_v/K_m)(\Delta e/\Delta V) \tag{10a}$$

$$H/\tau = -c_p(K_h/K_m)(\Delta T/\Delta V) \tag{10b}$$

Similarly, we have

$$E/\tau = -(\lambda\varepsilon/P)(h_v/h_m)[(e_z - e_0)/V_z] \tag{11a}$$

$$H/\tau = -c_p(h_h/h_m)[(T_z - T_0)/V_z] \tag{11b}$$

There is increasing doubt that K_m can be assumed to be equal either to K_v or K_h with the same certainty of assuming $K_v = K_h$. However, equality usually is assumed to permit profile estimates, and any resulting errors usually are small compared with other errors in plant-water research.

It is seen that E and H can be found from measurements of Δe, ΔT, and ΔV, provided a measurement of τ is available, e.g., with a stress meter or from wind profile structure. This does require information on K_v/K_m and K_h/K_m or equivalent information on the ratio of transfer coefficients. Previous remarks regarding the effect of fetch and surface inhomogeneities upon similarity between heat and vapor transport apply also to similarity with momentum transfer.

C. ENERGY BALANCE

The energy balance sums the energy fluxes at the surface, including the fluxes of radiation, sensible heat, latent heat, soil heat, and other miscellaneous fluxes. Though a two- or three-dimensional balance may be necessary for completeness, the simpler vertical energy balance will be of first concern. Sellers (1965), particularly, Webb (1965), Thornthwaite and Hare (1965), and Tanner (1967) have reviewed the energy balance, and further details on radiation exchange are available in Van Wijk and Sholte Ubing (1963) and Gates (1965).

1. Vertical Energy Balance

The vertical energy balance can be discussed conveniently as the radiation disposition at the earth's surface. The daytime radiation balance is illustrated in Fig. 1. The net radiation density is the balance of radiation which is converted to some other form of radiation:

$$R_n = (R_s\!\downarrow - R_s\!\uparrow) + (R_t\!\downarrow - R_t\!\uparrow) \tag{12}$$

where $R_s\!\downarrow - R_s\!\uparrow = a_s R_G$. The net radiation can be evaluated by measuring or

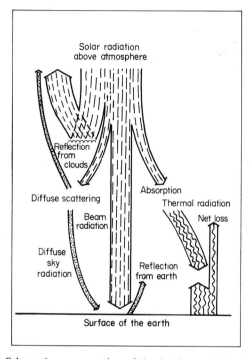

FIG. 1. Schematic representation of the daytime radiation balance.

calculating the flux density of each of the four radiation currents or by directly measuring the net radiation.

The vertical energy balance is

$$R_n = E + H + G + M \tag{13}$$

In Eq. (13), the net radiation and the ground heat flux are measured, and miscellaneous terms must then be either estimated, measured, or neglected. Since M usually is small, it is most frequently neglected, although this is a source of minor error. Figure 2 illustrates the usual daytime and nighttime energy

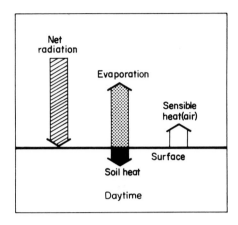

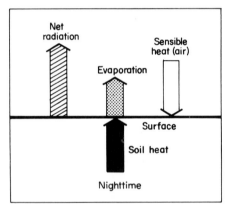

Fig. 2. Schematic representation of the daytime and nighttime energy balance.

balance. The magnitude of the nighttime balance is of the order of one tenth that at noontime. If dew occurs, the evaporation arrow is reversed to show vapor flow to the surface. When the surface is moist and the overlying air is warmer than the surface or has a large saturation deficit, heat also is available from the air as well as from the soil, as represented by Fig. 3.

2. Partitioning Latent and Sensible Heat-Flux Densities

Both E and H in Eq. (13) are unknown. H can be measured using either Eq. (6) or the profile method (19), as discussed later, and then E can be found as the only unmeasured term. E can also be measured by lysimetry and then Eq. (13) can be solved for H. These simple combination approaches, in which either H or E are measured, have proven useful.

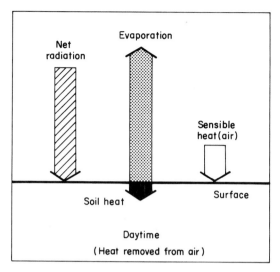

FIG. 3. Schematic representation of the daytime energy balance with advected sensible heat (temperature inversion).

H and E are most often resolved, using the similarity relation of (9), to give the final Eq. (14). The equation as written assumes that $(K_h/K_v) = 1$ or $(h_h/h_v) = 1$.

$$E = (R_n - G)/(1 + \beta) \tag{14a}$$

$$H = \beta(R_n - G)/(1 + \beta) \tag{14b}$$

The energy balance, coupled with similarity, or the Bowen ratio type of approach, can be extended to carbon dioxide flux density (Tanner, 1967).

Two basic advantages of the energy balance method are clear from the above equations. First, since the net radiation and the ground heat storage can be measured with reasonable accuracy, this places an upper limit on the sum of the sensible and latent heat. It is known that when the net radiation is high and water is available, evaporation generally is high, and when the net radiation is low, evaporation generally will be low. If there is no water available, then certainly there is an upper limit to the heat flux. Second, it can be seen from Eq. (9) that $\beta = \gamma(\Delta T/\Delta e)$ is set by assuming $(K_h/K_v) = (h_h/h_v) = 1$. Since β is in the denominator as $(1 + \beta)$, unless β is less than -0.5 the error in E will be less than the error in either $(K_h/K_v) = 1$ or $(h_h/h_v) = 1$. Similarly, any error in E is less than the error in either ΔT or Δe. The Bowen ratio of most vegetated surfaces and moist soil rarely exceeds the range -0.3–2.0.

3. Large Storage Terms

The heat storage term in water bodies which are a meter or more deep is large, and measurements of storage often cannot be made with reasonable

TABLE II

AVERAGE HEAT FLUX DENSITY IN $w\ m^{-2}$ FROM A
FOREST STAND OVER A 5-MINUTE PERIOD FOLLOWING A 1°C
STEP CHANGE IN TEMPERATURE FOR TWO WIND CONDITIONS[a]

Heat source	Wind = 2 m/sec	"Still" air
Trunks	0.2	0.2
Branch wood	1.5	1
Needles and twigs	4.0	1
Air	30	30
Soil	140	140
Total canopy storage	36	32
Canopy plus soil storage	175	170
High net radiation (for comparison)	550	550

[a] From Bergen (1967).

accuracy for an hour or even daily periods, although they can be made often with sufficient accuracy over periods of several days. Consequently, short period estimates of evaporation must rely upon the profile methods rather than energy balance measurements.

Tanner (1960) found canopy storage to be negligible for common crops; however, the mass of forest canopies is very large and consequently the heat storage could be appreciable. Bergen (1967) analyzed a white pine plantation with 30-foot high trees spaced at 4-foot intervals. He estimated the average heat flux in a 5-minute period following a step change of 1°C in the air and at the surface of the soil. The results of his analysis are listed in Table II. These data show that the canopy storage largely results from the air layer and is a relatively small part of the energy balance unless radiation is low. The flux density caused by air storage can be monitored readily.

D. PROFILE METHODS

Profile methods are based upon the similarity condition but use wind profile information to find the shearing stress for substitution in the similarity relation.

1. Wind Profile

When fetch is adequate and momentum transfer is one-dimensional, the wind profile in the atmospheric surface layer can be represented by Eq. (15). (Refer to Sellers, 1965, pp. 148–155, and Webb, 1965).

$$V_z = (V_*/k)\left\{\left[\ln \frac{z+D}{z_0}\right] + \Phi\right\} \qquad (15)$$

When an adiabatic profile obtains, all the turbulence is caused by frictional effects, none is caused by thermal buoyancy, $\Phi = 0$, and the wind velocity follows the log profile. When a temperature lapse obtains, and the profile is unstable, turbulence is increased because of the buoyancy of the lower, hotter air, which rises and is replaced by cool air from above. The effect of buoyancy is to increase mixing which produces smaller vertical gradients than would exist under neutral conditions. With stable conditions, or profile inversion, turbulence is damped because an air parcel, which moves up into less dense air, tends to settle back, and as it moves down into cooler air it tends to rise back to its initial position. Both stability and instability produce wind profile curvature. The diabatic profile parameter Φ is needed in Eq. (15) to describe the stability-induced curvature in the velocity profile. From Eq. (15), equations which give the shearing stress in terms either of $(V_2 - V_1)$ over heights z_2 and z_1 or of V_z at height z can be found. These also include corrections for the diabatic profile.

$$\tau = \rho k^2 (V_2 - V_1)^2 \left[\ln \frac{z_2 + D}{z_1 + D} \right]^{-2} \varphi^{-2} \tag{16a}$$

$$\tau = \rho C_z V_z^2 \qquad C_z = k^2 \left\{ \left[\ln \frac{z + D}{z_0} \right] + \Phi \right\}^{-2} \tag{16b}$$

where $\varphi - 1 = \partial\Phi/\partial \ln(z + D) \approx (\Phi_2 - \Phi_1)/\ln[z_2 + D)/(z_1 + D)]$.

One useful formulation of the diabatic profile model called the KEYPS profile sets $\varphi^2 = (1 - 18\,\mathrm{Ri})^{-1/2}$, where Ri is the gradient Richardson number.

$$\mathrm{Ri} = (g/T)(\Delta T \Delta z/\Delta V^2) \tag{17a}$$

$$\mathrm{Ri} = \{(g/T)(T_2 - T_1)[\ln(z_2 + D)/(z_1 + D)](V_2 - V_1)^{-2}\}(z + D) \tag{17b}$$

TABLE III

CORRECTION FOR STABILITY NECESSARY FOR
WIND PROFILE FOR GIVEN Δz, Δe, ΔV^a

Ri	φ^2	Φ	Ri	φ^2	Φ
0.05	3.161	0.584	−0.06	0.694	−0.192
0.04	1.891	0.308	−0.10	0.598	−0.283
0.02	1.250	0.109	−0.30	0.396	−0.552
0.01	1.105	0.049	−1.0	0.229	−0.967
0.00	1.000	0.000	−1.4	0.195	−1.105
−0.02	0.857	−0.077	−2.0	0.165	−1.261

[a] From Lettau (1962).

Formulation (17a) gives Ri at the geometric mean height of $(z_2 + D)$ and $(z_1 + D)$; however, (17b) has some advantage since the part in braces changes slowly with height and, consequently, Ri can be found at any height in the range of $(z_2 + D)$ and $(z_1 + D)$. The stability corrections provided by the KEYPS model for different Richardson numbers are shown in Table III. Since the Richardson number commonly varies between $0.03 > \text{Ri} > -0.05$ at 1 to 2 m, it is clear that corrections are necessary.

Other models of the diabatic profile have been formulated, as discussed briefly in Sellers (1965, p. 154) and Webb (1965); however, the above model is useful and is adequate for most needs.

2. Aerodynamic Formulas

By employing the similarity of (10a) and (11a) and the profile expressions for the shearing stress (16), one can find the profile expressions

$$E = \frac{(\lambda\rho\varepsilon k^2/P)(e_1 - e_2)(V_2 - V_1)}{[\ln(z_2 + D)/(z_1 + D)]^2\varphi^2} \tag{18a}$$

$$E = (\lambda\rho\varepsilon/P)C_z V_z(e_0 - e_z) \tag{18b}$$

These equations have assumed that $K_m = K_v$ and $h_m = h_v$ and that there is a known relation between τ and the wind profile for all conditions of thermal stability. Similar assumptions on heat transfer yield

$$H = \frac{\rho c_p k^2(T_1 - T_2)(V_2 - V_1)}{[\ln(z_2 + D)/(z_1 + D)]^2\varphi^2} \tag{19a}$$

$$H = \rho c_p C_z V_z(T_0 - T_z) \tag{19b}$$

Similar formulations of CO_2 transfer may be made.

It is noted that the Karman constant has an uncertainty of about 10%, so that there is an uncertainty in the stress Eq. (16) and in the evaporation Eq. (18) of about 20%. It can also be seen that the error in E is proportional to any relative error in assuming $K_v = K_m$ or in measuring ΔT or Δe.

E. EXPERIMENTAL REQUIREMENTS

One urgent practical requirement is to make all the gradient measurements as near to the surface as possible. Staying near the surface is desirable because (1) errors from thermal stratification are minimal within the first meter and (2), fetch requirement is minimized. If measurements are made close to the surface, they may be affected by surface inhomogeneities, and spatial sampling may be necessary. The inhomogeneity scale of forests is especially taxing. The problems of heat divergence and sampling are also of real importance.

1. Heat Divergence

Figure 4 represents the total energy balance of a volume containing the canopy. The vertical energy exchanges represented by Eqs. (13) and (14) and by (17) and (18) are shown as flux densities of the top and bottom of the box. The total flux density for two-dimensional exchange is given by

$$R_n = E + H + G$$

$$+ \int_0^z C_c(dT_c/dt)\, dz + \rho c_p \int_0^z (dT/dt)\, dz + (\lambda \rho \varepsilon / P) \int_0^z (de/dt)\, dz$$

$$+ \rho c_p \int_0^z [d(VT)/dx]\, dz + (\lambda \rho \varepsilon / P) \int_0^z [d(Ve)/dx]\, dz \qquad (20)$$

where all terms under the integrals are functions of z. The first line represents the simple vertical energy balance; however, if this box is at the edge of a canopy, the radiation must be integrated over the side area. The second line represents the heat storage of the canopy, the sensible heat in the canopy air, and the latent heat flux caused by changing vapor content. The third line represents the advection of sensible heat and latent heat.

Advection of sensible and latent heat will be present in the atmospheric surface layer above the canopy, provided there are horizontal temperature and vapor gradients. Since the horizontal change in heat must equal the vertical (i.e. $dH/dz = dH/dx$), for sensible heat

$$d[K_h(dT/dz)]/dz - VdT/dx = 0 \qquad (21)$$

This equation must be solved under appropriate boundary conditions (De Vries, 1959; Philip, 1959) to find the advection. A similar equation can be written for latent heat (vapor).

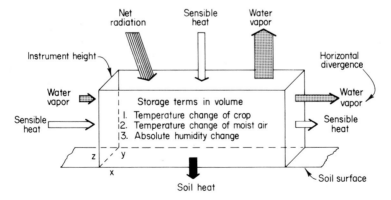

FIG. 4. Schematic representation of the complete energy balance of a canopy volume.

It also is noted that when wind moves from one surface to another of different roughness, the surface wind changes speed and there are net vertical velocities corresponding to advection of heat and vapor. This net $\langle w \rangle \neq 0$ carries vapor and heat that are not measured by the fluctuation correlations of Eq. (5) or by the gradients in Eqs. (7) and (8).

The horizontal wind gradients within canopies and above surfaces of different roughness can cause appreciable error, which is avoided only by having sufficient fetch. The "clothesline" heat exchange which occurs from flow through small plots or through large open canopies, such as orchards and forests with open trunk space, may limit many of the simple micrometeorological methods. Indeed, the effect of large-scale circulations in the forest canopy, which can be produced by thermal and/or structural differences (i.e., roughness, permeability or spacing, LAI, etc.) is a challenging and unresearched problem. When the divergence of heat and momentum can contribute serious errors to the simple vertical budget, it is necessary to measure the air movement, the vapor content, the heat, and the radiation at the sides of a hypothetical box surrounding the site. From this, the vapor and heat budgets are constructed.

The fetch distance is of considerable importance to meet the requirements for one-dimensional transfer. Wind tunnel data (see Brooks, 1961), an analysis of moisture and thermal discontinuities (Dyer, 1963), and an analysis of roughness discontinuities (Panofsky and Townsend, 1964) indicate that for approximately 90% adjustment of flux profiles at a height z the ratio of the height to fetch distance X should be approximately 1 : 100. If the discontinuity is not large, a smaller profile adjustment (e.g. 50%) may be sufficient and only a 1 : 50 or 1 : 25 height : fetch ratio may be required. On the other hand, if the discontinuity is very large or if an adjustment greater than 90% is required, a long fetch is mandatory. As a rough rule of thumb, height : fetch ratios should be at least 1 : 50 for minor discontinuities and at least 1 : 100 or 1 : 200 if the discontinuity is severe.

2. Sampling

The gradients and other terms must be sampled with the required accuracy. The easiest measurements are R_n, G, and ΔT; ΔV is somewhat more difficult, and Δe is still more difficult. The determination of D and z_0 in Eqs. (16), (18), and (19) is the most demanding measurement in either the Bowen ratio or profile method, since it depends on accurate measurement of the *second order* properties of the profile. Both wind and temperature profiles are required, extending 2 to 3 m above the surface, which increases fetch requirement. In addition, six to ten levels of precision wind measurements are needed. Errors in D occur, which cause large errors in $[\ln (z_2 + D)/(z_1 + D)]^2$

when $(z_1 + D)$ is small, unless considerable care is used to determine D. The measurement of D requires complete temperature and wind profiles. Since D and z_0 of vegetated surfaces may vary several centimeters with varying wind speed (e.g., Lemon, 1963; Udagawa, 1966), error may arise in profile methods from assuming D and z_0 are constant. Accordingly, the measurement of D and z_0 during each period may be necessary, using a diabatic wind profile model. It is seen that full wind and temperature profiles are needed as well as $\Delta e = (e_2 - e_1)$ for the profile method. Also, since complete profiles extend higher than ΔT and Δe measurements, more fetch is required.

As mentioned earlier, with high evaporation rates, the accuracy requirements for the ΔT and Δe used in the energy balance approach are not as severe as for the ΔV and Δe in the profile method because the Bowen ratio measurements are used as $[1 + (\gamma \Delta T/\Delta e)]$. Only Δe and ΔT over z_1 to z_2 are needed so that the height requirement is minimal, and the extensive profiles required to measure D are avoided.

The velocity V, the temperature T, and the vapor pressure e must be sampled at the same heights for the ΔV, ΔT, and Δe used in Eqs. (9), (10), and (11) if profile similarity is to be used. The Δe, ΔV used in Bowen's ratio can be measured using the same airstreams or from closely mounted, paired nozzles. This helps assure similarity since Δe, ΔT, ΔV are assumed to be measured over the same sections of the profile. When ΔV and Δe (or ΔT) are needed, it is difficult to sample for either Δe or ΔT where an anemometer is located; consequently, a similarity error may arise. This error is common and must be tested by comparing full velocity, vapor pressure, and temperature profiles for similarity.

Finally, the sampling period is considered. Webb (1964) shows that

$$\beta = \frac{\overline{H}}{E} = \frac{\gamma \langle \Delta T \rangle}{\langle \Delta e \rangle} \left[\frac{1 + \langle V' \Delta T' \rangle / \langle V \rangle \langle \Delta T \rangle}{1 + \langle V' \Delta e' \rangle / \langle V \rangle \langle \Delta e \rangle} \right] \tag{22}$$

where V', ΔT, and $\Delta e'$ are departures of short-period (e.g., 15 minutes) values from long-period means (e.g., several hours), and means are indicated by angle brackets. Since ΔT and Δe vary in the same way with the wind, the bracketed term is near unity.

The error in representing the average of the product by the product of the average, as needed in the profile method, is greater since

$$\langle \Delta V \cdot \Delta e \rangle = \langle \Delta V \rangle \langle \Delta e \rangle + \langle \Delta V' \Delta T' \rangle \tag{23}$$

where $\Delta V'$ and $\Delta T'$ are negatively correlated and the last term in Eq. (23) may be appreciable. If V at a single height and ΔT and Δe are measured, β can be calculated for an extended period, which can include short periods when $\beta \rightarrow -1$.

V. COMBINATION FORMULA FOR EVAPORATION

The combination method discussed in this section combines the energy balance and an aerodynamic formula into a very useful expression. This approach involves information about the surface and brings potential evaporation E_p into suitable perspective. Apparently, Penman (1948), Ferguson (1952), and Budyko (1965) (see Sellers, 1964 for Budyko's method) independently developed similar methods for estimating E_p. Penman's and Ferguson's approaches are similar and use the finite difference form of the saturation vapor pressure–temperature relation (Clausius–Clapeyron equation), whereas Budyko's approach is an iterative method that makes similar assumptions. These combination methods, which originally were suited only to E_p estimates, were recast in a general form by McIlroy (see Slatyer and McIlroy, 1961) and by Penman (1961). The Penman and the McIlroy formulas differ only in form and are discussed in detail by Penman et al., (1967) and by Monteith (1965).

The combination formula will be presented here and used to define potential evaporation. Its formulation will then be discussed in terms of a vapor diffusion resistance at the evaporating surface such as may occur with a mulched soil and with leaves.

A. GENERAL COMBINATION FORMULA

The combination formula is based upon the energy balance Eq. (13) and the transport Eqs. (8a)–(8c). Some of the concepts used in the discussion are shown with the saturation vapor pressure curve in Fig. 5. Some useful relations are established by approximating the chord between (T_d, e) and (T, e^*) with the slope at $(T_d + T)/2$ or at T.

When no radiative heat sources are present and $E = -H$, Eq. (9) applies, as illustrated in Fig. 5.

$$e = e_w - \gamma(T - T_w) = e_w - \gamma\delta \tag{24a}$$

Similarly, the relation between the saturation deficit and the wet-bulb depression holds:

$$(e^* - e) = s\delta + \gamma\delta = (s + \gamma)\delta = s(T - T_d) \tag{24b}$$

Finally, T may be written

$$T = T_w + (T - T_w) = T_w + \delta \tag{24c}$$

From Eqs. (24a) and (24c),

$$T_0 - T_z = (T_{w0} - T_{wz}) + (\delta_0 - \delta_z) \tag{25a}$$

$$e_0 - e_z = s(T_{w0} - T_{wz}) - \gamma(\delta_0 - \delta_z) \tag{25b}$$

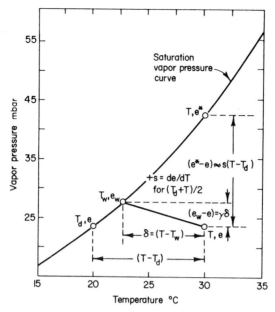

FIG. 5. Vapor pressure and temperature relations.

With Eqs. (25), (8), and (13) the combination formula is found as written by McIlroy (see Slatyer and McIlroy 1961; Monteith, 1965).

$$E = [s/(\gamma + s)](R_n - G) + \rho c_p h(\delta_z - \delta_0) \tag{26a}$$

which with Eq. (24b) can be written

$$E = [s/(\gamma + s)]\{(R_n - G) - (\rho c_p/s)h[(e_z{}^* - e_z) - (e_0{}^* - e_0)]\} \tag{26b}$$

and also as

$$E = [s/(\gamma + s)]\{(R_n - G) + (\rho c_p/s)h[(e_0 - e_z) - s(T_0 - T_z)]\} \tag{26c}$$

The result also can be written in the form Penman et al., (1967) used

$$E = \frac{(s + \gamma)(R_n - G) + (E_a/f_0)}{[s + (\gamma/f_0)]/\gamma} \tag{26d}$$

where E_a is defined after Penman (1948) as

$$E_a = (\lambda \rho \varepsilon/P)he_z[(f_0/f_z) - 1] \tag{27}$$

To find the evaporation, R_n, G, h, T_z, e_z, e_0, and T_0 must be known.

This form of describing evaporation is of interest because the available energy from radiation and soil storage ($R_n - G$) is separated from the convective heat supply terms. The wet-bulb depression and the saturation deficit describe the heat available from the air through convection.

The above combination equations assume only two things: first, that $h_v = h_h = h$ and, second, that the finite form of the Clausius–Clapeyron equation can be used. The second assumption is that $s = de^*/dT$ at $(T_0 + T_z)/2$ (or T_z provided $T_0 - T_z$ is small) can approximate the finite difference needed in Eqs. (24b) and (25b). The equations apply to surfaces such as leaves in which three-dimensional transport obtains as well as to an extended surface, where transport is one-dimensional provided h can be established for the surface and the other parameters can be measured.

B. TRANSFER COEFFICIENTS

The transport coefficients of interest are those describing surfaces with adequate fetch so that one-dimensional transport obtains and describing smaller surfaces where three-dimensional transport exists.

1. One-Dimensional Transport

The transfer coefficient h for Eqs. (8) and (26), when applied to surfaces with one-dimensional, turbulent transport, is obtained in several ways. Businger (1956) recommended the neutral wind profile resulting from Eq. (16b), when $\Phi = 0$. Tanner and Pelton (1960) and Van Bavel (1966) demonstrated that the combination method is satisfactory over irrigated crops when h is found as Businger suggested, assuming neutral conditions.

Fuchs and Tanner (unpublished results) have used Eq. (16b) over dry, bare soil with good results. In this instance, corrections for thermal stratification were required and were achieved adequately using Eq. (17) in appropriate form:

$$\text{Ri} = \{(g/T)(T_0 - T_z)[\ln(z/z_0)]V_z^{-2}\}z \tag{28}$$

where T_0, T_z, and V_z were measured at $z = 1$ m. From Ri, Φ was found, and then $h = C_z V$ was calculated via Eq. (16b).

Equation (16b) requires information on z_0. An empirical relation between z_0 and vegetation height has been developed by Kung and Lettau (1961):

$$z_0 = 0.058Z^{1.19} \tag{29a}$$

where z, the vegetation height, and z_0 are in centimeters. Equation (29a) provides a linear relation on a log–log plot. Tanner and Pelton, following Kung and Lettau, but using partly different data, found that

$$z_0 \approx 0.13Z \tag{29b}$$

where z_0 and Z are in centimeters. The above relations agree reasonably well for $Z < 2$ m; however, Eq. (29a) is preferable when $Z > 2$ m.

2. Three-Dimensional Transport

The transfer coefficient for leaves, sunken pans, etc. is found most conveniently using heat and mass transport correlations of the form

$$\text{Nu} = \text{C Pr}^n \text{ Re}^m \tag{30a}$$

$$\text{Nu}_m = \text{C Sc}^n \text{ Re}^m \tag{30b}$$

Correlations for flat plates, cylinders, and spheres are available in heat transport texts (e.g., Bird, et al., 1960). Monteith (1965) summarizes mass transport correlation data for leaves in air near $300K$ and finds

$$h = 0.50(V/L)^{1/2} \tag{31a}$$

The correlation for flat plates as given in transport books for $300K$ is

$$h = 0.37(V/L)^{1/2} \tag{31b}$$

or about three fourths that found by Monteith. Tibbals et al. (1964) indicate how h may be determined for conifer branches and other complex objects.

Many biologists compute the mean flux density of the leaf from the entire flux but use an area representing only one side of the leaf. This results in a flux density and transfer coefficient that is twice that obtained if the total area of the leaf is used. Conventionally, transport correlations determine the mean flux density from the total flux and the total area from which the flux derives. There is considerable ambiguity in the biological literature because the flux density and transport coefficients have not been reported according to convention.

3. Diffusion Resistance

Diffusion resistances, rather than transfer coefficients, are used when heat and vapor flow are in series through two or more pathways which differ in character. The diffusion resistance of a pathway is the reciprocal of the transfer coefficient.

C. POTENTIAL EVAPORATION

If E_p conditions are defined as those where water supply is not limiting, then $\delta_0 = (e_0{}^* - e_0) = 0$ and $f_0 = 1$. Then, the wet-bulb formulation (26a) reduces to

$$E_p = [s/(\gamma + s)](R_n - G) + \rho c_p h\delta_z \tag{32a}$$

and Eq. (26b) becomes

$$E_p = [s/(s + \gamma)][(R_n - G) + (\rho c_p/s)h(e_z{}^* - e_z)] \tag{32b}$$

which is the original Penman (1948) formula for potential evaporation.

By using the condition that the surface temperature and vapor pressure are related through the saturation vapor pressure curve, a measurement of T_0 or e_0 is eliminated from a determination of E_p. It is seen that the nonlimiting supply of water at the surface where sensible heat and evaporation originate is the crucial part of the E_p definition.

If the wind travels over a sufficiently long, wet fetch, then $(e_z{}^* - e_z)$ and δ_z of Eq. (32) approach zero. This is what McIlroy calls "equilibrium" E_p and is a "midoceanic" condition. Then,

$$E_p = [s/(s + \gamma)](R_n - G) \tag{33}$$

which is the *minimum potential evaporation obtainable*. The partitioning of $(R_n - G)$ into E and H is a function of temperature only, although this, in turn, must depend upon R_n and G.

The E_p given by Eq. (33) is the interesting condition of evaporation into a saturated atmospheric surface layer. This does not imply that there are no temperature or vapor pressure gradients but only that the gradients near the surface are adjusted to provide saturated vapor pressure and dew-point temperature profiles.

Monteith (1965) points out that the same condition can obtain over unsaturated surfaces provided the saturation deficit of the surface and of the air surface layer are equal. With this condition, changes in wind speed will cause no change in evaporation. Evaporation will always increase with wind speed when $(e_0{}^* - e_0) < (e_z{}^* - e_z)$ and decrease when $(e_0{}^* - e_0) > (e_z{}^* - e_z)$.

A suitable definition of potential evaporation is the evaporation that would obtain from a surface of any configuration under given meteorological conditions if there were no saturation deficit at the surface—a condition of adequate water supply. Thus, E_p is determined largely by the climatic conditions as given in Eq. (32); however, differences in the plant canopy and/or soil surfaces can affect the E_p through the albedo, which affects net radiation, and through the roughness length, which affects the transport coefficient.

A change in either the albedo or the roughness length can cause a difference in potential evapotranspiration between plant types. The albedo of different vegetation types may vary from 0.15 to 0.25, which could change the net radiation $\pm 5\%$. Changes in roughness can change the convective term of Eq. (32); however, changes are not drastic provided different surfaces have the same humidity, temperature, and wind profiles at the leading edge of the field. Although h will change with different vegetation, so also will $(e_z{}^* - e_z)$ in the opposite direction, and the product does not change as much as either term alone. The length of fetch and differences in the profiles at the leading edge provide the most pronounced differences between fields of different roughness.

From Eq. (33) it is seen that with infinite fetch, roughness has no effect.

With increasingly shorter fetches, E_p increases above $[s/(s + \gamma)]R_n$, and the effect of roughness differences becomes more pronounced. If upwind surface conditions are similar to the surfaces studied, this is equivalent to an increased fetch since the degree of adjustment to the new surface is small. Thus, surface roughness is expected to cause greatest differences when fetch is small and particularly when the upwind external area is dry so that air travelling over the E_p surface must make maximum adjustment. Reports of large E_p differences among plant types often refer to small areas and/or to arid regions where $(e_z{}^* - e_z)$ is large, making available large quantities of sensible heat from the surroundings.

D. RATIO OF ACTUAL TO POTENTIAL EVAPORATION

Tanner (1967) has summarized several empirical relations between E/E_p and soil moisture content that climatologists have proposed. Although evaporation from soils and plant leaves is influenced by soil moisture content, there is no simple relation between them. Empirical correlations of E/E_p to soil water, however bad, have been used with some success for seasonal estimates of evaporation. The success is due largely to the fact that the budgeting system has strong negative feedback and that local calibrations usually have been made. A rational modification of the combination formula to give E/E_p from surface measurements will be examined.

Penman and Schofield (1951) modified the potential evaporation estimate using a surface resistance which indicates an additional resistance to water vapor diffusion that is not shared by the heat flow. Slatyer and McIlroy (1961) and Monteith (1963) used similar concepts. Slatyer and McIlroy look to the way stomatal resistance affects transpiration from a leaf, whereas Monteith, as Penman and Schofield, views the canopy resistance as if the canopy has the properties of a large leaf. Monteith (1965) continues with this concept in his extensive treatment of evaporation from the combination formula viewpoint. These treatments involve a particular evaporation model and special assumptions; however, a general treatment will be made here and the more restricted models will be examined.

1. General Formula

Existing evaporation is related to the potential evaporation, using Eqs. (8a) and (26b), to give

$$E = [(\gamma + s)/s]E_p - (\rho c_p/s)h(e_0{}^* - e_z) \tag{34}$$

The only necessary surface measurement is T_0, which is needed to find $e_0{}^*$ and to find s at temperature $(T_0 + T_z)/2$.

At first glance, the last term in Eq. (32) would appear to be $(\gamma/s)E_p$; however, for the case of a dry surface layer, T_0 and $e_0{}^*$ are much higher than they would be if the surface were moist. Unless the soil is wet, $E_p < (\rho\varepsilon/P)h(e_0{}^* - e_z)$, where $e_0{}^*$ is the saturation vapor pressure corresponding to T_0. An upper limit to the surface temperature for a dry soil is given by Eq. (34). If the soil is wet, $e_0 = e_0{}^*$ corresponding to T_0, and Eq. (34) reduces to $E = E_p$.

This equation is different from those of Penman, Slatyer, and McIlroy and Monteith, which include an internal resistance for the surface. Equation (34) is general and assumes no particular diffusion model for a canopy, leaf, or other surface and has no internal resistance terms.

2. Evaporation Models

Two specific models represented by Fig. 6 will now be considered. In both models, the transport resistance between the surface and height z is $r_a = 1/h$ and is the same for both heat and vapor; however, the internal resistances for heat and vapor differ. The latent heat flux may be written in terms of the internal resistance to vapor transport:

$$E = (\lambda\rho\varepsilon/P)(e_0 - e_z)/r_a \tag{35a}$$

$$E = (\lambda\rho\varepsilon/P)(e_i - e_0)/r_i \tag{35b}$$

$$E = (\lambda\rho\varepsilon/P)(e_i - e_z)/(r_i + r_a) \tag{35c}$$

From Eqs. (34) and (35),

$$E = \frac{E_p - (\lambda\rho\varepsilon/P)[\gamma/(s + \gamma)](e_0{}^* - e_i)r_a{}^{-1}}{1 + [\gamma/(s + \gamma)](r_i/r_a)} \tag{36}$$

The first model assumes that vapor saturation occurs internally; then Eq. (36) can be written as a temperature expression without knowing the internal heat flow resistance. When $e_i = e_0{}^*$ corresponding to T_i, $e_i{}^* - e_0{}^* = s(T_i - T_0)$ and then Eq. (36) becomes

$$E = \frac{E_p - [\rho c_p s/(s + \gamma)](T_0 - T_i)r_a{}^{-1}}{1 + [\gamma/(s + \gamma)](r_i/r_a)} \tag{37}$$

Equation (37) represents the evaporation from a moist soil covered with a porous mulch or from a soil with a dry surface layer underlain by a moist sublayer.

The second model assumes that the internal conduction of heat is sufficiently high that $T_0 \to T_i$ and $[\rho c_p s/(s + \gamma)](T_0 - T_i)r_a{}^{-1}$ is negligible compared to E_p. If this is so and r_i still is not small compared with r_a, then $T_i \approx T_0$ and $e_i \approx e_0{}^*$, and Eqs. (36) and (37) reduce to

$$E/E_p = \{1 + [\gamma/(s + \gamma)](r_i/r_a)\}^{-1} \tag{38}$$

which is an equation put forth by Penman, McIlroy, and Monteith.

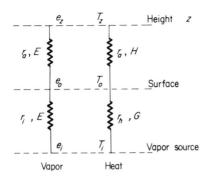

FIG. 6. Schematic diagram of external and internal diffusion resistances.

Because of the cuticle, stomata spacing, and leaf geometry, the transfer resistance for heat in leaves is much less than for vapor, and $T_i \approx T_0$. Accordingly, Eq. (38) is a suitable representation of leaves.

It is noted that if E/E_p is found, Eq. (38) can be used to compute an "effective" r_i for this second model that assumes $T_0 \approx T_i$, even though the surface does correspond to the model. Mulched and bare soils and leaves and canopies will be examined to see if Eq. (37) or (38) can reasonably represent them.

E. INTERNAL RESISTANCES

For Eq. (37) or (38) to represent mulched or bare soils and leaves or canopies, an internal diffusion resistance must be assigned to the surface that is meaningful with respect to the models these formulas represent. An internal resistance described by Eqs. (36), (37), and (38) may be assigned to mulched and bare soils and to leaves and plant canopies. These models can be examined to see if they are more reasonable than empirical relations of E/E_p to soil water content.

1. Mulched Soils

A mulched soil should follow the model described by Eqs. (36) and (37) with $e_i = e_i^* \sim T_i$, provided three conditions are met. First, no capillary flow through the mulch can occur; this is reasonably met by several types of mulches. Second, the capillary flow to the mulch–soil interface must exceed the vapor loss so that a significant decrease in relative humidity at the interface is prevented. Third, the diffusion resistance r_i of the layer must be known. When turbulent flow occurs above the surface causing pressure fluctuations, this resistance will be less than that calculated from molecular diffusion. Present theory is not adequate to evaluate the apparent diffusion resistance as influenced by pressure fluctuations.

2. Bare Soils

M. Fuchs and the author tried to apply, Eq. (36) to a Plainfield sand which had dried until a 1.5-cm-deep dry-sand surface layer had formed. In the early morning reasonable results were obtained; however, as the day progressed the diffusion resistance of the layer increased, even though the soil appeared moist under the dry layer and the thickness of the dry layer did not change measurably. The discrepancy could be caused by evaporation over a depth range, as described by Hanks and Gardner (1967), rather than at a plane as required by the model. This results primarily because of the distributed heat source and because of both upward and downward vapor gradients. Since the experiment by Fuchs and Tanner more nearly approximated a mulch condition than is found with other finer-textured soils, a simple model similar to Eq. (36) for soil is not likely.

When $E/E_p < 1$, the evaporation from soils can be treated satisfactorily by capillary flow principles, as shown in Chapter 5, without considering climatic effects.

3. Leaves

Because of the low resistance to heat flow in the leaf relative to the high resistance offered by the cuticle and the widely spaced stomata to vapor transport, the evaporation from leaves appears to fit the model described by Eqs. (35c) and (38).

The leaf internal resistance depends upon the water potential in the leaf and the light level at the leaf, although no unique relationship has been established even for a single species (Chapter 6). The leaf resistance can be found using either Eq. (35c) or (38). In either case r_a must be evaluated either from Eq. (35a) or from correlation relations (31a) and (31b). Usually r_a is so small that substantial error in defining r_a produces little error in r_i.

Independent means for evaluating r_i are discussed in Chapter 6. Stomatal aperture meters have been devised with the hope of measuring r_i directly. Correlations between r_i and permeability and leaf infiltration measurements have been used for indirect determinations.

4. Canopies

Penman and Schofield (1951) and Monteith (1963, 1965) and others have applied Eq. (38), or its profile equivalent, to the canopy as though the canopy were a large leaf. The concept of a canopy resistance, as described by Eq. (38) and which is based upon the model of a large leaf, is interesting but cannot be correct.

The sensible heat produced at the upper leaves of the canopy receiving strong radiation is transferred downward through the canopy to shaded leaves through a large temperature gradient, as illustrated by many data (e.g., Penman and Long, 1960; Brown and Covey, 1966).

The resistance models described by Eqs. (36) and (38) assume that the radiant energy exchange is at a plane, rather than being distributed over a volume. They also implicitly assume that the flux density at the surface under given total heat supply is independent of the distribution of heat sources and sinks and vapor sources. The effect of shading on stomatal resistance varies with position and time, as does the eddy diffusivity in the canopy space and the strength of radiative heat sources, and it is unrealistic to assume that any simple linear resistive network can provide a correctly integrated relation between the total vapor flux from a canopy to a forcing function at a plane near the canopy surface. Apparently, reasonable relations between stomatal resistance and canopy resistance derived, as by Monteith (1963, 1965), from an inapplicable model are fortuitous. It seems clear that canopy models, which consider the spatial distribution of heat sources and transfer coefficients, are necessary. The simple model proposed early by Penman and Schofield (1951) and elaborated by Monteith (1963, 1965) may prove more useful than the empirical correlation of E/E_p to soil water, but it provides no basic concept for evaporation from either canopies or soils and is useful potentially only in an empirical engineering sense.

VI. TRANSFER IN CANOPIES

The flux of vapor and heat within the canopy has been approached using the energy balance and also using wind fluctuation or profile models. A description of transport processes occurring within the canopy is much more complicated than in the atmospheric surface layer or from single leaves. An adequate discussion cannot be included in this chapter and, accordingly, only a few references to typical work are given.

Although several wind profile approaches to canopy transport have been proposed (Uchijima, 1962; Inoue, 1963; Uchijima and Wright, 1964; Cionco, 1965), they have not proven as successful as the energy balance approach; the same can be said of the wind-speed fluctuation approaches discussed by Uchijima and Wright (1964) and by Wright and Lemon (1966).

The energy balance approach to determining the flux of vapor and heat and the eddy diffusivities in the canopy is presented by Philip (1964). This description of canopy energy balance includes profiles of sources, diffusivities, and fluxes vs. either height or foliage density. Brown and Covey (1966) and Uchijima (1966) have extended Philip's approach to include the effects of stomatal resistance.

VII. EMPIRICAL ESTIMATES OF POTENTIAL EVAPORATION

A great many empirical climatological estimates of potential evaporation from field-size areas and larger areas have been proposed. The estimates can be grouped according to the principal climatological parameters used: radiation, temperature, humidity, and evaporation from evaporimeters. The principal empirical methods have been discussed by Tanner (1967) and are summarized briefly here.

Supplanting rational methods with empirical estimates may be justified if no data or measurements of the right kind exist; however, it should be recognized that this is the substitution of ignorance of results for ignorance of data.

A. CONSERVATIVENESS OF E_p

The variability between years of the monthly potential evaporation is low for any given location. This conservativeness also is true of the variables in Eq. (32) and more importantly, of measured evaporation where water is not seriously limiting (see data in Tanner, 1967, and Van Bavel, 1961). Because of the conservativeness of monthly E_p, coupled with the cyclic nature through the year, a high correlation is found between E_p and various empirical estimates.

When the empirical method has been calibrated against measured evaporation under conditions of nonlimiting water supply, the method provides reasonable quantitative estimates. This is because of the conservative character of E_p and because departures from average values are correlated with departures of many climatic variables from their means. In more conservative climates, such as arid regions compared with humid regions, empirical estimates and E_p are better correlated.

Methods based either on correlations with radiation and evaporation from shallow and sunken pans appear to provide the best estimates. Mean temperature methods are less valuable, and humidity methods appear to be least valuable.

B. EVAPORIMETERS

Evaporimeters include units ranging from large sunken pans to small atmometers, although the most commonly used evaporimeter probably is the Class-A U.S. Weather Bureau pan. Evaporimeters are described reasonably well by Eq. (32). Some atmometers and raised pans, such as the Class-A pan, have different areas of sensible heat and latent heat transfer, so that adjustments for different transfer coefficients for heat and vapor must be made (Kohler et al., 1955; Mukammal, 1961). The hourly and daily values of G in Eq. (32) may be different for pans and vegetated areas; however, over longer periods the differences decrease. The raised pan usually will have higher R_n and most often a higher transfer coefficient h than large, vegetated areas. In arid regions where $(e_z{}^* - e_z)$ is large, the potential sensible heat contribution to evaporation $(\rho\varepsilon/P)h(e_z{}^* - e_z)$ can be appreciably larger for pans than for large areas of vegetation. Nevertheless, the correlation between pans and E_p is usually high on a weekly to monthly basis.

Because atmometers usually are situated well above the surface where wind velocities are much larger than at the surface and because they are small in size, the transfer coefficient h is very large. Consequently, the contribution of sensible heat from the airstream toward evaporation is much larger than for extended vegetated surfaces. Atmometers are also subject to plugging and other problems and are less satisfactory than pans.

C. Radiation Methods

Radiation methods are among the better empirical methods. Their success rests on the fact that the radiation term of Eqs. (32) rarely is smaller than the convective term and that the convective term is correlated with net radiation.

Radiation methods employ either net radiation or solar radiation. The high correlation between net radiation and solar radiation is the reason for success of the estimates based on solar radiation. The degree of success also depends upon whether the net (or solar) radiation is either measured or estimated from cloudiness or percent sunshine using empirical formulas; there is considerable scatter in radiation estimates, particularly for periods shorter than a week or two.

The radiation either may be correlated directly with E_p or the radiation first may be weighted for effects of air temperature. The $[s/(s + \gamma)]$ in Eq. (32) is one type of temperature weighting term that is used, although other types also have been proposed.

D. Temperature Methods

Several relations between mean air temperature and E_p have been proposed, but those of Thornthwaite (1948) and of Blaney and Criddle (1950) have been used most widely. The Thornthwaite estimate depends only upon mean temperature, whereas the Blaney–Criddle estimate depends also upon "crop coefficients" that weight local conditions into the estimate. Both methods depend strongly upon the mutual correlation of both temperature and evaporation to radiation.

Some estimates use the difference between saturation vapor pressures corresponding to the maximum or minimum temperatures, which is an approximation of the convective heat supply term in Eq. (32). Other estimates use the saturation vapor pressure corresponding to the mean temperature.

Temperature methods have the apparent advantage that temperature data are readily available; however, the value of uncertain guesses of evaporation based on available but indirectly related data is debatable.

E. HUMIDITY METHODS

A variety of humidity methods has been used but most of them correlate $[CV(e_z^* - e_z)]$ to E_p^*. This type of humidity method provides a fair correlation with the sensible heat available for evaporation; however, the correlation with radiation is poor. Correlations between humidity and E_p have no advantage over temperature correlations and suffer the additional disadvantage that humidity data are not as available.

REFERENCES

American Meteorological Society. (1965). Agricultural meteorology. *Meteorol. Monographs* **6**, 188 pp.

Bergen, J. (1967). Some aspects of cold air drainage on a forested mountain slope. Ph.D. Thesis, Colorado State Univ., Fort Collins, Colorado.

Bird, R. B., Stewart, W. E., and Lightfoot, E. N. (1960). "Transport Phenomena," 780 pp. Wiley, New York.

Blaney, H. F., and Criddle, W. D. (1950). Determining water requirements in irrigated areas from climatological and irrigation data. *U.S. Dept. Agr. Soil Conserv. Serv.*, *SCS-TP-96*, 48 pp.

Brooks, F. A. (1961). Need for measuring horizontal gradients in determining vertical eddy transfers of heat and moisture. *J. Meteorol.* **18**, 589.

Brown, K. W., and Covey, W. (1966). The energy-budget evaluation of the micrometeorological transfer processes within a cornfield. *Agr. Meteorol.* **3**, 73.

Budyko, M. I. (1965). The heat balance of the Earth's surface. (Translated by N. A. Stepanova, 1958.) *U.S. Dept. Comm., Office Tech. Serv. PB131692*, 259 pp.

Businger, J. A. (1956). Some remarks on Penman's equations for the evapotranspiration. *Netherlands J. Agr. Sci.* **4**, 77.

Cionco, R. M. (1965). A mathematical model for air flow in a vegetative canopy. *J. Appl. Meteorol.* **4**, 517.

De Vries, D. A. (1959). The influence of irrigation on the energy balance and the climate near the ground. *J. Meteorol.* **16**, 256.

Dyer, A. J. (1963). The adjustment of profiles and eddy fluxes. *Quart. J. Roy. Meteorol. Soc.* **89**, 276.

Dyer, A. J., and Maher, F. J. 1965. The "evaporation": an instrument for the measurement of eddy fluxes in the lower atmosphere. *Australia, CSIRO, Div. Meteorol. Phys. Tech. Paper* **12**.

Dyer, A. J., Hicks, B. B., and King, K. M. (1967). The fluxatron—a revised approach to the measurement of eddy fluxes in the lower atmosphere. *J. Appl. Meteorol.* **6**, 408.

Ferguson, J. (1952). The rate of evaporation from shallow ponds. *Australian J. Sci. Res.* **5**, 315.

Gardner, W. R. (1965). Rainfall, runoff, and return. *Meteorol. Monographs* **6**, 138.

Gates, D. M. (1965). Radiant energy, its receipt and disposal. *Meteorol. Monographs* **6**, 1.

Hagan, R. M., Haise, H. R., and Edminster, T. W. (eds.) (1967). Irrigation of agricultural lands. *Agronomy* **11**, 1216 pp.

Hanks, R. J., and Gardner, H. R. (1967). Moisture and temperature profiles during evaporation as influenced by radiation and wind. *Soil Sci. Soc. Am. Proc.* **31**, 593.

Holmes, J. W., Taylor, S. A., and Richards, S. J. (1967). Measurement of soil water. *Agronomy* **11**, 275.

Holmes, R. M., Gill, G. C., and Carson, H. W. (1964). A propeller-type vertical anemometer. *J. Appl. Meteorol.* **3**, 802.

Inoue, E. (1963). On the turbulent structure of airflow within crop canopies. *J. Meteorol. Soc. Japan* **41**, 317.

Kaimal, J. C., and Businger, J. A. (1963). A continuous wave sonic anemometer-thermometer. *J. Appl. Meteorol.* **2**, 156.

King, F. H. (1910). "Physics of Agriculture," 604 pp. Publ. by author, Madison, Wisconsin.

Kohler, M. A., Nordenson, T. J., and Fox, W. E. (1955). Evaporation from pans and lakes. *U.S. Weather Bur. Res. Paper* **38**, 21 pp.

Kung, E. C., and Lettau, H. H. (1961). Regional and meridional distributions of continental vegetation cover and aerodynamic roughness parameters. *Ann. Rept. Ft. Huachuca Contract DA*-36-039-*SC*-80282.

Lemon, E. R. (1963). The energy balance at the earth's surface. I. *U.S. Dept. Agr. ARS Production Res. Rept.* **71**.

Lettau, H. H. (1962). Notes on theoretical models of profile structure in the diabatic surface layer. *Dept. Meteorol. Univ. Wisconsin Final Rept.*, *Contract DA*-36-039-*SC*-80282, 195.

McIlroy, I. C., and Angus, D. E. (1963). The Aspendale multiple weighed lysimeter installation. *Australia, CSIRO, Div. Meteorol. Phys. Tech. Paper* **14**, 29 pp.

Monteith, J. L. (1963). Gas exchange in plant communities, *In* " Environmental Control of Plant Growth " (L. T. Evans, ed.), p. 95. Academic Press, New York.

Monteith, J. L. (1965). Evaporation and environment. *Symp. Soc. Exptl. Biol.* **19**, 205.

Mukammal, E. I. (1961). Evaporation pans and atmometers. *Proc. Hydrol. Symp.* **2**, 84.

Nixon, P. R., and Lawless, G. P. (1960). Translocation of moisture with time in unsaturated soil profiles, *J. Geophys. Res.* **65**, 655.

Panofsky, H. A., and Townsend, A. A. (1964). Change of terrain roughness and the wind profile. *Quart. J. Roy. Meteorol. Soc.* **90**, 147. (See also discussions in *Quart. J. Roy. Meteorol. Soc.* **91**, 240–242.)

Pelton, W. L. (1961). The use of lysimetric methods to measure evapotranspiration. *Proc. Hydrol. Symp.* **2**, 106.

Penman, H. L. (1948). Natural evaporation from open water, bare soil, and grass. *Proc. Roy. Soc.* **A193**, 120.

Penman, H. L. (1961). Weather, plant and soil factors in hydrology. *Weather* **16**, 207.

Penman, H. L., and Long, I. F. (1960). Weather in wheat: an essay in micrometeorology. *Quart. J. Roy. Meteorol. Soc.* **86**, 16.

Penman, H. L., and Schofield, R. K. (1951). Some physical aspects of assimilation and transpiration. *Symp. Soc. Exptl. Biol.* **5**, 115.

Penman, H. L., Angus, D. E., and Van Bavel, C. H. M. (1967). Microclimatic factors affecting evaporation and transpiration. *Agronomy* **11**, 483.

Philip, J. R. (1959). The theory of local advection. I. *J. Meteorol.* **16**, 535.

Philip, J. R. (1964). Sources and transfer processes in the air layers occupied by vegetation. *J. Appl. Meteorol.* **3**, 390.

Robins, J. S., Pruitt, W. O., and Gardner, W. H. (1954). Unsaturated flow of water in field soils and its effect on soil moisture investigations. *Soil Sci. Soc. Am. Proc.* **18**, 344.

Sellers, W. D. (1964). Potential evapotranspiration in arid regions. *J. Appl. Meteorol.* **3**, 98.

Sellers, W. D. (1965). "Physical Climatology." 271 pp. Univ. Chicago Press, Chicago, Illinois.

Slatyer, R. O. and McIlroy, I. C. (1961). Practical microclimatology. *Australia, CSIRO, Plant Ind. Div. Canberra, Australia.* (UNESCO.)

Tanner, C. B. (1960). Energy balance approach to evapotranspiration from crops. *Soil Sci. Am. Proc.* **24**, 1.

Tanner, C. B. (1967). Measurement of evapotranspiration. *Agronomy* **11**, 534.

Tanner, C. B., and Pelton, W. L. (1960). Potential evapotranspiration estimates by the approximate energy balance method of Penman. *J. Geophys. Res.* **65**, 3391.

Taylor, S. A., Evans, D. D., and Kemper, W. D. 1961. Evaluating soil water. *Utah State Univ. Agr. Expt. Sta. Bull.* **426**, 67 pp.

Thornthwaite, C. W. (1948). An approach toward a rational classification of climate. *Geograph. Rev.* **38**, 55.

Thornthwaite, C. W., and Hare, F. K. (1965). The loss of water to the air. *Meteorol. Monographs* **6**, 163.

Thornthwaite, C. W., Superior, W. J., Mather, J. R., and Hare, F. K. (1961). The measurement of vertical winds and momentum flux. *Climatology* **14**, 1.

Tibbals, E. C., Carr, E. K., Gates, D. M., and Kreith, F. (1964). Radiation and convection in conifers. *Am. J. Botany* **51**, 529.

Uchijima, Z. (1962). Studies on the micro-climate within the plant communities. 1. On the turbulent transfer coefficient within plant layer. (In Japanese, English summary). *Nogyo Kisho J. Agr. Meteorol. [Tokyo]*) **18**, 1.

Uchijima, Z. (1966). Micrometeorological evaluation of integral exchange coefficient at foliage surfaces and source strengths with a corn canopy. *Nogyo Gijutsu Kenkyusho Hokoku, Butsuri Tokei (Bull. Natl. Inst. Agr. Sci. [Japan], Ser. A)* **13**, 81.

Uchijima, Z., and Wright, J. L. (1964). An experimental study of air flow in a corn plant-air layer. *Nogyo Gijutsu Kenkyusho Hokoku, Butsuri Tokei (Bull. Natl. Inst. Agr. Sci. [Japan], Ser. A)* **11**, 19.

Udagawa, T. (1966). Variation of aerodynamical characteristics of a barley field with growth. *Nogyo Kisho (J. Agr. Meteorol. [Tokyo]*) **22**, 7.

Van Bavel, C. H. M. (1961). Lysimetric measurements of evapotranspiration rates in the eastern United States. *Soil Sci. Soc. Am. Proc.* **25**, 138.

Van Bavel, C. H. M. (1966). Potential evaporation: the combination concept and its experimental verification. *Water Resources Res.* **2**, 455.

Van Wijk, W. R., and Scholte Ubing, D. W. (1963). Radiation, *In* "Physics of Plant Environment" (W. R. Van Wijk, ed.), pp. 62–101. Wiley, New York.

Webb, E. K. 1964. Further note on evaporation with fluctuating Bowen ratio. *J. Geophys. Res.* **69**, 2649.

Webb, E. K. 1965. Aerial microclimate. *Meteorol. Monographs* **6**, 27.

Wright, J. L., and Lemon, E. R. (1966). Photosynthesis under field conditions. VIII. Analysis of windspeed fluctuation data to evaluate turbulent exchange within a corn crop. *Agron. J.* **58**, 255.

CHAPTER 5

AVAILABILITY AND MEASUREMENT OF SOIL WATER

W. R. Gardner

DEPARTMENT OF SOILS, UNIVERSITY OF WISCONSIN, MADISON, WISCONSIN

I. INTRODUCTION

The importance of the relation of the state of water in the soil surrounding plant roots to the state of water in plant leaves has long been recognized. The pore space in the soil provides a reservoir for water that enables plants to survive and grow in a hydrological cycle in which rainfall is intermittent and undependable, but in which transpiration demand is unceasing and inevitable. Stated in simple terms, the supply of water to the plant on the average must equal the demand. Availability of water to plants depends largely on how the accommodation between supply and demand is accomplished.

A certain amount of disagreement has existed at times in the past among some workers in the field of soil–plant–water relations, and this is reflected in the literature. It is the intent in this chapter to deal more with the philosophy and concepts of water availability than to review the many published experiments. This is particularly desirable for those plant and soil scientists who have neither the time nor inclination to distill these concepts from the ever-expanding literature.

It should be stated at the outset that the term "water availability" seems increasingly meaningless except as a very general term that must be defined each time one wishes to use it in a quantitative sense. Much of the past controversy concerning the "relative availability" of soil water did not come to grips with this problem and instead became involved in semantics. That there is a relation between the water in the soil and that in the plant is clear to any layman who has seen a wilted plant. It was not different for early investigators to find that soil water content, per se, was not an adequate means of characterizing soil water. The gradual but steady recognition of the importance of the potential energy of soil water in understanding soil water relations constitutes the major part of the history of soil physics in the first half of this century and is well documented and thoroughly discussed elsewhere (e.g. Miller and Klute, 1967).

Two important concepts came out of the early work relating soil water to plant response. The first was the field capacity concept (Israelsen and West, 1922; Veihmeyer and Hendrickson, 1927), which became identified with the upper limit of available soil water. The second, the wilting coefficient (Briggs and Shantz, 1911), led to the permanent wilting percentage (Hendrickson and Veihmeyer, 1945) that gained wide acceptance as the lower limit of available water. The apparent utility of these two concepts is attested to by their almost universal usage, their deficiencies and associated controversies notwithstanding.

On the basis of their classic studies, Veihmeyer and coworkers (e.g. Veihmeyer and Hendrickson, 1933) concluded that between the aforementioned two limits it mattered little to the plant precisely what the physical state of the water in the soil might be. Soil water was said to be equally available over the available range, and it was not too important to be concerned with "how available?"

In one of the earliest and certainly the most thoroughly documented dissents from Veihmeyer's point of view, Richards and Wadleigh (1952) made a strong case for a concept of "decreasing availability" of water as the soil water content decreased between the field capacity and the permanent wilting point. The "unequal availability" concept was strengthened further by a number of papers that followed. Stanhill (1957) examined the results of 80 published studies and concluded that in 66 of them there was a significant plant response to soil water content within the so-called available range. The difficulty in settling unequivocally so basic a question as that of water availability stems from a number of factors. First, as was shown by Veihmeyer, it is virtually impossible to control the soil water content at any specified level. One usually has to allow it to fluctuate between field capacity or some similar value and a specified lower limit. Nor is the pattern of water extraction by plant roots necessarily uniform within the soil. Therefore, one is normally forced to integrate the soil water content over both space and time and to correlate this integrated soil water content with a plant response integrated over time. When this integration is taken over an entire growing season it is extremely difficult to evaluate directly the effect of limited water availability upon plant growth.

A fundamental issue that many workers failed to recognize was that one must distinguish between plant growth as opposed to transpiration as a measure of water availability. The fact that transpiration rate was found to be unrelated to soil water content over much of the "available range" was often cited as evidence of "equal availability" of water in the absence of any measure of plant growth. When plant response was measured, there were still disagreements about the availability of water since it made a difference whether one was concerned with vegetative growth, root growth, woody growth, or seed production. However, in view of the recent advances in understanding the physics of evaporation and water movement in soils there is little justification for prolonging the argument, since many of the issues can be or have been resolved by experiment. The problem now is mainly one of characterizing plant–soil systems quantitatively in terms of their water relations and exploring the basic principles underlying specific plant responses to water stresses.

An important consideration is to formulate the problem properly so that experiments designed to study the relation of plants to their environment can be interpreted unambiguously. Conceptually, this can be done in a relatively simple way. Water is required by plants to replace that which is lost by transpiration in much greater amounts than go into increasing the size of the plant. It is now quite clear, for reasons that are discussed in Chapter 4, that much of the time the atmospheric conditions may have a much greater influence than soil factors over the transpiration rate. Water movement in the liquid phase of the soil–plant system occurs in response to differences in the potential energy of water in different parts of the soil–plant system. The water potential in a plant must always be lower than that in the soil if water is to move from the soil into the plant. Thus, the energy of soil water always sets an upper limit to the energy of water in the plant. If one knows the potential energy of soil water, it follows that he knows the highest energy level possible in the plant. It seems quite apparent that whatever the influence of soil water upon plant response, it must be exercised through the effect upon the components of the potential energy of water in the plant. This is the justification for a great many of the studies of the relation between soil–water content and soil–water potential (soil moisture tension or soil suction). Once the importance of soil water potential was recognized, it was quite natural to attempt to relate the upper and lower limits of available water to specific values of soil water potential. This was relatively successful in the case of the lower limit, or permanent wilting point (Richards and Weaver, 1943), but thas proven largely fruitless in the case of the upper limit (Slater and Williams, 1965).

The main problem associated with attempts to relate plant response directly to soil–water potential is that the soil–plant–atmosphere system is a dynamic one that is never in equilibrium so long as the plant is transpiring. There is resistance to movement of water through the soil and the plant so that, although the soil–water potential may set an upper limit to the plant–water potential, the latter may be at a considerably lower value than the former. As a first approximation, if it is assumed that flow through the system is proportional to the potential difference, we may then write for a very simple plant–soil system:

$$\psi_p = \psi_s - ER \tag{1}$$

(this is not strictly true but adequate for our purposes), where ψ_p is the water potential in the plant leaf, ψ_s is the water potential in the soil, E is the transpiration rate, and R is the resistance to flow in the combined soil–plant system. The reference potential is taken as zero, so both soil and plant water potentials are negative, the latter being the more negative by an amount that depends upon both transpiration rate and resistance to flow. Since ψ_s will not be constant throughout the root zone from which water is being extracted, and R is a complex quantity which may depend upon many factors, Eq. (1) has a limited quantitative applicability and is more useful conceptually. E may be a function of the ψ_s as well as of atmospheric factors. That aspect of the problem is considered in other chapters. It will be the purpose of much of the remainder of this chapter to consider the factors that govern ψ_s and R and the manner in which they are related so that a quantitative or semiquantitative understanding of the environmental factors that determine the water potential in the plant can be developed.

II. SOIL WATER RELATIONS

A. RELATION OF SOIL WATER CONTENT TO POTENTIAL ENERGY

Very strong attractive forces between the surfaces of the soil particles and water molecules are responsible for lowering of the potential energy of water in the soil compared with water in bulk. Formally, this potential energy may be divided into several components though, in practice, this may be difficult to do. The potential due to these forces will be designated in this chapter as the matric potential $\psi_m = \psi_a + \psi_c + \psi_w$, where ψ_a is the adsorption potential resulting from adsorption forces operative mainly in the first few molecular layers adjacent to the particle surfaces. These forces are very strong and often result in the exclusion of dissolved ions from this region. ψ_c is the capillary potential derived from the curved meniscus at the air–water interface and related to the radius of curvature of this interface by the well-known relation

$$\psi_c = -2\sigma/r \qquad (2)$$

where σ is the surface tension. In coarse-textured soils this term is predominant throughout much of the soil water, especially at water contents corresponding to relatively high potential energies of the order of 0–0.5 bar. The third term, ψ_w, is due to the attraction between water molecules and ions in the electrical double layer at the charged surfaces of the clay particles. ψ_w is most important in fine-textured soils which have a large surface area, but it is difficult to separate from ψ_a and ψ_c. In practice, all three terms are usually lumped together since most methods of measuring matric potential measure the sum of all.

A second cause of a reduction in the potential energy of soil water is dissolved salts. The contribution to the potential due to salts is called the osmotic potential and is denoted by ψ_π. A third component of the potential energy is that resulting from external pressure. In the field this usually occurs in saturated soils as a result of the hydrostatic pressure attributed to the weight of the water above the point of measurement. This potential is given by $\psi_p = v \cdot \Delta p$, where Δp is the hydrostatic pressure in excess of atmospheric pressure and v is the specific volume of water (almost exactly 1 cm^3/gm). The final component of the potential energy is that caused by the earth's gravitational field and is given by $\psi_g = \rho g \cdot \Delta h$, where Δh is the elevation above the datum, g is the gravitational constant, and ρ is the density of water. In this chapter the Earth's surface will be taken as the reference level for this component unless otherwise specified.

The various means of defining and expressing the potential energy have been discussed in detail in Chapter 3. In this chapter, two expressions of energy are used. For some purposes it is more convenient to express the potential energy as that required to move a unit volume of water from the reference level to the point in the soil where it is to be specified. Since the specific volume of water is so nearly 1 cm^3/gm, this turns out to be the same numerically as the energy per unit mass, but it has the dimensions of pressure and is usually expressed in pressure units, normally in bars or millibars (1 bar = 10^6 dynes/cm^2 = 0.1 joule/cm^3). However, when dealing with water flow in soil it is much more convenient to use energy per unit weight of water. The energy then has dimensions of length and is usually expressed in centimeters of water. The gravitational potential in this system becomes simply Δh. The total potential less the osmotic component is designated as the hydraulic head:

$$H = (\psi_m + \psi_p + \psi_g)/g \qquad (3)$$

The negative of the matric potential has been traditionally known as the soil moisture tension or soil suction and has often been expressed in centimeters of water, though more recently bars and millibars are more common units. It should be noted that ψ_m is negligible in saturated soils and ψ_p is negligible in unsaturated soils. However, if ψ_m is thought of as an equivalent negative pressure, ψ_p and ψ_m may be considered as a single continuous pressure potential extending from the saturated to the unsaturated region. This concept is often found in the engineering literature.

The relation between the water content of a soil and its potential energy is an important physical characteristic of a soil. The potential energy is zero at or near saturation. Water held at energies less than -15 bars is of very limited value to the plant. The amount of water held at relatively high energies between zero and about -1 bar depends mainly upon the number and size distribution of the pores, whereas the amount of water held at lower than -15 bars is largely a function of soil texture. The water content at -15 bars is fairly well correlated with the surface area of a soil and would represent, roughly, about 10 molecular layers of water if it were distributed uniformly over the particle surface.

Curves relating the matric potential to the soil water content for different soil types are readily found in the soils literature. Figure 1 shows the soil suction as a function of soil water content by volume for Holtville silty clay for three different temperatures. The soil suction is the negative of the matric

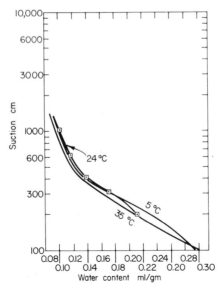

Fig. 1. Soil suction (matric potential) as a function of soil water content for Holtville silty clay.

potential expressed in centimeters of water. The data were obtained by E. J. Doering using the pressure membrane apparatus (personal communication). An adequate theoretical relation between the water potential and water content based upon soil properties has not been worked out. A number of empirical expressions have been developed to describe this relation analytically. An example is that given by Visser (1966)

$$\psi_m = A(P - \theta)^n/\theta^m \qquad (4)$$

where A, n, and m are constants, P is the pore space, and θ is the volumetric water content. At low water contents the numerator is relatively constant and Eq. (4) approximates a more frequently used relation, $\psi_m \sim \theta^{-m}$. Visser suggests that m is usually somewhat below 3 but may be near 0 for heavy clay soils, n varies between 0 and 10, and P usually falls between 0.4 and 0.6. Unfortunately, evaluation of the constants in Eq. (4) can be quite tedious.

The relation between the water potential and water content of a soil is not necessarily unique, and there is almost always some hysteresis present. Hysteresis is greatest in coarse-textured soils at high water contents where the pores may empty at a much lower potential than that at which they fill. It poses problems when one is dealing with nonsteady state flow systems. While the soil is continuously drying or continuously wetting, there is little problem as long as the appropriate relation between the two is known. The water potential is also a function of temperature, in general becoming lower as temperature is lowered.

B. Movement of Soil Water

1. Steady State Flow

The basic flow equation for describing water movement in soils is derived by assuming a linear system in which the flux is proportional to the driving force, with the driving force being the gradient of the potential energy. Since salts move rather freely through most soils, the osmotic component of the potential energy makes little or no contribution to the driving force. In this chapter we will also assume isothermal conditions so that we need not take into account temperature gradient effects since they are normally significant only at the soil surface. For an analysis of the movement of water when concentration and temperature gradients are important, the reader should see Cary and Taylor (1962). The flow equation in one dimension is:

$$q = -K[(d\psi_m/dz) + (d\psi_p/dz) + (d\psi_g/ds)] \qquad (5)$$

where K is the hydraulic conductivity, q is the flux density of water in the z direction, and the three terms on the right-hand side represent the gradients of the matric potential, pressure potential, and gravitational potential or head, respectively. As pointed out in Section II,A, the first term is omitted in saturated soils and the second in unsaturated soils. In a saturated soil, K is usually a function of position only, though in a soil with unstable structure, such as a sodic soil, it may be a function of the concentration of the soil solution as well as other factors. A serious complication occurs in unsaturated soils because the conductivity, which is usually denoted by k, is a very marked function of water content or water potential. Flow through a small pore varies roughly as the fourth power of its radius, so k depends very much upon the size distribution of pores that are filled with water. The relation between the capillary conductivity and the soil water content on a weight basis for Holtville silty clay is shown in Fig. 2. These data were obtained by Doering using the one-step method of analyzing pressure-plate outflow data (Doering, 1965). The temperature effect is greater than that which would be predicted from the temperature coefficient for the viscosity of bulk water. Several attempts have been made to calculate k from the water potential–water content curve, but they have met only limited success (Jackson *et al.*, 1965). An empirical expression that has been found useful for analytical purposes is

$$k = K/[(\psi_m/b)^s + 1] \tag{6}$$

where b and s are soil parameters. Physically, b is the potential at which $k = K/2$. The parameter s varies from about 1.5 for very fine-textured soils to

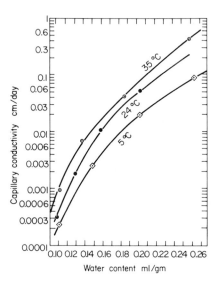

FIG. 2. Capillary conductivity as a function of soil water content by weight for Holtville silty clay.

as high as 10 or more for sandy soils. In the gravitational system for an unsaturated soil Eq. (6) becomes

$$q = -k[(d\psi_m/dz) + 1)]$$ (7)

where ψ_m is the matric component of the water potential given in centimeters of water. The depth z is taken as positive in the downward direction, while q in Eq. (7) is positive in the upward direction. Equation (7) may be integrated to describe steady state flow in one dimension if the relation between ψ_m and k is known. If no satisfactory analytical expression relating these two quantities can be found, no serious problem exists since integration by numerical methods is not difficult. Rearranging Eq. (7) gives

$$z_1 - z_2 = -\int_{\psi_2}^{\psi_1} d\psi/(1 + q/k)$$ (8)

Should k be a function of z as well as of ψ, the integration is a bit more cumbersome but not particularly difficult.

As pointed out above, the osmotic potential is omitted in Eq. (7) because salts tend to move with the water through the soil and do not usually affect the relative motion of the water with respect to the soil to any significant extent. However, salts must be taken into account when the total potential of soil water is related to plant water potential since the salts influence the latter. The exact nature of this influence is difficult to specify since it depends upon whether the salts pass freely through or are excluded by membranes in the plant roots. For practical purposes, it is often assumed that the osmotic and matric components are additive in their influence on water availability, and data such as those of Wadleigh and Ayers (1945) tend to support this as a reasonable assumption under some conditions. However, additivity of the two components cannot be a general rule since at least some salt is almost invariably taken up by the plant, resulting in an osmotic adjustment in plant cells. This aspect of the problem is more properly the subject of other chapters in this volume.

To the extent that salts are excluded by the root membranes, they tend to accumulate outside these membranes until a concentration gradient is built up sufficiently to cause diffusion of the salts away from the roots at the same rate at which they are transported up to the roots in the transpiration stream. If exclusion is complete, the steady state concentration of salt at a radial distance a from the axis of a cylindrical root is (Gardner, 1965)

$$C_a = C_b(b/a)^{w/2\pi D}$$ (9)

where C_b, which is presumed to represent the average concentration throughout the root zone, is the concentration at some distance b, one half of the distance between adjacent roots; w is the rate of water uptake per unit length of root; and D is the diffusion coefficient. C_a will probably exceed C_b significantly only in quite dry soils where D is small but where w is still appreciable. Any increase in C_a lowers the osmotic potential at the root surface accordingly.

2. Transient Flow

Many important flow problems do not fall into the steady state category. The equation for water movement during transient processes is obtained by combining Eq. (5) with the equation for the conservation of mass:

$$\partial\theta/\partial t = \partial q/\partial x + \partial q/\partial y + \partial q/\partial z \tag{10}$$

where t is time and θ is the volumetric water content of the soil. Combining with Eq. (5) gives:

$$\partial\theta/\partial t = \partial/\partial x(k\ \partial\psi/\partial x) + \partial/\partial y(k\ \partial\psi/\partial y) + \partial/\partial z(\partial\psi/\partial z) \tag{11}$$

or $\partial\theta/\partial t = \nabla \cdot k\ \nabla\psi$
as it is more conveniently written in vector notation. In order to solve Eq. (11), it is necessary to know θ as a function of position when $t = 0$ and to specify either the potential or the potential gradient along the boundaries of the system for all times $t > 0$. It is also necessary to know the relation between the water content and the potential. Solution of Eq. (11) would be relatively easy if it were not for the nonlinearity in the relation between ψ and θ and the variability of the conductivity k with θ and ψ, since Eq. (11) is mathematically the same as the heat flow equation, for which a large number of solutions are known (Carslaw and Jaeger, 1959). In the absence of exact solutions for variable k, which often require computers to obtain, the solutions for constant k can be extremely useful, as illustrated in later sections of this chapter.

Water uptake by the plant is taken into account mathematically by introducing an additional term to Eq. (11):

$$\partial\theta/\partial t = \nabla \cdot k\ \nabla\psi - Q \tag{12}$$

Q represents the rate of water uptake by the plant, per unit volume of soil, and may be a function of x, y, z, t, or ψ, as well as many other factors including the potential transpiration. The actual form this function might take is considered in Section IV.

A very convenient mathematical transformation can be made when a unique relation between the water content and the potential exists during the course of any given transient flow process. A new function called soil water diffusivity is defined by the relation

$$D = -k\ \partial\psi/\partial\theta \tag{13}$$

Introduction of this new parameter into Eq. (11) gives

$$\partial\theta/\partial t = \nabla \cdot D\nabla\theta + \partial k/\partial z \qquad (14)$$

which, except for the last term on the right that results from the gravitational gradient, is mathematically identical with the diffusion equation with a diffusion coefficient that is a function of concentration. One advantage of Eq. (14) over Eq. (11) is that it reduces the number of variables, and a second is that the diffusivity D does not vary quite so strongly with water content or potential as does the conductivity. The variation of soil water diffusivity with water content for Holtville silty clay is shown in Fig. 3 for three different temperatures. Comparison with Fig. 2 for the same soil shows that the diffusivity varies about a hundredfold while the conductivity varies about a thousandfold over the same range of water content. The two curves for 24°C represent duplicate runs and give an indication of the precision of the data. These data were also obtained by Doering (personal communication) by the pressure–plate outflow method (Doering, 1965). Therefore, the assumption of a constant diffusivity is often much better than the assumption of a constant conductivity. In many transient flow problems it turns out that the use of a constant average or weighted-mean diffusivity gives quite a good estimate of the flux into or out of a system, although prediction of the exact water content distribution history throughout the system is not nearly so good. A relation between diffusivity and potential or water content can be derived from analytical expressions

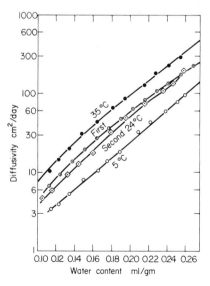

FIG. 3. Soil water diffusivity as a function of water content by weight for Holtville silty clay. The curves marked "first" and "second" represent duplicate runs at 24°C.

such as Eqs. (4) and (6) by differentiating the potential with respect to the water content and multiplying it by the conductivity. Over quite a wide range $\psi_m \sim \theta^{-m}$, and $k \sim \psi_m^{-s}$, so that $k \sim \theta^{ms}$ and $D \sim \theta^{m(s-1)-1}$. As an example, if m is 2 and s is 3, as might be the case for a fine-textured soil, the conductivity k varies as the sixth power of the water content while the diffusivity varies as the third power. Another convenient empirical expression, which has been found satisfactory for some soils, is of the form $D = D_0 \, e^{a\theta}$ where D_0 and a are soil parameters. D_0 if of the order of 1 or 2 cm²/day for medium-textured soils and a is of the order of 18–20. The capillary conductivity may range from 1 to 100 cm/day in a saturated soil down to about 10^{-6} cm/day in an air dry soil. The diffusivity varies from about 1 cm²/day to as high as 10,000 cm²/day. Theoretically, D goes to infinity at saturation but usually will not exceed about 1000 cm²/day at water contents less than field capacity for reasons explained below.

III. WATER AVAILABILITY TO PLANTS

A. The Upper Limit of Available Water

The maximum amount of water that can be held in a soil, neglecting swelling, is obviously limited by the total pore space. However, unless drainage is seriously impeded, a soil profile does not remain saturated if ever it does become saturated during infiltration. The infiltration process has been studied theoretically in considerable detail and the general features of the process are reasonably well understood. During the initial stages of infiltration into a uniformly dry (or wet) homogeneous soil, the principal water moving force is the matric potential gradient. The infiltration rate during the early stages of vertical infiltration is the same as that for horizontal water entry into soil and is described by the equation

$$I = (\theta_m - \theta_0)\sqrt{\bar{D}/\pi t} \tag{15}$$

where θ_m is the water content of the soil at saturation, θ_0 is the initial soil water content, t is the time, and $\bar{D}$ is a weighted-mean diffusivity. $\bar{D}$ depends more strongly upon the diffusivity near saturation than upon that near $\theta = \theta_0$. With the passage of time during infiltration, while the matric potential gradient is decreasing continuously the gravitational gradient remains constant, thus becoming increasingly important, relatively speaking. Philip (1957a) has shown that, except when t becomes too large, the infiltration rate can be represented by a good approximation:

$$I = (\theta_m - \theta_0)\sqrt{\bar{D}/\pi t} + B \tag{16}$$

where B is a constant that can be evaluated from the diffusivity and retention curves. As t approaches infinity, Eq. (16) is no longer valid since the gravitational potential then becomes completely dominant and $I = K$, where K is the hydraulic conductivity of the soil. Miller and Klute (1967) have suggested that an infiltration equation of the form

$$I = At^{-1/2} + K \tag{17}$$

be used instead, where A is a constant and B is replaced by K. Equation (17) sacrifices some precision when t is small in order to obtain agreement for $t = \infty$. The length of time required to approach a constant infiltration rate depends upon the initial water content and the diffusivity but may be of the order of a few minutes to a few hours in the field. Even after a constant infiltration rate is achieved, the water potential a short distance below the soil surface may be less than zero and the soil will not be completely saturated to any very great depth, though the wetting front will have assumed a constant shape and will move downward with a constant velocity.

After infiltration at the soil surface ceases, downward movement of water in the soil continues for some time. The rate of drainage or redistribution of the soil water decreases quite rapidly with time, so much so in some soils that after a few days this movement appears to cease. This apparent cessation of drainage has led to the concept of "field capacity." Field capacity is usually defined as the water content at which downward drainage becomes negligible. This definition has sometimes resulted in the erroneous conclusion that there is no water movement at water contents below field capacity or that such movement as there is is negligibly slow for all purposes. Such is not always the case.

Redistribution of water in the soil profile after irrigation or rainfall can be described by considering two different boundary conditions. If internal drainage of the soil profile is not limited by an impeding layer or a water table, then the soil will tend to drain at a fairly uniform water content, insofar as the soil profile is homogeneous. In terms of Eq. (7) the matric potential gradient $d\psi/dz$ has already become small compared with the gravitational gradient, if infiltration has gone on long enough to approach a constant rate. If $d\psi/dz \ll 1$, the drainage rate will be of the same order of magnitude as the capillary conductivity. The decrease in the drainage rate with time is due principally to the decrease in the capillary conductivity with decreasing water content. So long as the depth of wetting is sufficiently great, the rate of drainage of water out of the upper part of the soil profile will be virtually independent of the depth of the wetting and will depend only upon the water content, which determines the capillary conductivity. Since the conductivity is so strongly dependent on water content, varying from the fourth to tenth power of the latter, a very modest decrease in the water content can result in a decrease in the conductivity from a very high to an extremely low value. However, the conductivity remains finite even at low water contents, and it may take a long time in some soils before drainage becomes immeasurably small. A number of workers (e.g., Ogata and Richards, 1957) have found that water content can be related to time by an expression of the form

$$W = Ct^{-n} \tag{18}$$

where W is water content and C and n are constants.

In a well-drained profile, it may often be the case that succeeding irrigations or rains occur before the drainage from the previous addition of water has become negligible. In such cases the soil may approach a steady state water content that is reproducible from year to year and is taken as the upper limit of available water or the water-carrying capacity of the soil. It must be strongly emphasized, however, that where this is the case the downward drainage rate is no longer negligible, and the concept of field capacity has been redefined, at least implicitly, when applied to this situation. What happens is that the drainage or percolation rate adjusts so as to equal the difference between the rainfall rate and the evaporation rate. The gravitational component constitutes the major component of the total potential gradient. Because of the tremendous variation of capillary conductivity with water content, only a modest adjustment in the latter is necessary to maintain the appropriate conductivity. Thus, even with a crude estimate of capillary conductivity one can give a reasonable estimate of the average water content of the soil. This is one reason that it is necessary to be very careful when assuming that water movement is negligible below field capacity.

When drainage is impeded, a different boundary condition exists. The simplest situation is one in which drainage is to a fixed water table so that the matric potential is zero at that depth (Youngs, 1960; Gardner, 1962). As a first, though very rough, approximation the flow equation can be integrated to give the rate of drainage out of the profile according to the expression

$$q = -dW/dt = A e^{-Bt} = BW \tag{9}$$

where A and B are constants and W is the water content of the soil over and above that which remains when the profile has reached equilibrium with the water table. At equilibrium the matric potential will be equal and opposite to the gravitational potential so that the equilibrium soil suction equals the height above the water table and the equilibrium water content distribution with height will reflect the water retention curve. It is quite obvious that during drainage the suction can at no time exceed the height above the water table. Thus, for a water table at a depth of 2 m, the maximum possible suction within the root zone is 200 mbar, which would occur right at the soil surface. At 1-m depth the suction would be 100 mbar. Obviously, the all-too-frequent assumption that field capacity is given by the one-third atmosphere percentage (333 mbar) cannot be valid in this situation.

It can be shown that the time required for equilibration of the water content distribution is of the order of $t = L^2/D$, where L is the depth of the water table and D is an average diffusivity. D ranges from about 5000 cm^2/day near saturation down to about 500 cm^2/day at the traditional field capacity. Thus, a saturated profile with a water table at 1 m will drain to virtual equilibrium in a time between 2 and 20 days. It will approach 90% equilibrium much sooner than that.

It should be apparent from the above analysis that the field capacity depends more upon capillary conductivity or soil water diffusivity than upon the water potential. Therefore, any correlation between a given water potential and field capacity, as measured in the field, can be only fortuitous. Procedures, such as the now-obsolete moisture equivalent, that do not give some measure of conductivity or diffusivity cannot be expected to be of more than very limited value.

If one takes field capacity to be the upper limit of available water and also the water content at which drainage becomes negligible, he is confronted with the problem of accounting for the water the plant transpires prior to the time the field capacity is reached. Wilcox (1960) developed a procedure for including this water as part of the soil water available to the plant. An analytical approach to the problem suggested by the author (Gardner, 1967) will be outlined here. For illustrative purposes we will assume that the drainage rate is given by Eq. (19), although differentiating Eq. (18) to get dW/dt would give a more accurate result. In essence, it is assumed that the rate of drainage of water out of the root zone is a function of the water content in the root zone and independent of the rate of water uptake by roots. The justification for this assumption lies in the fact that linear combinations of solutions of the flow equation are also solutions of the equation. Thus,

$$-dW/dt = BW + E \qquad (20)$$

where W is the water content of the soil over and above that at which $dW/dt = 0$. It can be shown from the solution of Eq. (20) that the amount of water transpired by the plant which would have otherwise been lost from the soil profile by drainage is

$$W = Et = (E/B)\ln(L + W_i B/E) \qquad (21)$$

From the analysis of the drainage problem by Gardner (1962) it is shown that $B = \pi^2 D/4L^2$, where L is the depth of wetting or the depth to the water table.

A simple relation which takes the variability of D with water content into account is $D \sim W^n$, where n is a constant. For example, if D is assumed to decrease linearly with decreasing soil water content, which is a fair assumption over a limited range of water content, then Eq. (20) is replaced by

$$-dW/dt = BW^2 + E \tag{22}$$

which integrates to give

$$Et = \sqrt{E/B} \tan^{-1}(W_i\sqrt{B/E}) \tag{23}$$

where, as in Eq. (21), W_i represents the total amount of water transpired by the plant before drainage ceases.

B. UPWARD MOVEMENT OF WATER INTO THE ROOT ZONE

The problem is much more complex than is indicated above, however. Water which moves down below the root zone is still available for transpiration by the plant by virtue of its capability of being moved back up into the root zone in response to matric potential gradients set up as the surface soil dries. Some aspects of upward water movement have been examined and are worth outlining briefly here.

1. Steady State Movement

A simple case of a steady state water movement is that in which water moves upward at a constant rate from a water table at a fixed depth. Equation (8) describes this situation. Solutions of this equation have been published for conductivity–water potential relations of the form of Eq. (6) for $s = 1$, $\frac{3}{2}$, 2, 3, and 4 (Gardner, 1958). Quite interestingly, it turns out that for $n > 1$ there is a maximum rate at which water can be moved upward from the water table, regardless of how low the water potential at the soil surface becomes. This phenomenon sets an upper limit to the steady state rate at which water can evaporate or transpire. For those cases studied (Gardner, 1958), this limiting rate can be related to the depth of the water table d by the expression

$$E_{\lim} = A_s K(b/d)^s \tag{24}$$

where A_s is a constant which is different for different values of s and the other symbols have the same meaning as in Eq. (6). For upward water movement toward the root zone, d would represent the depth of the water table below the bottom of the root zone. The predicted rate of capillary rise or upward movement agrees quite well with that observed experimentally, with some exceptions (Gardner, and Fireman, 1958; Schleusener and Corey, 1959; King and Schleusener, 1961). One significant conclusion that can be drawn from the analysis is that appreciable quantities of water can be moved upward from depths of the order of 10 feet or more. For Pachappa sandy loam the limiting rate is about 1 cm/day with a water table at 1 m and 0.11 cm/day when d is 3m.

2. Transient State Movement

In the absence of a water table, upward movement of water into the root zone results in a decreasing water content in the soil below the root zone. The maximum possible rate of water loss from an infinitely deep soil is given approximately by the expression

$$q = (\theta_i - \theta_0)\sqrt{\bar{D}/\pi t} \qquad (25)$$

where $\bar{D}$ is the weighted mean diffusivity. The effect of gravity has been neglected in deriving Eq. (25), but the error is probably not serious. Equation (25) is identical with Eq. (15) for infiltration except that the weighted mean diffusivity is averaged slightly differently. θ_i is the initial water content of the soil, and θ_0 is the water content at the soil surface, which is maintained constant for all values of t. In deriving Eq. (25) it was assumed that θ was reduced to θ_0 when $t = 0$ and was maintained at this value thereafter so that the flux of water out of the soil is independent of external conditions. When external conditions influence the initial rate of water loss, solution of the flow equation is more difficult. Gardner and Hillel (1962) have obtained an approximate solution for an exponential diffusivity $D = D_0 \, e^{a\theta}$ and Covey (1963) has published an extensive analysis of the problem. To obtain their solution, Gardner and Hillel assumed that water was evaporated from a finite soil profile at a constant rate E. As evaporation continues, the soil surface eventually becomes air dry, after which time the rate E can no longer be maintained. If the initial water content of a profile of depth L is W_i, the total amount of water which can be evaporated at the rate E is

$$Et = W_i - (L/a) \ln (1 + EaL/2D_0) \qquad (26)$$

where t is the length of time during which E can be maintained constant. After this constant rate phase, the rate of evaporation decreases with time. To a first approximation, this decreasing evaporation rate is a function of the water content of the soil and is independent of external conditions. It is more straightforward to apply Eq. (26) to the problem of evaporation from bare soil than to apply it to the movement of water from below the root zone because the bottom of the root zone is ill-defined and one cannot really separate the soil profile into a region in which water movement is mainly through the soil and another in which it is all in the roots. Recent results obtained by the author, which will be published elsewhere, suggest that toward the bottom of the root zone the roots themselves offer resistance to water movement that is greater than the resistance to movement in a saturated soil, but substantially less than that of a soil at the wilting point. As a crude approximation it appears justifiable to assume that water transported by roots compensates for the decrease in transport by the soil as it dries, so that the apparent diffusivity of the root–soil complex tends to remain constant. With the assumption of a constant diffusivity, solutions of the flow equation are readily obtained. By examining results for different values of diffusivity one can gain some insight into the effect of a variable diffusivity. As an example,we can calculate how much water could be moved up into the plant root zone before the soil water content at the bottom of this zone drops to some value of θ that we will designate θ_w. This might be the permanent wilting point or any other specified lower limit. The solution to this problem for a constant upward flux E is

$$W = Et = \pi \bar{D}(\theta_i - \theta_w)^2/4E = \sqrt{\pi \bar{D}t}(\theta_i - \theta_w)/2 \qquad (27)$$

Equation (27) implies the existence of both an upper limit θ_i and a lower limit θ_w. These should be chosen with the discussion of the previous section in mind. Equation (27) applies to an infinitely deep soil or to a finite soil when E is relatively high and $\bar{D}$ is small. The solution for a finite soil is not difficult (Gardner, 1967). Again, by assuming a constant value of $\bar{D}$, one can predict the water content at the boundary between the root zone and the region below according to the equation

$$\theta = \theta_i - 2E\sqrt{t/\pi D} \qquad (28)$$

and the length of time that the rate of water uptake E can be maintained is

$$t_{\lim} = [(\theta_i - \theta_w)^2/4]\,\pi \bar{D}/E^2 \qquad (29)$$

The above equations have dealt exclusively with one-dimensional water flow. There are some interesting differences that occur when flow is in two or three dimensions. One example will illustrate this. Consider a single isolated plant with a hemispherical root system of radius a. Starting at $t = 0$, water is assumed to be extracted at a constant rate E_0 from the surrounding soil, neglecting any water stored within the root system itself. The water content at the boundary of the root system after a sufficiently long time is

$$\theta = \theta_i - (E_0/2\pi aD)(1 - a/\sqrt{\pi Dt}) \qquad (30)$$

which at $t = \infty$ becomes a constant. Therefore, the plant can maintain a constant transpiration rate indefinitely if it is sufficiently far from its nearest neighbors. The maximum rate that can be maintained is given by

$$E_0 = 2\pi aD(\theta_i - \theta_w) \qquad (31)$$

C. Extension of Plant Roots

The above equations are for a fixed root depth or a root distribution which is not changing sufficiently rapidly with time to influence the results. If the root system increases in length with time, this decreases the distance that water must move in order to enter the roots. An estimate of the amount of water that might thus be made available has been made by Kramer and Coile (1940). More recently, James Wolf (personal communication) examined this problem theoretically in a more rigorous fashion by simulating simultaneous water movement and root growth on a computor. Following the same approach, we can treat the problem approximately by assuming the diffusivity to be a constant, as we did in the preceding section. If the root system is extending downward at a constant rate U (in centimeters per day), then the additional amount of water made available to the plant per unit time is that in the region swept out by the root system, or $U(\theta_i - \theta_w)$. If the transpiration rate E is constant, then eventually a steady state condition is achieved at which time

$$(\theta_i - \theta) = E/U \tag{32}$$

As shown in the previous section, water movement upward toward the root system decreases continuously with time. If root growth continues at the same rate long enough, it will predominate over the water movement. Equation (32) will apply when $U > \sqrt{\pi \bar{D}/t}$. After a steady state is achieved, the amount of water made available to the plant due to root extension in one dimension will be equal to $L(\theta_i - \theta)$, where L is the total increase in length of the root system. An additional amount of water will have been made available to and transpired by the plant by virtue of water movement upward toward the roots. For a constant weighted mean diffusivity $\bar{D}$, this amount turns out to be

$$W = E\bar{D}/U^2 = (\theta_i - \theta)\bar{D}/U \tag{33}$$

Comparison of Eq. (33) with the amount of water within the extended root zone shows that the ratio $\bar{D}/U$ gives, in effect, the additional depth of influence of the root system by virtue of the ability of the soil to transmit water in the unsaturated state. As an illustration of the order of magnitude this effect might take, let us take for $\bar{D}$ a value of 500 cm^2/day at field capacity. A possible value for U might be 5 cm/day and for E about 0.5 cm/day. Thus, $E/U = 0.1$ so that the decrease in the volumetric water content of the soil is 0.1. Substituting these values into Eq. (33) gives $W = 10$ cm of water and an effective increase of the zone of influence of the roots of 100 cm. Equation (33) offers a relatively simple way of evaluating the adaptation of a particular plant species to its environment in terms of its rate of root growth and of the supply, storage, and demand characteristics of the hydrological part of the environment. In his analysis, Wolf considered individual root tips and allowed D to vary as a function of soil water content.

IV. WATER MOVEMENT TO PLANT ROOTS

In Section III some gross aspects of water movement to plant roots were considered. In the one-dimensional problems it was assumed that the soil water potential and water content had some constant average value at any given depth. In this section we consider in detail the problem of water movement to individual roots and the possibility that large gradients in water potential may occur adjacent to root surfaces. Details of the analysis to follow may be found in Philip (1957b) and Gardner (1960, 1964).

A. Water Movement to Individual Roots

If water is taken up by a cylindrical root of radius a at a constant rate q per unit length of root from a soil that at time $t = 0$ is at a uniform water content and potential, then the difference between the matric potential at the plant root surfaces and that at an infinite distance is

$$\psi - \psi_i = (q/4\pi k) \ln (4Dt/a^2 - \gamma) \qquad (34)$$

for all but very small values of t, where $\gamma = 0.577 =$ Euler's constant. Equation (34) is very similar in form to the steady state solution of the equation

$$\psi_a - \psi_b = (q/4\pi k) \ln (b^2/a^2) \qquad (35)$$

where b is the distance from which water is flowing toward the root. It is difficult to estimate probable values for q with any degree of certainty. We can expect the logarithmic term to be of the order of 10, so that $(\psi - \psi_i)$ will be of the order of q/k. It is doubtful that q would exceed $1.0 \text{ cm}^3/\text{cm-day}$, which for a value of $k = 1.0 \text{ cm/day}$ would give a value of $(\psi - \psi_i)$ of the order of 1.0 cm, which is negligibly small. Therefore, in nearly saturated soils we conclude that it is highly improbable that there is a significant potential gradient near the root. The capillary conductivity of a large group of soils is of the order of 10^{-3} cm/day when the potential is about -1 bar. For these values one would calculate a potential difference of 1000 cm or 1 bar, assuming the same rate of water uptake. The potential at the soil–root interface would be -2.0 bars. At -15 bars in the vicinity of the permanent wilting point the capillary conductivity reduces to 10^{-5} cm/day or less. For $q = 1.0 \text{ cm}^2/\text{day}$, $\psi - \psi_i$ is a prohibitively high 100 bars. Under these circumstances flow of water to the plant root is obviously limited by the low capillary conductivity. We can expect q to be greatly reduced, either through a reduced transpiration rate from the plant as a whole or a greater rate of uptake from a region at a higher water potential. In the former case, the transpiration rate is limited by the flow process and, given any sort of a reversible transpiration control function on the part of the plant, it would not be too surprising to find the transpiration rate under very dry conditions to be related directly to the rate at which water can move to the plant roots (Gardner, 1960; Gardner and Ehlig, 1963). Equation (34) assumes a constant rate of water uptake by the plant while Eq. (35) assumes completely steady state flow. In reality the transpiration rate fluctuates diurnally in response to the transpiration demand. While the above equations give the average potential about which the actual potential fluctuates, it is also of some interest to examine the amplitude of the fluctuation. The minimum water potential to which the plant drops in the heat of the day and the maximum to which it rises in the predawn hours may be as important in terms of plant response as the average.

It is assumed that the transpiration rate oscillates sinusoidally according to the expression

$$E = q(1 + \exp 2\pi it) \tag{36}$$

where $i = \sqrt{-1}$. The average daily transpiration rate is just q and the average potential at the root surface is given by Eq. (34). The solution of the flow equation for a constant average diffusivity D is (Carslaw and Jaeger, 1959, p. 263)

$$(\psi - \psi_i) = (q/4\pi k)[\ln (4Dt/a^2) - \gamma + [2 \exp (2\pi it)]K_0[a(2\pi i/D)^{1/2}] \tag{37}$$

where K_0 is a modified Bessel function of the second kind, tables of which are readily available. For $a/\sqrt{D}$ sufficiently small, as will normally be the case, one can replace Eq. (37) by the somewhat simpler expression

$$(\psi - \psi_i) = (q/4\pi k)[\ln(4Dt/a^2) - \gamma + \sin(2\pi t - e)(\ln 2d/\pi a^2 - \gamma)] \tag{38}$$

where e represents the phase lag. This is the amount of time the minima or maxima in the potential at the root surface lags behind the corresponding extremes in the transpiration demand and can be calculated from Eq. (37). The extent to which water in the vicinity of the root surface is restored at night is found from the minimum in Eq. (38), which occurs when $\sin(2\pi t - e) = -1$. This gives

$$(\psi - \psi_i)_{min} = (q/4\pi k) \ln (2\pi t) \tag{39}$$

It can be seen from Eq. (38) that the magnitude of the fluctuation is independent of time and is a function of the diffusivity and root diameter only. Therefore, the minimum and maximum potential differences between the soil and the root surface increase in the same way as the average. The maximum potential difference can be found in much the same way as the minimum by setting the sine equal to $+1$ in Eq. (39) to give

$$(\psi - \psi_i) = (q/4\pi k)(\ln 8D^2t/\pi a^4 - 2\gamma) \tag{40}$$

The difference between Eq. (40) and (34) may well be significant for a plant just approaching wilting since a high peak demand during the day may cause wilting and a reduction in growth, whereas the same demand, if averaged over the entire 24-hour day, might result in much less severe consequences.

An example will illustrate the magnitude of the effects being discussed. D may vary between about 10^4 cm²/day and 10 cm²/day. For a root diameter $a = 0.1$ cm, the ratio D/a^2 will fall between 10^6 and 10^3. Table I shows the

TABLE I

COMPARISON OF AVERAGE WITH SINE TERM IN EQ. (38)

D/a^2	$\ln 4Dt/a^2$		$\ln 2D/\pi a^2$
	$t = 1$	$t = 100$	
10^6	15.2	19.8	13.3
10^3	8.3	12.9	6.9

value of $\ln 2D/\pi a^2$ for these two values of D/a^2 and gives for comparison the time-dependent term in Eq. (38) for $t = 1$ and $t = 100$ days. To the extent that the approximation is valid for t as short as one day, we see that the approach to equilibrium is about 90% complete during the night following the first day. If the process goes as long as 100 days, the fluctuation in the potential stays the same but represents only about 60% of the average difference.

At this point a few words concerning the permanent wilting point concept are in order. Wilting is obviously a plant phenomenon related to the turgor pressure in the leaf cells, which we may expect to be related in some way to the total potential energy of the water in the leaves. The permanent wilting point is that water content below which the plant remains visibly wilted, even though transpiration is virtually prevented. If transpiration is prevented completely, the difference between the soil water potential at the root–soil interface and the average potential in the soil reduces at a rate given approximately by

$$\psi - \psi_i = (q/4\pi k) \ln [t/(t - t_1)] \tag{41}$$

where t_1 is the time at which transpiration ceased. Equilibrium should be virtually complete by the time t is greater than $2t_1$, unless the plant itself requires a large amount of water in order to equilibrate with the soil. If there is a definite leaf water potential at which the plant appears wilted, as seems to be the case (Gardner and Ehlig, 1965), then the soil water potential at which permanent wilting is observed will be limited by this value. Whenever the soil water potential is below this value, the plant will remain wilted, whatever the external conditions. As seen above, it is theoretically possible for the plant to fail to recover turgor when the soil is at a somewhat higher potential than this limiting value, particularly if water uptake continues, albeit slowly. More importantly, there is nothing in the physics of retention of water by soil or movement of water to roots which renders soil water unavailable to plants in the sense that roots are unable to extract water from the soil. While most soil scientists understand this fully, there are many plant and soil scientists who have been led to believe that water below the permanent wilting point cannot be extracted by the plant. The rate of transpiration may be very slow because of stomatal closure, but the true lower limit is the water content in equilibrium with the atmosphere. However, once the wilting concept is recognized and understood for what it is, it can be very useful for many purposes. Some wilting and reduction in transpiration rate can and will occur before the soil is reduced to the permanent wilting point because of the diurnal fluctuations in transpiration rate. Certainly, when this happens, the state of the soil water has an important effect upon that in the plant and a reduction in growth can be expected well before permanent wilting occurs.

B. Water Uptake by Root Systems

In order to extend the equations for a single root to an entire root system we write in analogy with Eq. (34):

$$W = A(\psi_{plant} - \psi_{soil})/R \tag{42}$$

where W is the rate of water uptake per unit volume of soil, ψ_{plant} is the water potential within the plant root, ψ_{soil} is the total water potential in the soil, which must now include the osmotic component because of the semipermeable membranes in the root, and R is the resistance to water movement in the soil and the plant. We then integrate Eq. (42) over the entire root system. This is easier to suggest than to carry out since the potential within the root system depends upon the water-transmitting properties of roots. The problem is essentially one of determining how to specify R. One way to do this is to assume that the soil and the plant resistances can be added in series so that $R = R_p + R_s$. The plant root resistance R_p is discussed in Chapter 6. By analogy with Eq. (34) we write for the soil resistance

$$R_s = A/kL \tag{43}$$

where A is a geometrical factor that depends only slightly on root distribution, L is the length of root per unit volume of soil, and k is the capillary conductivity. In an analysis of a very special situation, the author (Gardner, 1964) assumed R_p to be small compared with R_s so that the water potential could be assumed to be uniform throughout the entire root system of a sorgham plant. Equations (12) and (42) were solved simultaneously by replacing them by finite difference forms of the equations and dividing the soil profile into finite layers. The agreement between the predicted and the actual water uptake patterns was quite good except in the lower part of the root system during the late stages of water uptake. The assumption that root resistance was negligible apparently was not met toward the bottom of the root system.

When root resistance is not small in comparison to soil resistance the possibility of parallel flow through both root and soil exists (Gardner and Ehlig,

1962). No real attempt has been made to describe in mathematical terms the physics of water flow through a complex plant root system. A reasonably homogeneous root system might be described as a first approximation by an equation that assumed that vertical flow is proportional to some potential gradient that is the same everywhere at any given depth in the soil so that the root system can be considered one-dimensional. Then, within the root system we would have

$$W = d(K_p \, d\psi_s/dz)/dz \qquad (44)$$

where W must also satisfy Eq. (42) since the amount of water leaving the soil must equal that entering the plant. Combining Eqs. (10) and (44) gives

$$\partial\theta/\partial t = \frac{\partial}{\partial z} \, [K_s(\partial\psi_{\text{soil}}/\partial z) + K_p(\partial\psi_{\text{plant}}/\partial z)] \qquad (45)$$

Now, in some cases it may well turn out that ψ_{soil} is not greatly different from ψ_{plant} so that we may replace both by an average potential $\bar{\psi}$, and K_s and K_p by a conductivity equal to the sum of the soil and root conductivity. This results in the expression

$$\partial\theta/\partial z = \frac{\partial}{\partial z} \left(\frac{\bar{K} \, \partial\bar{\psi}}{\partial z} \right) \qquad (46)$$

Equation (46) is mathematically the same as the equation for the movement of soil water alone and is the justification for treating the lower portion of a root zone as a sort of composite porous medium. When this assumption is not adequate, some approach similar to that of Gardner (1964) or Visser (1966) seems the most promising.

The osmotic component of the potential requires special consideration. When salts are added from above, as in the case of irrigation with saline water, they will move down through the soil at a rate fC where f is the flux density of water and C is the salt concentration. As water is taken up by roots leaving the salts behind, the soil solution concentration increases. The steady state concentration in a one-dimensional flow system is given as a function of depth z by

$$C = IC_0/q(z) \qquad (47)$$

where I is the average rate of water application, C_0 is the initial salt concentration, and q is a function of depth that depends upon the uptake pattern. The relative amount of water extracted from the more saline portion of the root system depends to a great extent upon the total transpiration rate and the resistance to water uptake in all parts of the root system. Because water is not extracted to any great extent from the lower portions of some nonsaline root systems until the matric potential in the upper portion is quite low (Ogata *et al.*, 1960) one can argue that even less water would be extracted from this region if it were saline. Except when a soil is completely saturated, it seems quite probable that the osmotic potential at the bottom of the root zone seldom goes below the minimum total potential in the upper portion where the majority of roots are. There are two implications of this phenomenon: (1) If irrigation is always to the same depth, the plant may reduce the maximum stress to which it is subjected by developing more roots in the region that receives the irrigation water initially since this is the least saline water. More roots mean a lower resistance to water movement in this region. If irrigation is applied at the same minimum matric potential each time, root growth in the less saline portions of the root zone lead to more frequent irrigations and, very probably, increase leaching. (2) It may prove virtually impossible to concentrate some saline irrigation waters to a very high degree without allowing the upper part of the root system to achieve a corresponding matric potential, which may be detrimental to growth in itself. Much depends upon the root system and its resistance relative to that in the soil.

V. MEASUREMENT OF SOIL WATER

The foregoing analysis should make quite clear that it is necessary to measure four principal quantities in order to characterize availability of soil water to plants: (1) soil water content, (2) water potential, (3) capillary conductivity, and (4) soil water diffusivity. Methods for the measurement of all these have been the object of much research in soil physics. While improvements in all of them are needed, both laboratory and field techniques are presently available. These methods are described in detail in the monograph *Methods of Soil Analysis* (Black, 1965), which also cites many useful papers. This section is confined to a few comments concerning the suitability of some of the more common procedures.

A. WATER CONTENT

The gravimetric determination of water content by weighing soil samples before and after oven drying at 105° C is taken as the standard and is used to calibrate all laboratory and field methods of water content measurement. It is still frequently the most satisfactory method even in the field, despite the large number of samples that may sometimes be required.

In the laboratory, gamma-ray absorption techniques have proven to be very useful. Applications of this technique to plant water studies have been limited to date. The γ-ray absorption method has been used less extensively in the field than in the laboratory because the calibration depends also upon the bulk density of the soil. For large-scale field experiments the neutron soil moisture meter is proving increasingly useful. The principal difficulties of this method are generally in calibrating the instrument in the field and the not-infrequent malfunction of some commercial models of the instrument. One disadvantage of the method for some types of studies is the relatively large volume of soil over which it averages. However, this large sampling volume can be an advantage at times.

Several instruments, such as the gypsum resistance block, respond to the matric potential rather than to water content. These instruments, therefore, can be no better than the relation established between the potential and the water content.

B. WATER POTENTIAL

In the laboratory, the tension table and pressure plate apparatus are most frequently used for matric potential measurements. The osmotic potential is normally calculated from the soil solution concentration. The relatively recently developed thermocouple psychrometer (Richards and Ogata, 1958) is also used in the laboratory. The psychrometer measures the sum of the matric and osmotic potentials.

The tensiometer is the most widely used device for measuring matric potential in the field. With proper design and operation tensiometers work very well under a wide variety of conditions down to a potential of about $-\frac{2}{3}$ bar. In a few instances where the potential is changing rapidly with time and the capillary conductivity is very low, as in coarse-textured soils below -0.5 bar, the tensiometer may fail to respond satisfactorily, unless a null-type instrument is used.

Beyond the tensiometer range there is no equally satisfactory field method for measuring matric potential. The psychrometer has been adapted as a field instrument (Rawlins and Dalton, 1966), but the method is not too well suited for routine measurements. The most widespread method involves the use of resistance elements such as gypsum blocks. The resistance of these units depends upon their water content, which depends in turn upon the matric potential of the soil with which they are equilibrated. Their most important drawback, and it can be a very serious, one, is that their calibration tends to shift significantly from one drying cycle to the next and frequent recalibration is essential if quantitative results are required. They are most useful where only a qualitative estimate is needed.

Peck and Rabbidge (1966) have applied the tensiometer principle to the measurement of water potential over a wider range by incorporating a semi-permeable membrane in the instrument and filling the liquid chamber in the instrument with an aqueous solution of polyethylene glycol that cannot pass through the membrane. The hydrostatic pressure within the chamber is then measured by means of a pressure transducer. The success of this device depends upon the membrane since it must allow no glycol molecules to pass through. It will measure only matric potential so long as the solute molecules in the soil solution are able to pass freely through the membrane, but it will measure the osmotic potential of any molecules excluded by the membrane.

C. Capillary Conductivity and Diffusivity

Within the tensiometer range the capillary conductivity can be measured by a number of means (Richards and Weeks, 1953; Gardner and Miklich, 1962). At potentials below about 0.5 bar the pressure membrane outflow method seems to be the most satisfactory (Black, 1965). This method actually gives the diffusivity from which the conductivity is then calculated. The number of field methods for measuring the conductivity is small. Probably the most accurate procedure is that used by Richards and Ogata and analyzed in detail by Rose *et al.* (1965). This method requires that there be no water uptake by plant roots. The soil is wetted to a considerable depth and then covered to prevent evaporation during drainage. The flux across any depth is given directly from the rate of change of the total water content above that depth. The hydraulic gradient is obtained from tensiometric methods. The flux is divided by the gradient to give the conductivity.

A relatively rapid approximate method for measuring diffusivity in the laboratory was adapted from the outflow method by Doering (1965). This method has been found suitable for obtaining diffusivity from the rate at which core samples from the field dry. Actual *in situ* measurements of diffusivity in the field require more precise water content and gradient measurements than are normally made. Where these are obtainable (Watson, 1966), the calculation itself is not difficult.

Soil structure has a very important effect upon the retention and movement of water when the matric potential is above −1 bar. For this reason, the many measurements that have been made in the past upon fragmented soils are of limited value. However, at the other end of the scale soil texture is more important than soil structure since the water in relatively dry soils exists in very thin films, and measurements on fragmented samples tend to agree quite well with those on soil cores or in the field.

Because of hysteresis the diffusivity will not be a single valued function of the water content, just as the potential is not. For the same reason the capillary conductivity will not be a unique function of matric potential. However, it appears that the relation between the conductivity and the water content is reasonably unique, even in the presence of considerable hysteresis (Topp and Miller, 1966).

REFERENCES

Black, C. A. (ed.) (1965). Methods of soil analysis. *Am. Soc. Agron., Monograph* **9**.

Briggs, L. J., and Shantz, H. L. (1911). Application of wilting coefficient determinations in agronomic investigations. *J. Am. Soc. Agron.* **3**, 250.

Carslaw, H. S., and Jaeger, J. C. (1959). "Conduction of Heat in Solids," 2nd ed. Oxford Univ. Press, London and New York.

Cary, J. W., and Taylor, S. A. (1962). Thermally driven liquid and vapor phase transfer of water and energy in soil. *Soil. Sci. Soc. Am. Proc.* **26**, 417.

Covey, W. (1963). Mathematical study of the first stage of drying of a moist soil. *Soil Sci. Am. Proc.* **27**, 130.

Doering, E. J. (1965), Soil-water diffusivity by the one-step method. *Soil Sci.* **99**, 322.

Gardner, W. R. (1958). Some steady-state solutions of the unsaturated moisture flow equation with application to evaporation from a water table. *Soil Sci.* **85**, 228.

Gardner, W. R. (1960). Dynamic aspects of water availability to plants. *Soil Sci.* **89**, 63.

Gardner, W. R. (1962). Approximate solution of a non-steady state drainage problem. *Soil Sci. Soc. Am. Proc.* **26**, 129.

Gardner, W. R. (1964). Relation of root distribution to water uptake and availability. *Agron. J.* **56**, 35.

Gardner, W. R. (1965). Movement of nitrogen in soil. *Am. Soc. Agron., Monograph* **10**, 550.

Gardner, W. R. (1967). Water movement in the unsaturated soil profile. *Proc. Symp. Soil Water, Intern. Comm. Irrig. Drainage, Prague* **2**, 223.

Gardner, W. R., and Ehlig, C. F. (1962). Some observations on the movement of water to plant roots. *Agron. J.* **54**, 453.

Gardner, W. R., and Ehlig, C. F. (1963). The influence of soil water on transpiration by plants. *J. Geophys. Res.* **68**, 5719.

Gardner, W. R., and Ehlig, C. F. (1965). Physical aspects of the internal water relations of plant leaves. *Plant Physiol.* **40**, 705.

Gardner, W. R., and Fireman, M. (1958). Laboratory studies of evaporation from a water table. *Soil. Sci.* **85**, 244.

Gardner, W. R., and Hillel, D. I. (1962). The relation of external evaporative conditions to the drying of soils. *J. Geophys. Res.* **67**, 4319.

Gardner, W. R., and Miklich, F. J. (1962). Unsaturated conductivity and diffusivity measurements by a constant flux method. *Soil Sci.* **93**, 271.

Hendrickson, A. H., and Veihmeyer, F. J. (1945). Permanent wilting percentage of soils obtained from field and laboratory trials. *Plant Physiol.* **20**, 517.

Israelsen, O. W., and West, F. L. (1922). Water holding capacity of irrigated soils. *Utah State Univ. Agr. Expt. Sta. Bull.* **183**.

Jackson, R. D., Reginato, R. J., and Van Bavel, C. H. M. (1965). Comparison of measured and calculated hydraulic conductivities of unsaturated soils. *Water Resources Res.* **1**, 375.

King, L. G., and Schleusener, R. A. (1961). Further evidence of hysteresis as a factor in the evaporation from soils. *J. Geophys. Res.* **66**, 4187.

Kramer, P. J., and Coile, T. S. (1940). An estimation of the volume of water made available by root extension. *Plant Physiol.* **15**, 743.

Miller, E. E., and Klute, A. (1967). The dynamics of soil water. 1. *Am. Soc. Agron., Monograph* **11**, 209.

Ogata, G., and Richards, L. A. (1957). Water content changes following irrigation of bare-field soil that is protected from evaporation. *Soil. Sci. Soc. Am. Proc.* **22**, 122.

Ogata, G., Richards, L. A., and Gardner, W. R. (1960). Transpiration of alfalfa determined from soil water content changes. *Soil Sci.* **89**, 179.

Peck, A. J., and Rabbidge, R. M. (1966). Soil-water potential: Direct measurement by a new technique. *Science* **151**, 1385.

Philip, J. R. (1957a). The theory of infiltration. 1. The infiltration equation and its solution. *Soil Sci.* **83**, 345.

Philip, J. R. (1957b). The physical principles of soil water movement during the irrigation cycle. *Trans. 3rd Congr. Intern. Comm. Irrig. Drainage Question* 8, p. 8.125.

Rawlins, S. L., and Dalton, F. N. (1967). Psychrometric measurement of soil water potential without precise temperature control. *Soil Sci. Soc. Am. Proc.* **31**, 297.

Richards, L. A., and Ogata, G. (1958). Thermocouple for vapor pressure measurement in biological and soil systems at high humidity. *Science* **128**, 1089.

Richards, L. A., and Wadleigh, C. H. (1952). Soil water and plant growth. *In Agronomy* **2**, 13.

Richards, L. A., and Weaver, L. R. (1943). Fifteen atmosphere percentage as related to the permanent wilting percentage. *Soil. Sci.* **56**, 331.

Richards, S. J., and Weeks, L. V. (1953). Capillary conductivity values from moisture yields and tension measurements in columns. *Soil Sci. Soc. Am. Proc.* **17**, 206.

Schleusener, R. A., and Corey, A. T. (1959). The role of hysteresis in reducing evaporation from soils in contact with a water table. *J. Geophys. Res.* **64**, 469.

Slater, P. J., and Williams, J. B. (1965). The influence of texture on the moisture characteristics of soils. I. A critical comparison of techniques for determining the available water capacity and moisture characteristic curve of a soil. *J. Soil Sci.* **16**, 1.

Stanhill, G. (1957). The effect of differences in soil moisture status on plant growth: A review and analysis of soil moisture regime experiments. *Soil Sci.* **84**, 205.

Topp, G. C., and Miller, E. E. (1966). Hysteretic moisture characteristics and hydraulic conductivities for glass-bead media. *Soil Sci. Soc. Am. Proc.* **30**, 157.

Veihmeyer, F. J., and Hendrickson, A. H. (1927). Soil moisture conditions in relation to plant growth. *Plant Physiol.* **2**, 71.

Veihmeyer, F. J., and Hendrickson, A. H. (1933). Some plant and soil–moisture relations. *Am. Soil Survey Assoc. Bull.* **15**, 76.

Visser, W. C. (1966). Progress in the knowledge about the effect of soil moisture content on plant production. *Inst. Land Water Management, Wageningen, Netherlands, Tech. Bull.* **45**.

Wadleigh, C. H., and Ayers, A. D. (1945). Growth and biochemical composition of bean plants as conditioned by soil moisture tension and salt concentration. *Plant Physiol.* **20**, 106.

Watson, K. K. (1966). An instantaneous profile method for determining the hydraulic conductivity of unsaturated porous materials. *Water Resources Res.* **2**, 709.

Wilcox, J. C. (1960). Rate of soil drainage following an irrigation. II. Effects on determination of rate of consumptive use. *Can. J. Soil Sci.* **40**, 15.

Youngs, E. G. (1960). The drainage of liquids from porous materials. *J. Geophys. Res.* **65**, 4025.

CHAPTER 6

PLANT FACTORS INFLUENCING
THE WATER STATUS OF PLANT TISSUES

I. R. Cowan and F. L. Milthorpe

UNIVERSITY OF NOTTINGHAM SCHOOL OF AGRICULTURE,
SUTTON BONINGTON, LOUGHBOROUGH, ENGLAND

I. PRINCIPLES, PROPOSITIONS, AND PERTINENCES

A. Introduction

The water status of plant tissue may be defined (1) by the amount of water contained relative to what it can hold when fully turgid or (2) by the potential of the water. Two interrelationships occur. First, the *relative water content* is a function, dependent on the physical and chemical properties of the tissue, of the components of the chemical potential of the water. Second, the pattern and rate of flow in the tissue—and thereby the change of water content—are related to gradients of potential. In this chapter, discussion is confined to the detailed components of localized flow systems and their integration to form that part of the soil–plant–atmosphere continuum that exists between the surface of the root and the surface of the leaf. The system is very

137

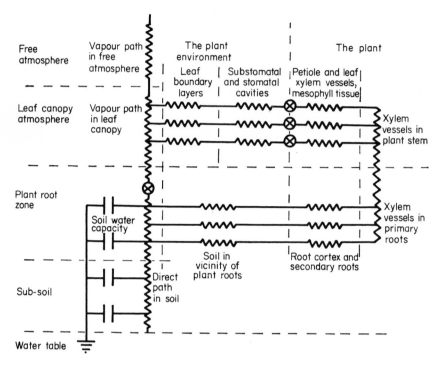

FIG. 1. Representation of pathways of water transport in the soil, plant, and atmosphere. Sites of changes of phase from liquid to vapor are distinguished by the symbol ⊗. After Cowan (1965).

complex, both geometrically and kinetically, and, of necessity, can only be treated approximately. Although an electrical analog cannot adequately describe the flow of water in a plant, the convenient symbolism of electrical circuits has been retained to describe qualitatively the various parts of the pathway of flow (Fig. 1). Flow takes place in a series parallel network of some intricacy—indeed, of greater intricacy than is indicated in this diagram. Either the whole or isolated parts of the system may be examined, of course, in any one experiment. Capacitors to represent storage of plant water have not been included in this analog. While changes in water content are of intimate concern here, the rate of change of water content in a transpiring plant is usually small compared to the magnitude of the flux of water through the plant. Indeed, crops often transpire more water in a single day than that contained within the plants themselves. The changes of flow and potential within the plant may be described therefore, with some reservations discussed later, by a sequence of steady states.

B. Basic Considerations

1. Flow Equations

The main channels of water movement in plants are provided by the xylem vessels in roots, stems, petioles, and leaf veins, with diameters of 2–500×10^{-4} cm, and the interstices between the fibrils of cell walls in root cortex and leaf mesophyll with widths of 1–100×10^{-7} cm. From a consideration of the Navier–Stokes equation of flow for small values of Reynold's number, the velocity of flow of water in a pore, $v(\text{cm}^3 \text{ cm}^{-2} \text{ sec}^{-1})$, may be described by

$$v = -k(\text{grad } P + \rho \text{ grad } gh - \rho F_w) \tag{1}$$

where k ($\text{cm}^4 \text{ sec}^{-1} \text{ dyne}^{-1}$) is the conductivity of the pore, P is pressure, ρ is density of water, g acceleration due to gravity, h is height in the earth's gravitational field, and F_w is the sum of all conservative forces, other than pressure gradient and gravitation, acting on unit mass of water in the direction of flow. Since ρ is nearly constant, Eq. (1) may be rewritten as

$$v = -k \text{ grad } \phi \tag{2}$$

where the hydraulic potential, ϕ, is the amount of work required to reversibly change the state of unit volume of free water at a standard pressure and height in the earth's gravitational field to that of the water in the pore. Equation (2) is readily integrated over a length of the pore defined by $0 < z < l$ to yield

$$v = -K \Delta\phi \tag{3}$$

where $K = 1 \big/ \left(\int_0^l dz/k \right)$

If diffusible solutes are present in the water, the forces acting both on the solute and the water must be considered. Assuming that only one species of solute is present,

$$v = -k[\text{grad } \phi - \rho_s(F_s - F_w)] \tag{4}$$

where ρ_s is the concentration of solute and F_s the sum of the forces, other than pressure gradient and gravity, acting on unit mass of solute in the direction of flow. v, ϕ, and ρ are now, respectively, the velocity, hydraulic potential, and density of the solution—not of the water alone. It is convenient to write the difference in forces in the form

$$F_s - F_w = -\text{grad}\left(\frac{RT}{M} \ln a_s\right) \tag{5}$$

where R is the gas constant, T the absolute temperature, M the molecular weight of the solute, and a_s the relative activity of the solute associated with its position in the force field $F_s - F_w$. Using the approximate relation for osmotic pressure

$$\pi = \frac{RT\rho_s}{M} \tag{6}$$

and substituting Eq. (5) in Eq. (4),

$$v = -k\left(\text{grad } \phi + \frac{\pi}{a_s} \text{ grad } a_s\right) \tag{7}$$

This relation cannot be integrated unless the distribution of solute in the pore is known. The flow of solute is (see de Groot, 1961)

$$J = \rho_s v - \rho_s u_s[\text{grad}(\mu_s - \mu_w) - (F_s - F_w)] \tag{8}$$

where μ_s and μ_w are the chemical potentials per unit mass of solute and water respectively and u_s is the mobility of unit mass of solute. u_s may be expressed in terms of the diffusion coefficient of the solute in water, D, by the relation

$$u_s = \frac{MD}{RT} \tag{9}$$

For dilute solutions, approximately,

$$\rho_s \text{ grad}(\mu_s - \mu_w) = \text{grad } \pi \tag{10}$$

Substituting Eqs. (5), (6), (9), and (10) in Eq. (8),

$$J = \frac{M}{RT}\left(\pi v - D \text{ grad } \pi - \frac{D\pi}{a_s} \text{ grad } a_s\right) \tag{11}$$

2. Convection of Solute

The simultaneous Eqs. (7) and (11) may be integrated over a finite length of the flow path. First, suppose that the differential force $F_s - F_w = 0$, and so $a_s = 1$ and grad $a_s = 0$. Then the solution of Eq. (7) is given by Eq. (3) as before. Assuming that the conductivity, k, and thus the velocity of the solution, v, is constant along the flow path, Eq. (11) gives

$$J = \frac{Mv}{RT} \frac{\pi_0 \exp(vl/2D) - \pi_l \exp(-vl/2D)}{1 - \exp(vl/D)} \tag{12}$$

If J is zero,

$$\pi_l = \pi_0 \exp(vl/D) \tag{13}$$

This relationship describes the accumulation of solutes at an impermeable boundary, due to convection.

3. Differential Permeability

Equations (7) and (11) may be solved for situations where the activity $a_s \neq 1$. Important examples relate to the passage of water through pores in cell membranes and protoplasm and particularly through the root endodermis. Since the thickness of the plasmalemma is of the order of 10^{-7} cm and that of the cytoplasm is 10^{-4} cm, vl/D is sufficiently small to allow the approximation $\exp(vl/D) \approx 1 + vl/D$. It may then be shown that

$$v = -K\left\{\Delta\phi - \pi_l\left[1 - y_l\left(1 + \frac{v}{lD}\int_0^l \left(\frac{1}{y}-1\right)\int_0^z y\,dz \cdot dz\right)\right] \right.$$

$$\left. + \pi_0\left[1 - y_0\left(1 - \frac{v}{lD}\int_0^l \left(\frac{1}{y}-1\right)\int_z^l y\,dz \cdot dz\right)\right]\right\} \quad (14)$$

$$J = -\frac{DM}{RTl}\left[\pi_l y_l\left(1 - \frac{v}{lD}\int_0^l \int_0^z y\,dz \cdot dz\right) - \pi_0 y_0\left(1 + \frac{v}{lD}\int_0^l \int_z^l y\,dz \cdot dz\right)\right]$$

$$(15)$$

where $y = a_s/\bar{a}_s$, $\bar{a}_s$ being the average value of a_s over the length of the pore. It is important to note that a_s is a function of the position within the pore only and not, at least directly, of the solute concentration—see Eq. (5). Equation (14) represents hydrodynamic bulk flow through a membrane under the influence of an osmotic pressure difference and provides a generalized description of the phenomenon discussed by Ray (1960), Dainty (1963), Kuiper (1963), and Dick (1966).

Some particular examples may be considered. First, suppose that a_s is constant within the pore and unity outside the pore. That is $y = 1$ for $0 < z < l$ and $y_1 = y_0 = y'$, say, at $z = 0$ and $z = l$.
Then

$$v = -K[\Delta\phi - \Delta\pi(1 - y')] \quad (16)$$

and

$$J = -\frac{DMy'}{RTl}\Delta\pi + \frac{M\bar{\pi}}{RT}y'v \quad (16a)$$

where $\bar{\pi} = \frac{1}{2}(\pi_l + \pi_0)$. The term $1 - y'$ is the " reflection coefficient," σ, introduced by Staverman to describe the interaction between the flows of solution and solute in membranes (cf. Dick, 1966). It gives the ratio of the hydraulic potential difference to the osmotic potential difference when there is no volume flow. Examination of Eq. (16a) shows that $y'(= 1 - \sigma)$ is the fraction of the solute concentration that is carried through the membrane with the bulk flow of solution when there is no difference of solute concentration.

If y is zero—representing an infinite value of a_s in the membrane and complete impermeability to solute—the volume flow of solution (and of water, since the two are the same) is

$$v_w = -K(\Delta\phi - \Delta\pi) = -K(\Delta\psi + \Delta\rho gh) \tag{17}$$

where ψ is the water potential, as defined by Slatyer and Taylor (1960), and $\Delta\rho gh$, the difference of hydraulic potential, is a negligible quantity in this system.

Small differences between the apparent conductances to flow through membranes induced by hydraulic and by osmotic potential differences are not necessarily associated with values of σ less than unity. Suppose that $y = y'$ for $0 < z < b$ and $l - b < z < l$ and that $y = 0$ for $b < z < l < b$; in other words, there is an infinitely high barrier to the passage of solute in a central length $l - 2b$ of the pore, but the solute may diffuse freely in the rest of the pore. Then, from Eq. (14),

$$v = -K\left(\Delta\phi - \Delta\pi + \frac{2b\bar\pi v}{lD}\right)$$
$$= -K\left(\Delta\psi + \frac{2b\bar\pi v}{lD}\right) \tag{18}$$

The apparent conductivity will decrease by an amount proportional to the mean concentration of solutes and the velocity of flow because, as a result of the convection of solute, the osmotic potential difference across the barrier $b < z < l - b$ is less than the overall difference $\Delta\pi$. The effect will increase if the osmotic potentials are determined not at the pore ends but at some point in the external solution. Dainty (1963) has discussed the practical implications of this on measurements of membrane permeability. The effect may in part account for the differences found by Mees and Weatherley (1957) between pressure-induced flow and osmotically induced flow into root systems (cf. p. 150).

Finite permeability of a membrane to solute does not imply *per se* that the reflection coefficient σ is less than unity, except in a trivial sense. Suppose that v and K in Eq. (16) refer not to a single pore but to the volume flow of solution and conductance per unit area of membrane due to the pores in the membrane. Let us further suppose that the solute may pass through the membrane by an additional pathway independently of the flow of water. The total volume flux, v^*, then becomes

$$v^* = v - \frac{p_s v_s}{RT}\Delta\pi = -K\left[\Delta\phi - \Delta\pi\left(1 - y' - \frac{k_s v_s}{KRT}\right)\right] \tag{19}$$

where p_s is the additional permeability (in centimeters per second) of the membrane to solute and v_s is the partial molar volume of solute. Here, the apparent reflection coefficient is

$$\sigma^* = 1 - y' - \frac{p_s v_s}{KRT} \qquad (20)$$

with a maximum value for $y' = 0$ of

$$\sigma_m^* = 1 - \frac{p_s v_s}{KRT} \qquad (21)$$

Slatyer (1962, 1966) presented estimates of the apparent reflection coefficients for uptake of mannitol and sucrose by tissue of tomato, eucalyptus, and cotton leaves and of potato tuber and obtained an average value of $\sigma^* \approx 0\cdot9\sigma_m^*$. Slatyer's experiments were not free of possible convection effects of the type described above and, in view of the relatively small interaction between water and solute which appeared to occur, it may be assumed that $\sigma^* \approx \sigma_m^*$ and $y' \approx 0$. Therefore, Eq. (17) may be accepted as valid for the movement of water across plant membranes, with v_w and K being referred to unit area of the membrane.

C. APPLICATIONS AND APPROXIMATIONS IN PLANT SYSTEMS

1. Cell–Water Relations

Philip (1958a,b,c) analyzed the uptake of water by individual cells following a sudden change in the potential of water in an external solution. The potential of water in the cell is given by

$$\psi = \psi_1 + (\psi_2 - \psi_1)\{1 - \exp[-K_c(\varepsilon + \pi_0)At/V_0]\} \qquad (22)$$

where ψ_1 and ψ_2 are the values of ψ before and after equilibration, K_c is the conductance of the cell surface to water (and thus involves cell wall, plasmalemma, cytoplasm, and tonoplast), ε is the elastic modulus of the cell, π_0 and V_0 are the osmotic potential in the cell and cell volume, respectively, when the cell is at zero turgor pressure, A is the surface area, and t is the time. The half-time of the change in water potential (and in relative water content) of the cell is

$$t_{1/2} = \frac{V_0 \ln 2}{K_c(\varepsilon + \pi_0)A} \qquad (23)$$

Typical values of the parameters in Eq. (23) are $V_0/A = 5 \times 10^{-3}$ cm, $K_c = 2 \times 10^{-5}$ cm sec^{-1}atm^{-1}, and $\varepsilon + \pi_0 = 100$ atm (Philip, 1966). Using these, $t_{1/2} \approx 2$ seconds. Even allowing for likely errors, it is clear that half-times are of the order of seconds rather than minutes and that appreciable differences of water potential between cell walls and protoplasm are very transient.

Most measurements of half-times of changes of water content have been made, for obvious reasons, on sections of plant tissue rather than individual cells. Philip (1958b) analyzed the propagation of turgor and of potential through cell aggregates resulting from a change of concentration of the external solution. He finds that these phenomena may be described by a diffusion equation, the diffusion coefficient being

$$D = \frac{K_c(\varepsilon + \pi_0)Al^2}{2V_0} = \frac{l^2 \ln 2}{2t_{1/2}} \tag{24}$$

where l is the length of each cell and $t_{1/2}$ is given by Eq. (23). Setting $l = 5 \times 10^{-3}$ cm, $D \approx 5 \times 10^{-6}$ cm^{2}sec^{-1}. The half-time for water uptake by a linear aggregation of cells, of length l^*, is $t_{1/2}^* \approx 0.05\, l^{*2}/D$. Taking $l^* = 10l$, $t_{1/2}^* = 25$ seconds, Philip (1966) points out that $t^* = l^{*2}/D$ is a characteristic time for the propagation of a disturbance through a diffusion system. Using the values given, he finds $t^* \approx 8$ min and concludes that the quasi-steady state model of plant–water relations may not be valid for fluctuations of transpiration with this, or a smaller, characteristic time (see also Kohn and Dainty, 1966).

In the above analysis, Philip assumes that the pathway for water movement is from protoplast to protoplast. Weatherley (1963) suggested that a disturbance of water pressure is propagated rapidly through the cell walls and is followed by a slower equilibration of the cell contents with cell-wall water. If this is so, it is important to distinguish the characteristics of flow in tissue immersed in a medium of changing osmotic potential from those in intact tissue experiencing a change of hydraulic pressure. In the former, rates of change of tissue-water content are likely to be limited by diffusion of solutes through the cell walls and will be slower the larger the aggregation of cells. Rates of change of water content induced by hydraulic pressure differences will be limited by the process of water exchange between individual protoplasts and their cell walls and will be more rapid than osmotically induced changes. Fluctuations of transpiration rate will be reflected initially in a change of the hydraulic potential of the solution in the cell walls of the mesophyll; it seems likely that the propagation of this change and the subsequent changes in protoplast water content may take place very rapidly. The deficits of leaf water content that are commonly found to persist in crop plants at night after rapid transpiration during the day are almost certainly associated with the slow recovery of the water potential in the soil around the roots rather than with components within the plants (Philip, 1966).

2. Plant–Atmosphere Relations

It has been emphasized above that flow within the xylem vessels and cell walls takes place in response to gradients of hydraulic potential rather than water potential. Nevertheless, because the gravitational component is usually negligible and the gradient of solute concentration is small, the two are very similar. In the steady state, the water potential in the xylem and cell walls will be similar to that within the adjacent cells. Then, neglecting all but the most essential geometry of flow,

$$E = \frac{\psi_r - \psi_l}{R} \tag{25}$$

where E is the rate of transpiration, ψ_r and ψ_l are, respectively, the water potentials at the root surfaces and at the evaporating sites within the leaves, and R is the resistance to water flow through the plant. In dealing with plants in natural conditions it would be apposite, if not conventional, to reverse the terms in Eq. (25). In most instances, rates of flow in the plant are controlled by the environment, and the potential gradients that develop are the result of these. It commonly has been held that the resistance to vapor transfer away from the mesophyll is greater than that to liquid flow through the plant. This contention, though first made 20 years ago, is still the cause of misunderstanding, and it is therefore desirable to examine it in detail. It was noted by van den Honert (1948) that $\psi_r - \psi_l$ is about 10 atm in living plants, whereas the difference of water potential between the leaves and the ambient atmosphere is usually about 1000 atm. He concluded that the resistance to transport in the vapor phase is greater than that in the liquid phase. His argument is incomplete since vapor transport is a function of differences of vapor pressure —not of water potential. However, a similar approach can be pursued more rigorously. Water potential and vapor pressure are related by the equation

$$\psi = \frac{RT}{V} \ln \frac{e}{e'} \tag{26}$$

where e and e' are respectively the actual and saturation vapor pressures of water at temperature T and V is the specific volume of liquid water. The ratio e/e' is also the relative activity of liquid water of potential ψ and is a state variable whether or not there is an equilibrium vapor phase present. Since e/e' is not less than 0.95 in living plants, a sufficient approximation of Eq. (26) is

$$\psi = \frac{RT}{V} \left(\frac{e}{e'} - 1 \right) \tag{27}$$

Provided the plant is isothermal,

$$E = \frac{e_r - e_l}{R'} \tag{28}$$

where $R' = RVe'/RT$ is a new resistance. It is likely that the vapor pressure at the air–water interfaces in transpiring plants is approximately reflected by measurements of water potential in the leaf tissue; if so, then $e_r - e_l$ rarely exceeds 1 mbar. The difference in vapor pressure of water between the leaves and the ambient atmosphere is of the order 6 to 30 mbars. Clearly, the resistance in the vapor phase is greater than that in the liquid phase. The conclusion that the mechanism of vapor transport is more important than that of liquid transport in determining the rate of transpiration is true under nonisothermal conditions also. The relative extent to which the vapor pressure difference between leaves and atmosphere may be altered by changes of e/e' in the leaf is small under all normal circumstances of transpiration (Table I). Any slight change of rate of transpiration that may occur due to a change of water potential in the leaf is diminished because it is followed by a change of leaf temperature and thus of vapor pressure in the opposite direction.

TABLE I

APPROXIMATE MAGNITUDES OF POTENTIAL AND RELATIVE
ACTIVITY OF WATER IN THE SOIL–PLANT–ATMOSPHERE CONTINUUM

Component	Turgid plant		Wilting plant	
	Water potential (atm)	Activity	Water potential (atm)	Activity
Soil	−0.1 to −10	1.000 to 0.993	−10 to −20	0.993 to 0.986
Leaf	−5.0 to −15	0.997 to 0.990	−15 to −30	0.990 to 0.980
Atmosphere	−100.0 to −2000	0.934 to 0.253	−100 to −2000	0.934 to 0.253

3. Characteristics of Plant Conductance

The application of Eq. (25) is limited. As will be illustrated later, the conductances of the roots and leaves vary with the potential and the rate of flow. This is not surprising: As indicated above, water potential, or indeed any other single-state variable, is inadequate to describe the movement of water. The flow of solutes must be considered also. Changes of salt concentration may affect conductivity directly by modifying the properties of membranes. Heat flow within the plant may be linked with water transport, but the possibility of strong interference between the two is unlikely on thermodynamic grounds (Spanner, 1964). Changing conductances in the plant probably also arise from changes in the geometry of the flow system associated with differing degrees of hydration. On the other hand, the shearing forces associated with flow through the plant are very great and their effect on tissue geometry must be complex—but unpredictable without a much greater knowledge of the elastic properties of cell components than is available at present.

Despite these considerations and the clear need to examine the range of validity of the quasi-steady state model, information on the variation of conductivity with velocity and potential differences and knowledge of the magnitudes of these components can lead to a partial understanding of the system. We must perforce assume that the model is an acceptable approximation in the rapidly changing conditions that occur in a natural environment. The problem of describing the factors that affect the water status of plant tissue then becomes one of definining and evaluating the conductances of plant components together with the external factors influencing the supply and loss of water. It is convenient to deal with these supply and loss aspects separately.

II. SUPPLY OF WATER TO THE LEAVES (LIQUID PHASE)

A. INDIVIDUAL ORGANS

1. The Root

In any one root at a given instant, two components of flow may be recognized. One concerns the entry of water from the soil solution, the other the flow along the root xylem. These are defined by

$$f = L \, d\phi_x/dx \quad \text{and} \quad df/dx = -S(\psi_s - \psi_x) \tag{29}$$

where $f(\text{cm}^3 \text{ sec}^{-1})$ is the flow upward in the root, x is the distance along the root, ϕ_x is the hydraulic potential in the xylem, ψ_s and ψ_x are respectively the potential of water surrounding the roots and within the xylem, and L and S are respectively the transmission coefficients for flow along the root and across the root. Provided the concentration of solute in the xylem is small, the gradient of ϕ_x will be similar to that of ψ_x. When ψ_s is constant over the length l of the root, the conductance of the root as a whole K_r is defined by the ratio $f/(\psi_s - \psi_x)$ at $x = 0$. With S and L constant it may be shown that

$$K_r = (SL)^{1/2} \tanh(S/L)^{1/2}l \tag{30}$$

If $Sl^2/L \ll 1$ this relation may be rewritten $K_r \approx Sl$, the resistance to flow along the xylem being negligible compared with that to flow across the cortex. More generally, S and L will vary along the root; it may be shown $K_r \approx \int_0^l S \, dx$, provided $\int_0^l 1/L \int_x^l S \, dx \cdot dx \ll 1$. Most workers have not measured the size of the roots or root systems they have worked with, so there are few comparative values of K_r available. Cox (1966) has attempted to apply Eqs. (29) to whole root systems of young wheat plants. L decreased and S increased with distance along the root, values being in the ranges $12\text{--}2 \times 10^{-4}$ cm^4 sec^{-1} atm^{-1} and $0.4\text{--}2 \times 10^{-6}$ cm^2 sec^{-1} atm^{-1} respectively. The conductances K_r for the whole root systems were $8\text{--}2 \times 10^{-5}$ cm^3 sec^{-1} atm^{-1} and for individual primary roots $1.2\text{--}0.4 \times 10^{-5}$ cm^3 sec^{-1} atm^{-1}. These values are considerably greater than those of 10^{-7} to 10^{-6} cm^2 sec^{-1} atm^{-1} obtained for a root of a broad bean plant by Brouwer (1965). In general, the conductance of the roots appeared to be dominated by that of the root cortex. However, the estimated decrease in water potential across the cortex near to the tips of the longest roots was small compared with that along the xylem vessels of the roots, and therefore the uptake of water by the lower parts of the root system was limited by the resistance to flow in the xylem.

An individual root varies along its length. It consists of undifferentiated meristematic cells behind the root cap (1–2 mm), followed by a zone of elongating and differentiated cells (2–10 mm) and finally a region of mature cells. The root-hair region extends from just behind the zone of differentiation; here, water uptake is facilitated by the intimate contact between root hairs and soil and the presence of differentiated xylem elements in the root. With the passage of time, cutin is deposited in the walls of the epidermal cells and the root hairs and the latter may often degenerate (Brouwer, 1965). Suberin is also deposited in the walls of the endodermal cells as Casparian strips on radial walls and secondary suberin lamellae over the whole wall (Esau, 1962); usually, such cells are completely suberized at a distance of 10–12 cm from the root tip, although this distance is inversely related to the rate of root extension (Brouwer, 1965). Both cutin and suberin are waxy materials and presumably provide a barrier through which water can pass only by distillation. Studies of individual roots of onion and maize suggest that the most active region of absorption is 4–10 cm from the tip (Rosene, 1937; Hayward et al., 1942; Slatyer, 1960), although the conductance of old suberized regions of roots of fruit trees is appreciable (Kramer, 1946). Indeed, Kramer and Bullock (1966) have pointed out that suberized roots of a large loblolly pine contribute about 93 % to the total absorbing area; although their conductivity is about one tenth that of unsuberized roots, they absorb three fourths of the total water taken up.

It is now generally believed that most of the water passing through the cortex does so in the cell walls, the conductivity of the cytoplasm being relatively small. However, Woolley's (1965) studies of the diffusional exchange of tritiated water in maize roots suggest that neither the endodermis nor epidermis are especially large barriers and that possibly 70 % of the transport is through cytoplasm. The experiments of Jensen and Taylor (1961), Kuiper

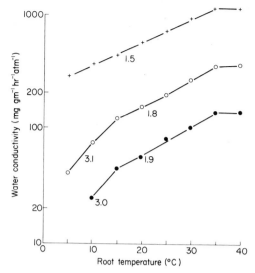

Fig. 2. The relationship between the conductivity of the root for water (logarithmic scale) and the temperature of maize roots when conductivities are measured by imposed pressure differences (crosses), transpiration (open circles), and osmotic potential gradients (closed circles). The figures indicate values of Q_{10}. After Brouwer (1965).

(1963), and Brouwer (1965) show that the activation energy for water transport in roots is higher than that associated with viscous flow; it decreases with increase of temperature, the Q_{10} changing from 3–4 to 1.2–2 (Fig. 2).

Appreciable controversy exists concerning the relative contributions from the osmotic and pressure components to the potential of water in the root xylem. The osmotic concentration may often exceed that of the external solution (Table II). It tends to decrease with increase in the rate of transpiration. Intact plants are generally able to absorb water against much lower

TABLE II

Osmotic Pressures (atm) in the Xylem and External Medium of Transpiring and Detopped Bleeding Plants[a]

Species	Transpiring plants	Bleeding plants	Medium
Maize	1.2		0.4
Maize	1.9	4.0	0.8
Tomato	2.3	2.4	0.4
Peas	0.4	1.5	0.8
Barley	1.0	2.1	0.8

[a] Calculated from Brouwer (1965), assuming solute concentration of 1 meq l^{-1} $\approx$ 0.049 atm.

water potentials than are the root systems of detopped plants. The rate of exudation from the latter is usually only 5% of the rate of transpiration. However, (Brouwer, 1965) found that the rate of exudation from detopped maize plants approximated to the rate of transpiration.

Estimates of the conductance of whole root systems have been made in various ways: (1) from measurements of π_s, π_x, and the rate of exudation with severed root systems, (2) from the increase of flow due to the imposition of pressure on the water surrounding the roots, and (3) from estimates of ψ_x in relation to the rate of transpiration in intact plants. Investigations by Brouwer (1965) show that appreciably divergent values are obtained from the various methods (Fig. 2). Mees and Weatherley (1957) obtained essentially similar results, the conductivity for flow induced by hydraulic pressure gradients being 1.3 times that induced by osmotic gradients. The discrepancy may arise partly from differences in pathway, compression of gas in air spaces, and transport of solutes.

The effect on water uptake of pressure gradients changing from low to high values differs from that found when the change is in the opposite direction; the former results in a logarithmic relation between water uptake and pressure difference, whereas the latter gives a linear relation (Fig. 3). This effect is found with excised root systems (Brouwer, 1965; Kuiper, 1963; Mees and Weatherley, 1957) and with intact transpiring plants (Weatherley,

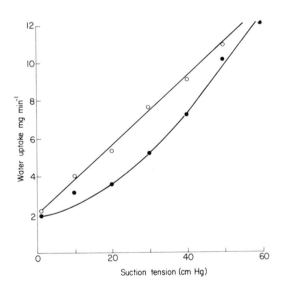

FIG. 3. The relationships between water uptake of roots of a bean plant and suction tensions applied to cut end of the stem. Closed circles indicate values when suction was progressively increased; open circles, when suction decreased. After Kuiper (1963).

1965). With increasing suction the conductivity increases more in the regions distant from than close to the root apices.

The species of solute surrounding roots influences conductivity to water greatly (Kuiper, 1963). Various inhibitors, such as cyanide, fluoride, and dinitrophenol decrease the conductivity (Brouwer, 1965; Ordin and Kramer, 1956) under all circumstances but more markedly when osmotic gradients are primarily concerned (Mees and Weatherley, 1957). Kuiper (1963) interprets these responses as indicating that the main barrier to flow is in the lipoprotein membranes of the endodermal cells, the protein layers being stretched by increased suction and their structure affected by the nature of the ions present. The free volume for water transfer through the membrane, and also possibly through the protoplasm itself, is increased.

The conductivity of a root or root system, then, may change by at least an order of magnitude with changes in the physical and chemical environment. [Changes of the same order in permeability to water of cells between the unplasmolyzed (0.2×10^{-7}) and plasmolyzed $(4 \times 10^{-7} \text{ cm}^3 \text{ cm}^{-2}$ surface $\text{sec}^{-1} \text{ atm}^{-1})$ states have been found (Myers, 1951)]. Most workers have not measured the size of the systems they have worked with and so there are few comparative values. For most flow studies, it is convenient to express conductivity per unit length of root.

2. The Stem

The stem is possibly the best documented of all the flow components in the plant, and its features are examined only briefly here. In herbaceous and short woody plants water is conducted as continuous columns in the xylem vessels and tracheids; in tall trees the mechanism is less certain. Despite the inadequacy of the experimentation—compensated only by the vigor of associated polemics—it is likely that flow is similar to that in herbaceous plants. Most of the experiments (cf. Greenidge, 1957; Kozlowski, 1964; Zimmermann, 1964, 1965) indicate that there is little real evidence against this contention. The concentration of solutes in the xylem sap is about 0.2–0.4%, and the negative water potential is identified with a negative pressure. Both experimental and theoretical estimates show that the intrinsic pressure of water is greater than the negative pressure required ($\sim$ 15–25 atm) to transport water to the top of the tallest tree. Experiments using tracers and other techniques indicate that flow is normally in the tracheids (of conifers) and vessels (of angiosperms). If these conducting elements are broken, transient interruption of water flow occurs but new channels, including lateral transport through the vessel walls, come into operation. It seems likely that the conductance along walls of the tracheary elements and along xylem rays (Kozlowski et al., 1966) is adequate to maintain flow when short lengths of the lumina are disrupted (as by air embolism). Species with diffuse–porous xylem (i.e., with uniformly distributed vessels of equal diameter) differentiate new xylem slowly, whereas those with ring–porous xylem (vessels of unequal diameters with largest vessels formed in spring) produce new xylem more quickly. In the latter, probably only those elements formed during the current or previous season function as conducting elements (Preston, 1952; Peel, 1965). In conifers, most of the water moves in the larger tracheids only of all xylem rings (Kozlowski *et al.*, 1966).

The specific conductivity of xylem, k_x, is conveniently defined by

$$f = - \frac{k_x A}{l} \Delta\phi \qquad (31)$$

where f is the rate of flow in the xylem, A is the cross-sectional area of xylem lumina, and $\Delta\phi$ is the increment of hydraulic potential in length l of the xylem (ϕ is approximately equivalent to the hydraulic pressure). The data of Peel (1965) indicate that the xylem cylinders of diffuse–porous species in the limited range of 0.3–0.8 cm radius have approximately uniform conductivities, whereas those of a ring–porous species have uniform conductivities only when less than 0.5 cm radius, the conductivities of larger stems not being proportional to the xylem area. Some values of k_x are given in Table III.

The value of k_x would be expected to vary with the number and diameters of the conducting elements involved in the functional xylem. Vessels range from 2×10^{-3} to 7×10^{-2} cm in diameter and have few transverse septa; tracheids are about 2–3×10^{-3} cm in diameter and have many transverse septa containing pores of about 6×10^{-6} cm diameter (Preston, 1952).

TABLE III

SPECIFIC CONDUCTIVITIES OF XYLEM, k_x, RECORDED FOR VARIOUS SPECIES;
THE CONDUCTIVITIES OF THE XYLEM LUMINA ARE PROBABLY 4 TO 5
TIMES THESE VALUES

Species	k_x (cm^2 sec^{-1} atm^{-1})	Authority
Roots of deciduous trees	10–160	Huber (1956)
Stems		
Conifers	0.6	Huber (1956)
Deciduous trees	1.6–3	Huber (1956)
Lianas	7–36	Huber (1956)
Fraxinus excelsior (ring-porous)	5.9–6.7	Peel (1965)
Acer pseudoplatanus (diffuse-porous)	3.2–4.6	Peel (1965)
Salix atrocinerea (diffuse-porous)	1.3–1.8	Peel (1965)

Maximum values for linear velocities of flow, measured by the thermo-electric method, are 45 m hr^{-1} in ring–porous and 6 m hr^{-1} in diffuse–porous trees (Zimmermann, 1964) and 0.1–0.7 m hr^{-1} in conifers (Huber, 1956); values of a similar order of magnitude are obtained by using dyes, salts, and radioactive tracers (Crafts et al., 1949). Values for herbaceous plants appear to be similar to those for diffuse–porous trees.

As a crude approximation, for diffuse–porous species $k_x \approx \pi N r^4/(8\eta)$ $\approx 2.5 \times 10^2$ cm^2 sec^{-1} atm^{-1} where there are N vessels per square centimeter ($\approx 6.4 \times 10^2$) of radius r ($\approx 10^{-2}$ cm). Calculations of this nature contain many oversimplifications, especially as the xylem consists of an intercon-necting system of many vessels of radii of different sizes arranged in parallel. A closer approximation to the true value of k_x is given by $\pi \sum_j [N_j r_j^4/(8\eta)]$ where N_j and r_j are the numbers and mean radii of vessels in different size classes. Dimond (1966) has analyzed flow in the tomato plant using this approach. In this plant, the radii of vessels of a large vascular bundle vary from 5 to 75μ, the frequency distribution being log normal. However, the largest 6 vessels in a vascular bundle of 82 vessels would be expected to trans-port about 60% of the water. The data for a sample of the internodes and petioles in a plant, in which flow rates were induced by known pressure differences, show that the main resistance to flow is in the petioles (Table IV) Each conductance refers to the particular organ as a whole, but values of k_x may be calculated. The three large bundles in a tomato stem have a total area of vessel lumina of about 6.4×10^{-3} cm^2; with a conductance of 180 $\times 10^{-3}$ cm^3 sec^{-1} atm^{-1} over a length of 6 cm, $k_x \approx 1.7 \times 10^2$ cm^2 sec^{-1} atm^{-1}. Values of $k_x A$ were about 4×10^{-4} cm^4 sec^{-1} atm^{-1} which compare

TABLE IV

LENGTHS AND CONDUCTANCES OF INTERNODES AND PETIOLES
AT DIFFERENT POSITIONS OF A TOMATO PLANT WITH 16
UNFOLDED LEAVES[a]

Position of internode or petiole numbered from base	Length (cm)		Conductance $(k_x A/l, 10^{-3}$ cm^3 sec^{-1} atm$^{-1})$	
	Internode	Petiole	Internode	Petiole
1	6.3	8.0	175	0.12
4	4.3	11.4	470	0.48
7	6.0	11.3	189	1.17
10	7.2	11.3	107	2.00
13	8.2	10.1	86	5.16
16	0.5	1.1	2.4	0.15

[a] Data after Dimond (1966).

closely with values of 3.3×10^{-4} obtained by Jensen *et al.* (1961), also with the tomato plant. The values of k_x were close to those calculated above for diffuse–porous trees but were two orders of magnitude larger than those given in Table III. Part of this discrepancy is accounted for when actual areas of xylem are taken into account; nevertheless, it would seem that not all vessels in diffuse–porous trees are involved in water transport.

Conductance in conifers is more complex; here, it probably is controlled by the number and dimensions of the pores in the many septa of the tracheids. Although Stamm (1946) determined the dimensions, no adequate analysis has been attempted. However, Kozlowski *et al.* (1966) have shown that flow occurs predominantly through the tracheids of largest diameter—it is not known whether the sizes of the pores of the septa are related to tracheid diameter.

With vessels of radius 10^{-2} cm and maximum linear flow velocity of 10^{-1} cm sec^{-1}, the required pressure drop along a vessel is calculated as 10^{-2} atm m^{-1}. This is lower than the values of 0.05 atm m^{-1} quoted by Zimmermann (1964) and 10^{-1} atm m^{-1} calculated much earlier by Dixon (1914). Dimond's data (see above) for the rate of transpiration in his experiment also suggest a pressure drop of 10^{-1} atm m^{-1}. To these values must be added the gradient of 10^{-1} atm m^{-1} required to lift the water against gravity.

3. *The Leaf*

Water enters the leaf via the petiole and midrib and flows through the network of subsidiary veins and individual vessels; finally, it has to move through cell walls and/or protoplasts to the evaporating surface located within cell walls bordering on substomatal cavities. There is much uncertainty and few quantitative data concerning the relative magnitudes of the resistances in the several parts of this pathway. The facts that severance of the main veins (Wylie, 1938; Mer, 1940) has little effect on transpiration over appreciable periods and that a leaf or even half a leaf exposed to high insolation will wilt while a shaded adjacent leaf or half-leaf remains turgid (Rawlins, 1963) suggest that the conductances of the veins are high relative to that in the wall/protoplast part of the pathway. Evidence from the movement of fluorescent dyes (Strugger, 1943; Ziegenspeck, 1945) suggests that most of the water moves via the cell walls. Weatherley (1963) studied the rate of water uptake through the petioles of severed leaves of red currant and pelargonium before and after transpiration was suddenly retarded. The decrease in rate appeared to involve two exponential decay processes, one having a half-time of approximately 10^2 seconds and the other of 2×10^3 seconds. The initial rate of uptake associated with the first process was about 60 times that associated with the second. Weatherley interpreted these results as indicating a rapid propagation (in effect, diffusion) of pressure through the leaf via the xylem and cell walls and a slower equilibration between the cell-wall water and the cell protoplasm and concluded that most of the water moving through the leaf of a transpiring plant does so along the cell walls. An unsatisfactory aspect of this interpretation is that it also predicts that the total uptake of water by the cell walls, following the cessation of transpiration, would be about 3 times the uptake by the cells themselves.

The flow pattern in leaves probably is somewhat as follows. In a leaf that is not transpiring (in the early morning, for example), the potential of water in the cell walls adjacent to a substomatal cavity is equal to that in the protoplasts of the adjacent cells. In the absence of components of potential in the cell wall resulting from solutes and forces originating from the pore surfaces, both potentials equal the pressure of water in the cell walls, P_w. P_w is less than the pressure of the atmosphere by the sum of the water potential in the soil and the gravitational potential associated with the height of the plant. The air–water interfaces in the capillaries are negatively curved according to the relation

$$P_w = P_a - \gamma(1/R_1 + 1/R_2) \qquad (32)$$

where P_a is the pressure of the atmosphere, γ is the surface tension of water, and R_1 and R_2 are the principal radii of curvature. If water now begins to evaporate, the interfaces take up an increasingly negative curvature and P_w diminishes. A hydraulic potential gradient is set up in the cell walls and xylem and a difference of water potential between the cell walls and protoplasm, and water moves toward the air–water interfaces. Initially, the supply of water is provided by the plant tissue, but later an increasing amount is withdrawn from the soil. If the rate of transpiration were to remain constant, and if the hydraulic conductivity of the soil around the roots was sufficient to prevent rapid changes of water potential there, a nearly steady state would be achieved in which virtually the whole of the flow would be supplied by the soil, and potentials in the plant would diminish only as the potential of water in the bulk of the soil diminished. In practice, the rate of transpiration exhibits both diurnal and irregular fluctuations and, at any one time, the transient effects of previous fluctuations are present in the plant. If the pressure, P_w, of water in the cell walls diminishes sufficiently, the menisci in the larger pores recede. The pressure difference when this occurs is the "air-entry value" and, for pores with hydrophilic internal surfaces, is given by a modification of Eq. (32):

$$P_a - P_w = 2\gamma/r \approx \frac{1.5 \times 10^{-4}}{r} \text{ (atm)} \qquad (33)$$

where r is the effective radius of the pores. If P_w now decreases further, more pores empty and the pressure is related to the amount of water in the walls. It may now be identified as a matric potential, τ, this being the component of water potential related to the water content of the matrix. The two may also be identified at pressures greater than the air-entry value if the pores of the wall were to contract under the influence of negative pressure, but it is not certain that they do so. If there were extensive electric fields originating at the inner surfaces of the pores, the effects of these would be included in the matric potential; the gradient of τ would remain zero at right angles to the lines of flow, but P_w would now increase with proximity to the surface. Only at points removed from the electric field would $P_w = \tau$. A similar restriction would be placed on Eq. (32), and Eq. (33) would no longer be valid. It is doubtful, however, whether surface effects of this kind can be of much importance in the largest cell-wall pores, for which $r \approx 5 \times 10^{-6}$ cm. The air-entry value for these, then, is calculated as being roughly 30 atm. If the cell walls contained a large number of pores of approximately this size, appreciable amounts of water could be lost with little further decrease of pressure. In the short term, this water could supply the demands of an increased rate of transpiration but, if sustained, would result in a drastic lowering of the pressure and a loss of water from the cell protoplasm.

The wall water would thus " buffer " the effects of short-period fluctuations in transpiration rate. This possibility has been explored by Carr and Gaff (1961), who estimate that in leaves of the sclerophyll *Eucalyptus globulus* 100 gm turgid tissue contain 20 gm dry cell wall, 20 gm dry protoplast, 30 gm cell wall water, and 30 gm protoplast water. (The values for water contents of the tissues and especially of the protoplast are very much lower than those of mesophytes.) An appreciable " buffering " effect, however, can only operate when the mean pressure in the walls is slightly greater than the air-entry value for an appreciable volume of pores. It depends, therefore, upon the size-distribution of the pores and the combination of factors that determine the mean pressure.

The elasticity of the cell walls is also an important characteristic. An approximate expression for the change of cell volume, V, with change of water potential is (Philip, 1958a)

$$\frac{1}{V_0}\frac{dV}{d\psi} = \frac{1}{\varepsilon + \pi_0} \tag{34}$$

where V_0 and π_0 are respectively the volume and internal osmotic pressure of the cell when its turgor pressure is zero (incipient plasmolysis) and ε is the elastic modulus of the cell wall defined by $V_0\, dP/dV$. If the elastic modulus of the walls is high, a large decrease in ψ is accompanied by a small loss of water from the protoplast. A combination of large elastic modulus and osmotic pressure provides a mechanism for maintaining the water supply to the metabolic components while sustaining large gradients of potential associated with water flow to the leaf. There are appreciable differences between species in the curves relating relative water content to leaf water potential (Altman and Dittmer, 1966).

Excised leaf discs lose water very rapidly; they also take up water rapidly when floated on water (Weatherley, 1965). This suggests that the conductance through the protoplasts is not particularly low and that the water potential in the protoplast is not greatly different from that in the cell wall at any moment. Metabolic activity is probably most closely related to the relative water content of *protoplasts* (not the relative water content of *tissue*). Assuming $\psi = \pi - P$, variation in π can obviously influence the hydrostatic pressure at any given value of ψ. Slatyer (1963) discussed the variation of π: generally, it is about 5 atm in shade plants, 10–20 atm in crop plants, 30–40 atm in xerophytes, and 100 atm or greater in halophytes. Much of this variation appears to be associated with differences in external solute concentration (cf. Chapter 8) rather than with intrinsic genetic parameters. However, the osmotic pressure does vary with internal factors, usually being greatest during dormancy and lowest during active growth, increasing during the growth of a leaf and decreasing during its senescence, increasing during the day and decreasing at night, and increasing with decreasing water potential.

The significance of solutes in this part of the transpiration pathway has not been explored. However, the air–water interfaces in the cell walls of the leaf mesophyll form an impermeable boundary and Eqs. (12) and (13) are applicable. It is important to know whether the vapor pressure of water there may be substantially reduced by an accumulation of salts due to convection. The average distance of the evaporating surface from the nearest xylem vessel may be taken as $l = 2 \times 10^{-2}$ cm and the average effective radius of the interstices in the cell wall as $r = 10^{-6}$ cm. The approximate conductance is found from the Poiseuille expression $k = r^2/(8\eta)$, where η is the dynamic viscosity of water (10^{-2} poise). If the difference of hydraulic pressure between xylem and evaporating surface is 5 atm, $v \approx 3 \times 10^{-3}$ cm sec^{-1}. The diffusion coefficient of salts in water is about 2×10^{-5} cm^2 sec^{-1}; therefore, $vl/D \approx 3$, and $\pi_l/\pi_0 \approx 10$. The osmotic pressure in the xylem is about 0.2 atm and, therefore, in the present example, that at the evaporating surface is about 2 atm—sufficient to reduce the vapor pressure of water by only 0.14%. The calculation neglects, of course, the uptake of salt by mesophyll cells and probably overestimates the magnitude of the accumulation. As in the root, there is much indirect evidence suggesting that the conductance to flow in the leaf is not constant but varies with the rate of flow and other factors (Rawlins, 1963).

Few direct measurements of the variation of water potential between different leaves at any time are available. Begg *et al.* (1964) found that the water potential in all leaf layers of a crop of *Pennisetum* was around −8 atm in the early morning and evening and fell during the day to −18, −20, and

−21 atm in the upper, middle, and lower layers, respectively. Recovery occurred during the afternoon. Lemon (1963) quotes values in a maize crop during the time of maximum evaporation ranging from −1.5 in the lower leaves to −4.5 atm in the upper leaves. Čatsky (1965) has measured the relative water contents of different leaves on an isolated plant during a drying cycle. Most of the leaves had similar values when the plant was growing in moist soil. These were around 98–95% (say, −1 to −4 atm water potential). Values for different leaves diverged as the soil dried. After 5 days, for instance, the relative water content of a very young leaf was 80% (about −12 atm), whereas that of the oldest leaf was 45% (about −30 atm). This is usual: the older leaves of a plant experiencing a water deficit tend to wilt and die first. The reasons for this behavior are not clear but must be associated with physiological parameters such as less-responsive stomata in old leaves or failure of the metabolism to produce osmotically active solutes rapidly. (Microclimates of the different leaves on an *isolated* plant are similar, and resistances in the pathway to old leaves are less than those to young leaves).

4. The Fruit

Certain organs with a high resistance to vapor loss, such as fruits, tubers, or stems of succulent plants, often act as reservoirs, the water flowing to the leaves during periods of high transpiration (Bartholomew, 1926; Furr and Taylor, 1935). It is doubtful if such a supply is sufficient to influence the relative water content of leaves, although the transient drain can reduce the growth of the fruit.

B. THE PLANT AS A WHOLE

1. Resistances to Flow

The flow of liquid water through the plant may be described in general terms by Eq. (25). This may also be written as

$$f = E = \frac{\psi_r - \psi_l}{R_{\text{root}} + R_{\text{stem}} + R_{\text{leaf}}} \tag{35}$$

Jensen *et al.* (1961) attempted to measure the resistances of these three components in small plants of sunflower and tomato totally immersed in water and subjected to pressure differences. Their technique probably over-estimated the leaf resistance. There were appreciable discrepancies between the resistances of intact plants and the sum of their component resistances measured separately (Table V); approximately, the resistance to flow through the leaf was equal to that through the stem and one half to one third that through the root. Cox (1966) compared the conductance for flow through

TABLE V

VALUES OF RESISTANCES TO FLOW THROUGH WHOLE
PLANTS AND THEIR COMPONENTS[a]

Component measured	Resistance (10^2 atm sec cm^{-3})	
	Sunflower	Tomato
Whole plant	14.7	8.9
Stem and roots	9.2	5.1
Stem and leaves	5.5	2.7
Stem only	2.7	1.5

[a] After Jensen *et al.* (1961).

leaves (including petioles) with that through the roots plus stems of sunflower plants by measuring fluxes and potential differences (1) with all leaves present and (2) with one of each pair of opposite leaves removed. He found that the resistance of the leaf was about twice that of the roots plus stem. The total resistance to flow in his plants was 17.6×10^2 atm sec cm^{-3}, a value very similar to that obtained by Jensen *et al.* (1961).

A number of recent experiments have shown that resistance in the plant decreases with increase in the transpiration rate. For instance, Macklon and Weatherley (1965) found, over a threefold variation of transpiration rate, no change in the leaf water potential of *Ricinus* plants with their roots in water culture. There were significant changes in plants with their roots in soil; these were attributed to the resistance to flow in the soil. Cox (1966) obtained decreases in leaf water potential of sunflower with increases of transpiration rate, but the resistance was not constant (Fig. 4). Gardner and

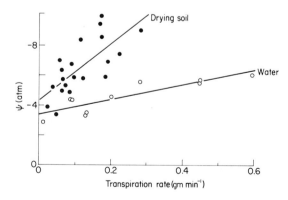

FIG. 4. The relationship between the leaf water potential and the transpiration rate of plants with roots in soil (closed circles) and in water (open circles). After Cox (1966).

colleagues (cf. Slatyer and Gardner, 1965) obtained essentially the same result. It would seem that the leaf water potential is substantial at "zero transpiration." This is difficult to explain, especially as it is also appreciable in leaf discs floated in water. It may reflect inadequacy of the methods used to estimate leaf water potential; nevertheless, it is the common finding of a number of workers using two different types of thermocouple psychrometer and the hanging-drop osmometer (cf. Chapter 8).

2. The Supply System

The extent of the root system of crop plants is very great; systematic quantitative studies of many species have been made by Weaver (1926), Troughton (1957), and many others (Table VI). The depth at which roots grow in the soil can be considerable, annual crops penetrating 150–250 cm wherever physical and chemical conditions are suitable (Kramer, 1949). The numbers and lengths of roots in the soil make it doubtful whether the hydraulic conductivity of the soil, as such, is ever a limiting factor influencing the rates of water uptake. The hydraulic resistance of roots when immersed in an aqueous medium does not appear to be particularly large. Data of Jensen and Taylor (1961) indicate that a 10-atm difference between the potential of water in the medium and that in the stem xylem would support a transpiration rate of 1.09×10^{-2} cm^3 sec^{-1} and 1.96×10^{-2} cm^3 sec^{-1} for small plants of sunflower and tomato, respectively. These are equivalent to a rate of 1 cm evaporation per day from leaf areas of 940 and 1520 cm^2 respectively—both of which exceed liberal estimates of the actual leaf areas.

The roots are frequently regarded as cylindrical absorbing surfaces in a homogeneous medium, the flow pattern in the soil being radially symmetrical

TABLE VI

CHARACTERISTICS OF ROOTS OF VARIOUS CROPS IN UPPER 6 INCHES OF SOIL[a]

	Roots			Root hairs			
Crop	Length per unit volume (cm^{-2})	Surface area per unit volume (cm^{-1})	Mean radius (10^{-2} cm)	Length per unit volume (10^2 cm^{-2})	Mean length of individual hairs (cm)	Surface area per unit volume (cm^{-1})	Mean radius (μ)
Soybeans	4.2	0.59	2.2	0.9	0.01	0.4	7
Oats	6.6	0.46	1.1	11.6	0.13	4.9	7
Rye	9.2	0.72	1.3	24.2	0.13	11.1	7
Bluegrass	55.3	3.06	0.9	74.3	0.10	22.7	5

[a] Data of Dittmer given in Russell (1953).

and conforming to the Darcy relation for unsaturated flow. These are sensible first approximations to make and have led to an improved understanding of plant–soil interrelationships. However, the root is not a cylindrical absorbing surface in the strictly mathematical sense—such would require that it cut through the soil without respect for the solid phase or disturbance of the water films. Supposing that it does, then the surface makes contact with solid, liquid, and gas in the proportions in which these phases exist in the soil as a whole. In particular, the fraction of the surface area in contact with liquid water is the volume concentration of water in the soil, θ. If the conductance to the entry of water per unit length of root is S when the entire root surface is in contact with liquid water, the effective conductance of the root is $S\theta$ and decreases as the soil dries. If S is small but the extent of the root system is great, this conductance is small compared with the hydraulic conductance to flow through the soil. When θ is 0.2, say, the resistance of the whole root system is 5 times as great as if it were completely immersed in water. This picture is an absurd one in several respects. It does emphasize, however, the importance of considering the geometry of both soil and root on a microscale and the nature of the contact between root and water. There is little quantitative information available, and we can only indicate some of the factors involved.

Table VII shows the sizes of some components of the system under consideration. It is evident that even the finest roots and root hairs cannot penetrate freely through the pores of the soil matrix.

TABLE VII

APPROXIMATE MAGNITUDES (cm) OF SOME COMPONENTS
OF THE ROOT–SOIL MATRIX

Radii of roots	Primary	3×10^{-2}
	Secondary	1×10^{-2}
	Tertiary	5×10^{-3}
Length of root hairs		1×10^{-1}
Radius of root hairs		6×10^{-4}
Diameters of soil particles	Sand	$5 \times 10^{-3} - 1 \times 10^{-1}$
	Silt	$5 \times 10^{-4} - 5 \times 10^{-3}$
	Clay	$<5 \times 10^{-4}$
	Colloidal clay	$<2 \times 10^{-4}$
Radii of curvature	-0.1 atm	1.5×10^{-3}
of air–water interfaces	-1 atm	1.5×10^{-4}
at various soil matric	-10 atm	1.5×10^{-5}
potentials		
Depth of electric double layer		1×10^{-6}

Evidence reviewed by Cowan and Milthorpe (1967) suggests that the constraints placed on the growth of roots by the pore structure and by the shear strength in soils are considerable. Possibly, roots will not extend into rigid pores less than 0.2 mm in diameter nor through systems with shear strength greater than 300 gm cm^{-2}; the shear strength of many soils is frequently in excess of this value. More generally, there is evidence that root growth in soils is restricted at bulk densities of the order of 1.3–1.5 gm cm^{-3}. It is likely that many pores in compact soil aggregates cannot be occupied by roots. A realistic model of water flow probably requires that the soil be regarded as an assembly of spheres (of differing radii) in which water flows radially outward toward the roots.

Roots that occupy the larger interstices in a soil may become isolated as the water recedes into the adjacent small pores. Contact between the roots and structurally normal water will be limited since the radii of even the root hairs are large compared with the radii of curvature of the air–water interfaces at matric potentials as high as −1 atm. The mucigel outside the epidermal cells may serve a role in preserving hydraulic continuity (Jenny and Grossenbacher, 1963), and the function of the cortex in transporting water towards the endodermal cells of the root becomes increasingly important. If the conductivity of the cortex is large it may transport water longitudinally as well as radially and thus serve to overcome the effects of limited liquid contact at the root surface. At low matric potentials, and particularly if the roots tend to shrink, substantial areas of the root surface may become isolated from liquid water, and the resistance of those epidermal cell walls that preserve contact will become important. A substantial proportion of the water may move toward the root in the form of vapor. (This observation has little to do with the question of vapor vs. liquid flow in the bulk of the soil when the water potential is near wilting level.)

The possible magnitude of such vapor movement to roots may be calculated. Allowing for the return flow of heat when water distils across a vapor gap, it may be shown that the gradient of the water potential is related to the flux of vapor, E, by

$$\text{grad } \psi = \frac{-RTE}{V} \frac{1}{\chi} \left(\frac{1}{D} + \frac{\varepsilon}{k} \right) \tag{36}$$

where V is the molar volume of liquid water in soil and root, χ is the mean concentration of water vapor in the gap, D and k are the molecular diffusion coefficients in air of water vapor and heat respectively, and ε is the rate of increase of the latent heat content of saturated air with increase of sensible heat content. Taking the temperature to be 20°C, $RT/V = 1.3 \times 10^3$ atm, $\chi = 1.7 \times 10^{-5}$ gm cm^{-3}, $D = 0.26$ cm^2 sec^{-1}, $k = 0.22$ cm^2 sec^{-1}, and $\varepsilon = 2.1$. Then, with grad ψ in atm cm^{-1} and E in gm cm^{-2} sec^{-1}, grad $\psi \approx -E \times 10^9$ numerically. If the gap surrounding the root (of radius r) is cylindrical and of width w, and the rate of water uptake per unit length of root is q, then $\Delta\psi = 1.6 \times 10^8 q \ln(1 + w/r) \approx -1.6 \times 10^8 \ q \ w/r$, if w/r is small. Suppose that transpiration from a crop takes place at the high rate of 1 gm cm^{-2} of soil surface day^{-1} or 1.2×10^{-5} gm cm^{-2} sec^{-1}, that the plant roots extract water to a depth of 20 cm, that there are 7 cm of roots, of radius 1×10^{-2} cm, per cm^3 of soil (see Table VI) and that the difference of water potential between the roots and the soil is 5 atm. Then the width of the air gap, w, is 4×10^{-3} cm. If the transpiration rate were only 0.5 gm cm^{-2} day^{-1}, $w = 1.1 \times 10^{-2}$ cm. In these computations the role of root hairs has been neglected; these will effectively increase the surface area and radius of the roots in the way visualized by Passioura (1963) for ion uptake. It would seem possible that root systems are capable of satisfying a substantial part of the plant's water requirements by absorption of vapor from a root–soil air gap when the width of this gap is of the same order of magnitude as the radius of the root itself. This presents a rather different picture of root–water relations from the models of liquid flow to roots presented by Philip (1957), Gardner (1960), Visser (1964), and Cowan (1965). The difference lies partly in the values assigned to root concentration. Those assumed or measured in numerical applications of the liquid flow model have usually been very much smaller than that taken here. There is a need for more quantitative data concerning root concentrations and diameters than are available at present.

Within the root system, as with the single root, the entry of water into and the movement of water along the xylem vessels must be considered. Equation (29) may be modified as

$$v = k_r \frac{d\psi_x}{dz} \quad \text{and} \quad \frac{dv}{dz} = -h(\psi_s - \psi_x) \tag{37}$$

where v is the upward flow of water, per unit area of soil surface, in the roots at depth z in the soil. The coefficients in this equation are related to those of Eq. (29) by $k_r = lt^2L$ and $h = lS$, where l is the length of root per unit volume of soil and t is a root tortuosity factor, being the mean cosine of the angles made between roots and the vertical. The approximations inherent in these relations are the common ones in plant and soil science of dealing with functions of averages rather than averages of functions. Observations made by Wind (1955) indicate that k_r decreased with depth under a sward of *Lolium perenne*, being roughly proportional to the concentration of main roots in the upper soil. k_r was estimated to be 2×10^{-3} cm^2 sec^{-1} atm^{-1} near the surface with 30 primary roots per square centimeter soil surface, each root having xylem of equivalent hydraulic radius of approximately 12μ. Measurements made by Cox (1966) on a young wheat root system immersed in water showed a similar pattern. However, h appeared to remain relatively constant with depth in spite of the decreasing number of roots—due, presumably, to an increasing permeability with distance along the individual roots. Estimated values of h/k_r in the upper parts of root systems were approximately 10^{-3}–10^{-2} cm^{-2}, there being large differences between different root systems of similar size and age. The conductances of the root systems were primarily determined by the values of h; therefore, it seems likely that the second part of Eq. (37), with ψ_x being taken as constant, may be used to describe the uptake of water from soil.

The application of the second part of Eq. (37) would be simple if the changing root–liquid contact and hydraulic conductivity in drying soils could be neglected. In practice, it needs to be modified so that h is defined as the conductance to the flow of water from the soil in bulk between the roots where the potential is ψ_s; h then decreases with decreasing concentration of roots. In moist soils, for example, extraction of water usually takes place most rapidly from the upper parts of the root zone. As the water content of the soil in these regions is diminished, the water potential, hydraulic conductivity, and root–water contact decrease, and the region of maximum rate of water uptake moves progressively downward. Gardner (1964) attempted to analyze this process making the assumption that the root conductance is large compared with the conductance in the soil, and thus h is proportional to the concentration of roots and the hydraulic conductivity of the soil. The analysis was tested against the measured patterns of water extraction by sorghum roots in a cylinder of soil (Fig. 5). (The water extraction was determined using tensiometers and resistance blocks.) The initial pattern of water extraction when the soil was wet was taken to reflect the distribution of roots in the cylinder. Subsequent rates of water extraction were predicted, using the estimated root distribution together with a knowledge of the hydraulic

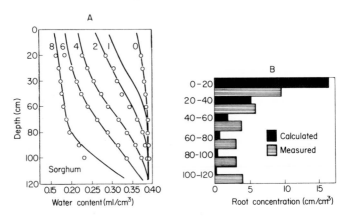

FIG. 5. The relationships between (A) soil–water content and depth and (B) root concentration and depth during the drying cycle. The curves 0–8 represent the respective numbers of days after wetting. The circles indicate experimental data, and the curves were calculated from theory. In B the black histograms represent calculations from theory, and the white actual measurements. After Gardner (1964).

characteristics of the soil. They agree satisfactorily with the actual rates of extraction; however, subsequent measurement of the number of roots in the cylinder did not agree very well with the estimated pattern. It is probable that the discrepancy resulted, in part, from neglect of cortex resistance and resistance along the xylem elements of the longer roots in the cylinder.

Some aspects of crop responses in relation to the supply system can be examined using a simplified model of flow through the soil, plant, and atmosphere in series (Philip, 1957; Gardner, 1960; Cowan, 1965). Assuming that the concentration of roots and rates of water extraction are substantially uniform throughout the depth of the root zone and that there is quasi-steady state flow, the second part of Eq. (37) may be integrated through the depth of the root zone to yield the total rate of transpiration from the crop. Some computations based on such a model are illustrated in Fig. 6. It is assumed that the stomata are fully open during the daylight hours, provided the plant water potential ψ is less than a critical value, ψ_w, (taken to be -15 atm) and that transpiration is then determined by climatic factors. If $\psi = \psi_w$, however, the stomata close to the extent necessary to prevent further decrease of water potential and transpiration is controlled by soil and plant factors. These assumptions are an approximate description, only, of stomatal behavior—as will be evident from later discussion. Other model characteristics requiring specification involve the hydraulic properties of the soil, depth of penetration and concentration of roots in the soil, the internal resistance of the crop to water flow, and the rate of transpiration from the crop if stomata are fully open. During the sequence of four days illustrated in Fig. 6, the rate of

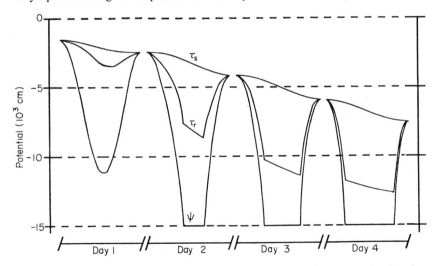

FIG. 6. Soil water potential and leaf water potential during four successive days in a drying cycle. τ_s and τ_r are the average soil water potential in the root zone and at the root surfaces, respectively; ψ is the potential of water in the leaves. After Cowan (1965).

transpiration falls below the potential rate for periods of the day that succes-
sively increase in length as the soil becomes drier. Initially, the major part of
the potential difference in the system is located in the plant, but later it is in the
soil surrounding the roots. The decrease of daily transpiration with time for
this model is illustrated by curve 2 in Fig. 7. The other curves represent the
same phenomenon with different assumed concentrations of roots. If the

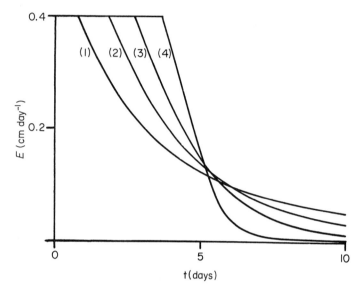

FIG. 7. Decrease of daily transpiration (E) with time (t) for crop having different
densities of rooting. Curves 1–3 are for root densities of 0.125, 0.25, and 0.5 cm root per
cm³ soil and curve 4 is for very dense rooting. After Cowan (1965).

root system is sparse, a water deficit develops in the leaves, the rate of transpiration falls, and water is conserved while soil water potential is still high.
Eventually, however, soil water content and mean rate of transpiration are
greater than in crops having greater concentrations of roots. In the latter, the
rate of transpiration falls later but more rapidly.

III. LOSS OF WATER FROM LEAVES (VAPOR PHASE)

A. Individual Leaves

As described by Penman (1956), Monteith (1965), and others (cf. Chapter
4), the rate of transpiration from a leaf, E(gm cm^{-2} sec^{-1}), may be expressed
by

$$E = \frac{\varepsilon H/\lambda + \rho[q'(T) - q]/r_a}{\varepsilon + 1 + r_l/r_a} \tag{38}$$

where ε is the increase of latent heat content with increase of sensible heat content of saturated air at the temperature of the ambient air T, H (cal cm^{-2} sec^{-1}) is the net rate of absorption of radiant heat by the leaf, λ (cal gm^{-1}) is the latent heat of vaporization of water, ρ(gm cm^{-3}) is the density of air, $q'(T)$ and q are the saturation and actual specific humidities respectively of the ambient air, and r_a and r_l (sec cm^{-1}) are external and internal diffusive resistances respectively.* That is, r_a is the time required for unit volume of air to exchange heat or water vapor with unit area of the aerodynamic surface and r_l may be regarded as the time required for unit volume of water vapor to diffuse from the evaporating surface to unit area of the aerodynamic surface. As these two resistances are the only plant parameters involved, the discussion here is confined to these. The weather components are discussed in Chapter 4. It is assumed in deriving Eq. (38) that the vapor pressure of the evaporating surface is effectively that of free water at the same temperature and that the temperature of the evaporating surface is the same as that of the leaf surface.

1. The External Resistance (r_a)

The external resistance depends partly on the speed of the air stream and partly on the geometry of the surface. It is best determined empirically for leaves of any given size and shape by measuring the water loss from wet surfaces (such as wet blotting paper) of the same dimensions with the same external conditions. Then,

$$r_a = \frac{\rho(q_0' - q)}{E} \tag{39}$$

where q_0' is the specific humidity of saturated air at the mean temperature of the surface.

For a plane surface parallel to a smoothly flowing stream of air, the mean resistance is

$$r_a = c(b/u)^{1/2} D^{-2/3} v^{1/6} = r_1(b/u)^{1/2} \tag{40}$$

say, where c is a constant for surfaces of a given shape, b is a characteristic dimension of the surface, u is the wind speed, D is the diffusion coefficient of water

$$*\varepsilon = \frac{M_w}{M_a}\frac{\lambda}{CP}\frac{de'}{dT} = \frac{1}{\gamma}\frac{de'}{dT} \approx 1.515\frac{\Delta e'}{\Delta T}$$

where M_w and M_a are the molecular weights of water and air respectively, λ the latent heat of vaporization of water, C the specific heat of air, P the atmospheric pressure, e' the saturation vapor pressure (mbar), γ the psychrometric constant and T (°C) the temperature, and $\Delta e'/\Delta T$ is obtained from tables of saturation vapor pressure in relation to temperature. The specific humidity q (the mass of water vapor per mass of moist air) is most readily obtained as $M_w e/(M_a P)$ or $6.22 \times 10^{-4}e$ where e is the vapor pressure.

vapor in air, and v is the kinematic viscosity of air. For an elliptical surface with b (cm) as the length of the axis downwind, $c = 1.4$; with $D = 0.26$ cm^2 sec^{-1} and $v = 0.15$ cm^2 sec^{-1}, the arbitrarily defined component r_1 equals 2.5 sec$^{1/2}$ cm^{-1}. The resistance to evaporation from a broad surface at a finite angle to the wind direction does not differ greatly from that for a similar surface parallel to the wind. Therefore, Eq. (40) may be applied to give the approximate mean resistance for leaves of random orientation. Taking the mean value of b to be $(4A/\pi)^{1/2}$, where A(cm^2) is the area of each leaf, numerically,

$$r_a \approx 2.6A^{0.25}/u^{0.5} \tag{41}$$

Equation (40) gives the resistance to transfer of sensible heat also, provided D is replaced by k, the thermal diffusivity of air. Since $D/k = 1.19$, resistances to transfer of heat are 12% greater than those to transfer of vapor.

The complications that may occur with real leaves in outdoor conditions —resulting from atmospheric turbulence, leaf flutter, and the like—are not well understood. Monteith (1965) has reviewed existing data and suggests, for both heat and vapor, that Eq. (40) with $r_1 \approx 1.3$ sec$^{1/2}$ cm^{-1} is most representative of leaves in open air, b being the diameter of broad leaves or the breadth of narrow leaves. This value is about one half that found for artificial surfaces in wind tunnels. With slow wind speeds, free convection may take place and r_a becomes a function of the temperature and humidity differences between the evaporating surface and the air (Gates, 1967). In all situations, r_a is a significant component and must always be taken into account. Its neglect, for example, has led to much erroneous thought concerning stomata (cf. p. 174). It is clear from Eqs. (38) and (41) that the transpiration rate *per unit area* will be less from large than from small leaves and at low than at high wind speeds, all else being equal.

2. The Internal Resistances of the Leaf (r_l)

The internal resistances of the leaf comprise the complex represented in Fig. 8. That is, on each of the two surfaces of the leaf, the cuticular and stomatal pathways are parallel; therefore, the total internal leaf resistance, r_l, is given by

$$\frac{1}{r_l} = \frac{1}{r_c} + \frac{1}{r_s + r_i + r_w} \tag{42}$$

where r_c, r_s, r_i, and r_w are the resistances to diffusion of vapor through the cuticle, stomata, substomatal cavities, and cell walls, respectively (Milthorpe, 1961a). Each is expressed per unit area of leaf surface and may be represented by l_e/AD, where l_e is the effective length of the diffusion path, A is the cross-

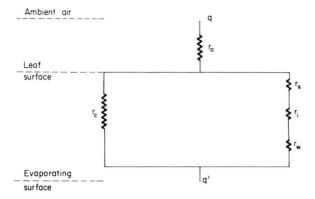

Fig. 8. Arrangement of resistances in the path of water vapor diffusing from the leaf. After Milthorpe (1961a).

sectional area, and D is a diffusion coefficient depending on the molecular species and pore dimensions.

a. The Cell-Wall Resistance (r_w). Since the days of Livingston and Brown (1912), the significance of the influence of the cell wall on transpiration has been controversial. It is now well established that the liquid evaporating surface is contained within the cell wall, which is covered with a thin, waxy layer (Scott, 1950). Electron photomicrographs show a continuous layer of waxy material extending around the guard cells, into the substomatal cavity, and on all walls bordering intercellular spaces. The thickness of the layer over the cell walls of the substomatal cavity is much less than that on the guard cells; in the wheat leaf it is about 0.06 μ. Inside this layer the cell wall contains further areas of osmiophilic substances. It seems likely that the liquid water is contained in pore spaces between the cellulose microfibrils, the water surface being where hydrophilic and hydrophobic wall surfaces meet and having a vapor pressure almost equal to that of free water at the same temperature. With high rates of transpiration, some of the larger pores would be expected to be emptied, causing an increase in the length of pathway for vapor diffusion. Exposure to air could allow waxy deposits to be formed, and so the size of this resistance could well increase during the age of the leaf and with the intensity of the transpiration to which it is subjected.

In unpublished experiments, the transpiration rates were determined from the mesophyll surfaces of *Antirrhinum* leaves from which the epidermis had been removed (E_1) and after the stripped surface had been washed with a detergent and several changes of water (E_2). Then,

$$r_w = \frac{\rho(q_1' - q_1)}{E_1} - \frac{\rho(q_2' - q_2)}{E_2} \qquad (43)$$

Values of 0.22 sec cm^{-1} were found; in these experiments the total internal resistance of intact leaves was 3.8 sec cm^{-1}, and the external resistance was of a similar value. Klemm (1956) carried out similar experiments with leaves of *Sedum* (and other species) in a constant humidity chamber. Temperatures of the evaporating surface were not measured. Assuming isothermal conditions, his experiments indicate that r_a was about 2.3 sec cm^{-1} and that r_w was 1.66 sec cm^{-1} when the leaf was turgid and twice this value after the loss of 25–30% of the leaf water. The change during drying was reversed on reabsorption of water.

Meidner (1965), Gregory *et al.* (1950), and Milthorpe and Spencer (1957) have all shown small changes in transpiration rates without measured changes in stomatal resistance to diffusion (cf. Fig. 12). Although it is not certain in these experiments that differences in the vapor pressure gradient may not have been responsible, they provide further indirect evidence that the walls may present a variable resistance to vapor diffusion. In the mesophytes studied the value of this resistance appears to be small; however, it is conceivable that this resistance may be appreciable in xerophytes with thick walls and possibly a thick, waxy internal layer. [The high values for $r_s + r_i + r_w$ obtained for xerophytes from diffusion measurements (Table VIII) possibly reflect a high value of r_w.]

b. *The Resistance of the Substomatal Cavities* (r_i). Representing the long and short axes of a stomatal pore by a and b respectively (Fig. 9), where $a \gg b$ as in wheat, the substomatal cavity may be regarded as consisting of two coaxial half-cylinders of length a, one of area A_1 and radius $b/2$ and the other of area A_2 and radius $L + b/2$, where L is the mean distance from the stoma to the mesophyll (Heath and Russell, 1954). The mean surface area for diffusion, A, is $(A_2 - A_1)/\ln (A_2/A_1)$. In wheat, $a = 33$, $b = 2$, $L = 30\mu$; the number of stomata on the lower surface $N_1 = 3100$ and on the upper $N_2 = 3900$ and the diffusion coefficient for water vapor $D_0 = 0.26$ cm^2 sec^{-1} at 25°C. Then, r_i of the lower surface is given by $L/(AD_0N_1) = 0.22$ sec cm^{-1} and r_i of the upper surface $= 0.17$ sec cm^{-1}.

The assumed shape of the substomatal cavity should approximate as closely as possible the actual shape for the species being considered. Bange (1953) observed that the cavity in *Zebrina* more closely approximated a sphere; he obtained a value of 0.4 sec cm^{-1} for the stomatal surface of this hypostomatous leaf but also included the lower part of the stomatal pore in his calculation. This value is, therefore, an overestimate.

c. *Stomatal Resistance to Diffusion* (r_s). The stomata provide a variable resistance in the pathway of flow and are the most effective means at the plant's disposal for controlling the rate of water loss. Because they are one of the two most important plant parameters influencing the water status of tissue and because much of what has been written about their role in diffusion is misguided, a reasonably comprehensive treatment is attempted.

   i. Diffusive flow through stomata. The formal equation for diffusive flow is $f = DA\rho \, dq/dl$, where f(gm sec^{-1}) is the rate of flow, D(cm^2 sec^{-1}) is the appropriate diffusion coefficient, A (cm^2) is the cross-sectional area of the path, ρ (gm cm^{-3}) is the density of the atmosphere, and dq/dl (cm^{-1}) is the gradient of specific concentration (mass fraction) over the length l (cm) of path. For one stoma,

$$\frac{\rho \, \Delta q}{f} = \int_0^l \frac{dl}{AD} = r_D \qquad (44)$$

where r_D (sec cm^{-3}) is the resistance to diffusion.

   The shape of the cross section of the stomatal pore and the dimensions along its length vary greatly between species (Copeland, 1902; Haberlandt, 1914). In many mesophytic dicotyledons, the pores are elliptical in cross section with a narrow throat of area $\pi a_t b_t/4$ flaring approximately symmetrically and exponentially to the mouth of area $\pi a_0 b_0/4$ (Fig. 9). In most Gramineae the longitudinal section of the pore is similar but the cross section approximates to a rectangle. Milthorpe and Penman (1967) have given a detailed treatment for wheat. In this (as in all other) species, there is no precise information on $b_0 = f(b_t)$ and $a_0 = f(a_t)$ over the range of apertures from closed to fully open; it was assumed that, over the entire range of b_t, $b_0 = b_t + 1\mu$ with an exponential section and that a shortened partially as b_t decreased. It is convenient for computation to use the *mean* hydraulic radius, h, that is,

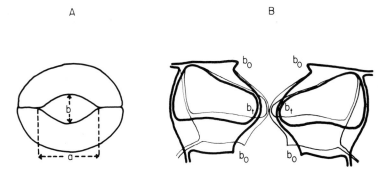

FIG. 9. *A*: Diagrammatic surface view of elliptical stoma defining dimensions denoted by a and b. *B*: Section of stoma of *Helleborus* sp. in the open (thick lines) and closed (thin lines) conditions. From an original diagram of Schwendener, reproduced in Haberlandt (1914).

the ratio of the sectional area to perimeter. In the rectangular pores of wheat where $a \gg b$, the mean hydraulic radius is given by

$$h = \frac{b_0 b_t}{2(b_0 - b_t)} \ln \frac{b_0}{b_t} \tag{45}$$

Then, resistance to diffusion through the pore is given by $l/(2ahD)$ to which an end correction must be added—Eq. (47).

The diffusion coefficient, D, varies from that appropriate to diffusion in free air, D_0, at wide apertures to that appropriate for narrow channels, D_1, when almost closed. The effective coefficient is given by $1/D = 1/D_0 + 1/D_1$ (Carman, 1956), where D_0 at 25°C is 0.26 cm^2 sec^{-1} for water vapor and 0.17 cm^2 sec^{-1} for carbon dioxide and

$$D_1 = \frac{8}{3} h \frac{\delta}{k_1} \left(\frac{2RT}{M}\right)^{1/2} \tag{46}$$

There is little experience to guide the choice of correct values for δ and k_1. Probably, δ can be taken as 0.6 for pores of all shapes and dimensions and k_1 can be calculated from the details given in Eq. 3.18 and Table XV of Carman (1956); k_1 will vary with h. Allowing for appropriate end corrections, detailed in Milthorpe and Penman (1967), an approximate relation is given by

$$r_D = \frac{l}{2ahD} + \frac{2.5}{D_0 a\pi} \ln \frac{1.6 \times 10^{-4}}{b_0} \tag{47}$$

$$= Nr_s$$

where r_s (sec cm^{-1}) is the stomatal resistance with N pores per square centimeter of leaf surface.

It is clear that r_D and r_s are not simple functions of any pore dimension, although relationships can be derived from a knowledge of the geometry of the pore. The significance of some of these components in diffusion through wheat stomata is illustrated in Fig. 10. In particular, attention may be drawn to the diffusion coefficient that varies from about two thirds to nine tenths of the free diffusion coefficient over the effective range of resistances normally found (say, 60 to 1.4 sec cm^{-1}). Generally, in previous analyses, it has been assumed that the walls do not interfere with diffusion but the above treatment, based on experience of diffusion through inert materials, shows that it is a significant factor. It will also be noted in Fig. 10 that the end correction at the widest apertures is greater than the quantity being corrected.

The treatment applied by Milthorpe and Penman (1967) to the rectangular pores of wheat can be extended to elliptical pores. Unless the geometry of the population of pores is known with precision, a sophisticated treatment is not warranted. For most purposes, an approximate analysis incorporating

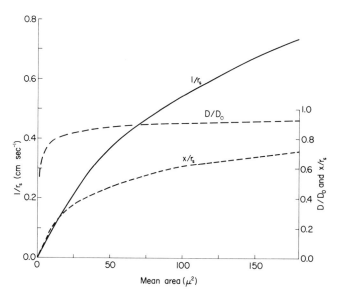

FIG. 10. Relationship between diffusive conductance of stomata ($1/r_s$) per cm^2 of lower surface of a wheat leaf and the mean cross-sectional area of the pore together with the diffusion coefficient for water vapor as a fraction of that in free air (D/D_0) and the proportion of the total resistance contributed by the end correction (x/r_s).

the main features stated above and by Penman and Schofield (1951) suffices. With pores of the shape shown in Fig. 9, the radii at the throat and mouth may be taken as the geometric means of the respective axes, that is, $r_t = (a_t b_t)^{1/2}/2$ and $r_0 = (a_0 b_0)^{1/2}/2$, and the mean hydraulic radius h is given by $r_0 r_t \ln (r_0/r_t)/[2(r_0 - r_t)]$. Then,

$$r_s = \frac{1}{N} \left\{ \frac{l}{4h^2 D} + \frac{1}{4hD_0} \right\} \tag{48}$$

With pores varying along their lengths in a more complex manner, it may be necessary to treat sections of the pore separately—analogous to the procedure followed by Bange (1953) but with appropriate "effective" diffusion coefficients and end corrections.

ii. Some remarks concerning diffusion through stomata. Arising from misplaced emphasis in interpretation of some experiments first carried out by Brown and Escombe (1900) and inadequate appreciation of the significance of pore dimensions in diffusion, several distortions have become entrenched in the standard texts. For example, it often is stated that "the quantities of water-vapor diffusing through small openings in a given period of time (per unit concentration gradient) are proportional to the perimeters and not to the areas of the pores" and that "the diffusion per pore increases with increase in distance apart of the apertures, although not proportionally" (for example, Meyer and Anderson, 1952). The so-called "perimeter law" arose from neglect of the external resistance; inadequate agreement of experimental data with this "law" led to the elaboration of the vague and equivocal concepts of "interference" between adjacent pores. In turn, the wider application of both misconceptions resulted in general confusion.

Although the importance of the external resistance to the bulk diffusion of vapor away from the surface as a whole has been pointed out by various workers over the years, repetition of the experiments—including the misinterpretations—has led equally to the perpetuation of the misunderstandings and extension from them to absurd conclusions. Brown and Escombe, Sayre, and others in carrying out these experiments with artificial uniperforate or multiperforate septa considered flux/concentration difference solely in relation to pore dimensions. In addition to flow to and from the septum as a whole, the gas has to diffuse up to the entry of and through each tube and away from its outlet; the flow rate will correspond to that through a tube of the same cross-sectional area but having a length greater than its measured length. This "end correction" is approximately equal to $2\pi r/4$ with circular tubes (also see above) and was recognized by Brown and Escombe. As Penman and Schofield (1951) indicated, however [cf. Eqs. (38) and (42) above], after allowing for the external resistance, estimates of stomatal resistance as $(l + \pi r/2)/(NDA)$ were close to those observed. Recently, Lee and Gates (1964) and Ting and Loomis (1965) pointed out that as l is constant, if $l \gg r$, then the resistance approximates to l/NAD, whereas if $l < r$, l/A is small relative to $\pi r/2$. With all the artificial septa used, l has been much smaller than r; therefore, the "perimeter" relation is favored. With stomata, however, l is usually greater than r; therefore, the "area" relation is favored. (Nevertheless, the end correction is substantial at wide apertures; cf. Fig. 9).

Discussions such as the foregoing serve useful pedogogic purposes but are somewhat remote from the real world of the stomata, which are never right-cylindrical tubes and which approach dimensions in which slip flow is significant. They also divert attention from the real problems concerned with diffusion through complex geometrical shapes. It is clear that diffusion to and from the surfaces within a leaf cannot be expressed simply in terms of one dimension of the stomata: All components of the system must be considered and the stomatal component alone is related to pore dimensions by the complex relation expressed in Eqs. (47) and (48).

    iii. Measurement of diffusive resistance. Although the above analysis expresses stomatal resistance to diffusion in terms of pore geometry, there is considerable doubt, arising mainly from imperfect knowledge of that geometry, of the exact values to use for some of the parameters. Moreover, the dimensions of the pores on any one leaf vary greatly and the light microscope does not permit measurements of dimensions less than about 0.2 μ. From direct measurements of the pores, therefore, even the most diligent worker cannot determine values of stomatal resistance larger than about 10 sec cm^{-1}; estimates of values smaller than these also contain many uncertainties.

More precise estimates are possible if a viscous-flow porometer is used (cf. Chapter 8 and Heath, 1959). The relationship between the resistance to viscous flow and pore dimensions can be derived in a manner analogous to that for diffusive flow given above (Milthorpe and Penman, 1967). By appropriate separation of the components of flow directly attributable to the stomata (Penman, 1942), resistances to viscous flow can be measured and converted to resistances to diffusion, using the derived relationships. Errors arising from uncertain geometry or " slip " factors are then very much reduced as both curves are displaced in the same direction, although not exactly to the same degree. For example, the assumption that all pores are of the same width at any instant—rather than having a log-normal distribution with a standard deviation of ~ 0.10 about the mean—only produces a tiny displacement of the calibration curve. It is essential, however, when using either viscous-flow or diffusive-flow porometers to separate out those parts of the flow arising from components other than the stomata. Most of the viscous-flow porometers in current use allow estimates of resistances up to about 80–100 sec cm^{-1}.

iv. Values of minimum stomatal resistance. Values of stomatal resistance in different species have been measured by porometry, calculated directly from pore dimensions, or estimated from concentration gradient/flux measurements (Table VIII). Those obtained from pore measurements will be generally about 10% too low because the free diffusion coefficient has been assumed; however this is negligible relative to other sources of variation. With those values obtained from flux measurements, allowance has been made for the external resistance to diffusion, but the contributions arising from the cell wall, substomatal cavities, and cuticle are also included. It will be seen that generally the conifers have higher minimum values than mesophytes and that the resistance generally is very high in xerophytes (possibly because of a high cell-wall resistance).

v. Factors influencing stomatal resistance. Stomatal movements result from turgor changes in the guard cells, these changes being due to unknown metabolic reactions (Heath, 1959; Meidner and Mansfield, 1965; Zelitch, 1965); there may also be direct effects associated with the water supply. Two broad groups of plants may be recognized according to the diurnal course of stomatal movement (Fig. 11): (1) the succulents whose stomata are closed during most of the day and (2) the nonsucculents whose stomata are open for most of the day. In the nonsucculents the stomata open in response to an

TABLE VIII

MINIMUM VALUES OF STOMATAL RESISTANCE[a]

Species	r_s (sec cm^{-1})	Species	$r_s + r_i + r_w$ (sec cm^{-1})
Mesophytes		Mesophytes	
Beta vulgaris	0.5	*Alocasia* sp.	2.4
Solanum tuberosum	0.9	*Brassica* sp.	1.6
Triticum aestivum	3.0	*Gossypium hirsutum*	1.8
Helianthus annuus	0.7	*Hyoscyamus niger*	4.8
Medicago sativa	0.8	*Lycopersicon esculentum*	4.8
Pinus resinosa	2.3	*Phaseolus vulgaris*	4.8
Zebrina pendula	1.0	Xerophytes	
		Atriplex sp.	24
		Haloxylon articulatum	26
		Kochia indica	8
		Pinus halepensis	17
		Reaumuria hirtella	14
		Zygophyllum dumosum	8

[a] The first three values only of r_s were obtained from viscous-flow measurements and the remainder were calculated from pore dimensions; the entries under $r_s + r_i + r_w$ were obtained from flux measurements. Table modified from Altman and Dittmer (1966).

increase in light supply and a decrease of CO_2 concentration in the substomatal cavity. Although the quantitative changes at high light intensities are not well documented, it would seem that the form and position of the curve relating stomatal conductance to light intensity is somewhat similar to that relating rate of photosynthesis to light intensity. Changes in temperature may have two opposing effects: one, associated with increase in the CO_2 concentration within the leaf, causes closure at high temperatures and the

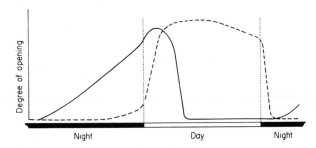

FIG. 11. Diagram indicating the diurnal course of stomatal movement in a succulent (continuous line) and normal nonsucculent plant (broken line). After Meidner and Mansfield (1965).

other, acting independently of the response to CO_2, produces greater opening at high temperatures. Detailed considerations of these responses are outside the context of this chapter; however, two other factors—the effects of age and of water supply—are relevant.

Generally, the reponses associated with the age of the leaf are not well documented; these represent a sequence of changes in the metabolic complex within the guard cells and possibly also in the efficiency of the mesophyll cells to reduce the CO_2 concentration in the substomatal cavities. However, the available evidence suggests that the stomata on very young leaves close tightly in the dark and open slowly and to a limited extent in the light; those on mature leaves are most responsive, closing tightly in darkness and opening rapidly and widely during the light phase of a diurnal cycle; and those on old leaves are very sluggish, neither closing greatly in the dark nor opening widely in the light. These changes can influence the water loss from isolated plants but have much less significance in plant stands, where the redistribution of sensible heat is such that effectively smaller loss from one leaf layer is compensated by greater loss from another (Section III,B, and Chapter 4). There is a sequence of changes associated with flowering, however, that may have important consequences. For example, in an experiment made by Krizek and Milthorpe, two groups of decapitated, debudded plants of *Xanthium* were kept under constant conditions of radiation, temperature, and ventilation: one group was exposed to short days to initiate the flower-induction reactions while the other was kept in the nonflowering state by supplying a light-break during the dark period. The leaf areas of each group were similar throughout the experimental period. Large differences in stomatal behavior and associated changes in transpiration rate were found. These changes were in the direction of a decreased stomatal resistance to diffusion soon after "flower initiation," quickly followed by a very large increase in resistance; they probably reflect internal changes in guard-cell metabolism. Fritschen and van Bavel (1964) have obtained similar responses from sudan grass in the field.

The stomatal changes associated with water supply are important, the stomata providing the only effective means for the control of water loss when the water supply to a leaf is restricted. The partial closure of stomata accompanying a water deficit in the leaf appears to involve two mechanisms: one concerns purely passive changes in turgor of the guard cells and the other involves an active metabolic reaction associated with increases in the intercellular CO_2 concentration (Heath and Meidner, 1961) and possibly reflects direct effects of water shortage on the photosynthetic reactions. The direction of movement following passive changes depends on the rate of change of the leaf water content (Stålfelt, 1955; Milthorpe and Spencer, 1957; Meidner, 1965). If a leaf is suddenly deprived of its water supply, the first response is a transient opening of the stomata, and this is soon followed by gradual closure (Fig. 12); if the water supply is restored, the stomata close further while the leaf water content is increasing, but they slowly reopen after the leaf regains full turgor. These effects appear to arise because water moves from the veins to the epidermal cells directly above and thence via a number of epidermal cells to the guard cells. Interruption of the water supply leads first to a rapid loss of turgor of the epidermal cells before much change in the guard cells, but later the turgor of the guard cells also decreases; restoration of the supply leads to reverse changes. The transient opening appears to occur only when

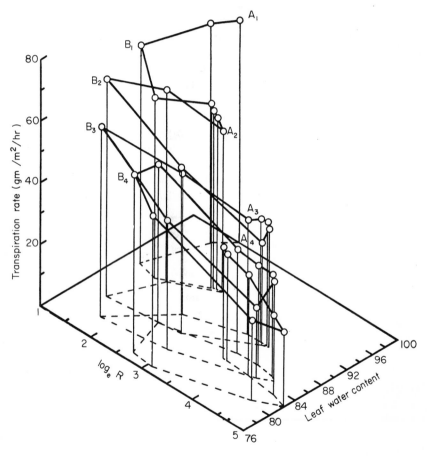

FIG. 12. Diagram of a three-dimensional model showing the relationships between transpiration rate, logarithms of resistance of stomata to viscous flow (log$_e$ R), and relative leaf water content of a wheat leaf during four successive cycles of wilting and recovery. Water supply removed after the periods marked *A* and restored after the periods marked *B*; each point represents an 8-minute period. After Milthorpe and Spencer (1957).

the leaf water content decreases rapidly, as with sudden interruption of the water supply. With normal plants in soil during a drying cycle, the stomata respond by closing earlier each day as the soil becomes drier and perhaps finally fail to open during the light phase. There are also situations when the plant is unable to maintain its leaf water content throughout the whole diurnal cycle; midday closure of the stomata is then observed (Begg et al., 1964). Changes in the intercellular CO_2 content may also be concerned in midday closure (Meidner and Mansfield, 1965).

Changes in relative transpiration rates of plants of the same size in the same environment are also a function of changes in stomatal resistance, but not a direct function because of associated changes in the heat balance— H and T in Eq. (38). Data of this nature have been obtained by Ehlig and Gardner (1964) for four species in drying soil and with high potential transpiration rates. No unique relation was found between transpiration rate and leaf water potential, the stomata commencing to close at leaf water potentials between -5 and -12 atm, depending on species, and reaching constant closed values at -10 to -20 atm, then giving transpiration rates equivalent to about 20% of the potential rate. The data of Denmead and Shaw (1962) and others relating transpiration rates to potential transpiration and soil water also essentially reflect changes in stomatal resistance.

Short-term cyclic changes in the transpiration rate, that is, periodic fluctuations with a phase of 20–40 minutes, have been detected in laboratory experiments. These may arise following a sudden change in the evaporation potential of the atmosphere as found by Ehrler et al. (1965) or even spontaneously under constant conditions as found by Cox (1966). These changes are accompanied by changes in leaf temperature and in stomatal resistance and possibly are initiated by an inadequate supply of water to the epidermal and guard cells. The resulting partial closure reduces transpiration and allows an adequate supply to be restored and the stomata to reopen to the original extent only to result in a repetition of the sequence.

Considerable interest has been shown recently in substances that induce partial stomatal closure, thereby reducing transpiration without greatly interfering with photosynthesis. This is possible because in photosynthesis there is a resistance in addition to those enumerated in Eq. (42)—the resistance to diffusion of CO_2 in the liquid phase between the cell wall and the chloroplast. This so-called mesophyll resistance is of the order of 2 to 10 sec cm^{-1} (Gaastra, 1963). Waggoner and Zelitch (1965), Waggoner and Hewlett (1965), Zelitch (1965), and Monteith et al. (1965) reviewed current progress in the search for inhibitors of stomatal opening. The most successful found to date are phenylmercuric acetate and the monoethyl and monoglyceryl esters of decenylsuccinic acid. Use of these has reduced the transpiration rates of isolated plants and of barley in the field by 15–30% but has not significantly influenced the stream flow of a watershed when applied to the upper surfaces of a community consisting of oaks, hickory, and other species. Because these substances appear not to be translocated, this result may simply represent failure of the chemical to reach the stomata (but see p. 183).

d. Cuticular Resistance to Diffusion (r_c). The cuticular resistance can only readily be measured for a surface that has no stomata. It is given by

$$r_c = \frac{\rho(q_c' - q_c)}{E_c} - \frac{\rho(q_0' - q_0)}{E_0} \tag{49}$$

where the subscripts c and 0 refer respectively to determinations made from the surface of a leaf without stomata and from a wet surface of the same shape in the same environment. The usual procedure of taking the transpiration rate from a nonstomatal surface as "cuticular transpiration" and sub-. tracting this value from the rate from a stomatal surface is, of course, inexact because no account is taken of the external resistance. If the cuticular conductance is the same for both surfaces of a leaf with stomata present on the lower surface only, then the "stomatal" transpiration is $\{r_c/(r_c + r_s)\}E_L$ and is given by $E_L - [E_U(E_0 - E_L)/(E_0 - E_U)]$, where E_L, E_U, and E_0 are the evaporation rates per unit vapor pressure difference from the lower surface, the upper surface, and a free water surface respectively (Milthorpe, 1961a). However, there is no point in separating "cuticular" from "stomatal" transpiration; *account must always be taken of all resistances in the pathway.*

It is difficult to measure independently the cuticular conductance of a surface that also possesses stomata, as it is impossible to ensure that the stomata are ever completely closed. Possibly, the most satisfactory estimate is given by determining the transpiration rate per unit vapor pressure difference over a range of measured stomatal conductances and extrapolating the curve to zero stomatal conductance. Values of r_c of stomatal surfaces are therefore always approximate.

The measured values of r_c are about 50 sec cm^{-1} for mesophytes and are very much higher for some xerophytes (Table IX). In other words, the cuticular resistance is 30–50 times the minimum stomatal resistance and usually about 100 times the external resistance. Near or full closure of the stomata therefore leads to a very substantial reduction in the transpiration rate.

e. Ranges of Leaf Resistance to Diffusion. The limited information presented above indicates minimum values of $r_s + r_i + r_w$ of 1–5 sec cm^{-1} with mesophytes and 8–20 sec cm^{-1} with xerophytes. The values quoted for xerophytes may be greater than possible minimum values as they were obtained from plants growing in the field. They conflict with the early findings of Maximov (1929) that transpiration is as high from xerophytes as mesophytes when

TABLE IX

MEASURED VALUES OF CUTICULAR RESISTANCE[a]

Mesophytes		Xerophytes	
Species	r_c (sec cm^{-1})	Species	r_c (sec cm^{-1})
Alocasia sp.	60	Atriplex spp.	160
Gossypium hirsutum	60	Haloxylon articulatum	400
Helianthus annuus	43	Kochia indica	44
Lycopersicon esculentum	19	Pinus halepensis	140
Phaseolus vulgaris	19	Reaumuria hirtella	48
		Zygophyllum dumosum	96

[a] After Altman and Dittmer (1966).

grown under laboratory conditions and plentifully supplied with water. (However, the external resistance of his xerophytes may have been less than of his mesophytes.) Estimates of cuticular resistance suggest values of the order of 20–50 sec cm^{-1} for mesophytes and, say, 50–400 sec cm^{-1} for xerophytes. The leaf resistance, as defined by Eq. (42), then may be expected to vary over the range of 1–50 sec cm^{-1} in mesophytes and, say, 10–400 sec cm^{-1} in xerophytes. These are values that are one and two orders of magnitude greater than those of the external resistance at wind speeds normally found in the field.

The transpiration from a leaf is the sum of the transpiration from the upper and lower surfaces: each surface has the same external resistance varying with the wind speed, but the leaf resistances vary with the respective stomatal resistances. As the sizes of stomata vary inversely with their density, it is likely that the stomatal resistances of the two surfaces will be approximately the same within the range of ratios of stomatal numbers of the lower to upper surface of, say, 0.75–1.33. Then, the rates may be expressed per unit area of leaf, treating the leaf as consisting of two surfaces in parallel. The values of the internal and external resistance per unit area of leaf are half the respective values for a single surface. Outside this range, separate values need to be estimated for each surface. Waggoner (1965) carried out an analysis and obtained experimental data consistent with this approach.

B. THE CANOPY AS A WHOLE

The role of leaf resistance, r_l, in determining the rate of transpiration from the leaves of a crop—and thus affecting the potential of water in the plant—is intimately related to the microclimatology of the crop. A full analysis of this relationship is outside the present context, and only a brief outline of the factors involved can be given.

Within a dense canopy of foliage, the streams of water vapor from the individual leaves merge to give the upward flux of water vapor E. The rate at which E increases with height, z, in the canopy depends, at a given height, on the surface area of leaf per unit volume of the canopy atmosphere a, the mean values of the internal and external resistances of the leaves, and the difference between the humidity of air at the evaporating surfaces within the leaves (taken to be that of saturated air at leaf surface temperature) and the humidity outside the boundary layers of the leaves. Thus,

$$\frac{dE}{dz} = \frac{a\rho(q_0' - q)}{r_l + r_a} \qquad (50)$$

Similar considerations apply to the upward flux of sensible heat, F, in the canopy. The difference in temperature between leaf surface and ambient air may conveniently be converted into the difference of the specific humidities of saturated air at the same temperatures:

$$\frac{dF}{dz} = \frac{a\lambda\rho(q_0' - q)}{\varepsilon r} \qquad (51)$$

Neglecting the small amounts of energy involved in photosynthesis and changing heat storage in the foliage,

$$\lambda E + F = H - G \qquad (52)$$

where H is the net downward flux of radiation in the canopy and G is the flux of heat down through the soil surface. Equations (50), (51), and (52) may be combined to give

$$\frac{dE}{dz} = \frac{\varepsilon(dH/dz)/\lambda + a\rho\delta/r_a}{\varepsilon + 1 + r_l/r_a} \qquad (53)$$

where $\delta = q' - q$. Equation (53) is essentially similar to Eq. (38) discussed earlier. The upward fluxes of vapor and heat may also be related to the gradients of humidity and temperature in the canopy through the relations

$$E = -K\rho \frac{dq}{dz}, \qquad F = -K \frac{\lambda\rho}{\varepsilon} \frac{dq'}{dz} \qquad (54)$$

Then,

$$E = \frac{\varepsilon(H - G)/\lambda + K\rho \, d\delta/dz}{\varepsilon + 1} \qquad (55)$$

Given knowledge of the transport characteristics r_l, r_a, and K, the leaf area density a, the variation of the net radiation H, the soil heat flux G, and the humidity deficit at the top of the canopy, Eqs. (53) and (55) may be solved for E and δ (Cowan, 1968; see also Cowan and Milthorpe, 1967). The solution is approximate since the spatial variations of ε and of the thermal emission of the leaves (which contributes to H) are ignored; errors are not serious provided the variation of temperature in the canopy does not exceed 2–3°C. Once E and δ have been obtained it is a simple matter to derive profiles of humidity and temperature (both at the leaf surfaces and in the canopy atmosphere) amd of the transpiration per unit area of leaf. Some results of such computations are shown in Fig. 13; these indicate the effects of leaf resistance (assumed constant through the canopy) on the distribution of transpiration. They refer to a canopy having hypothetical characteristics, the transport coefficients being derived from semitheoretical considerations and the form of the net radiation profile being assumed. Generally, in any given set of weather conditions, increase in the leaf resistance leads to the transpiration rate becoming more uniform through the different layers of the crop, the total rate of loss decreasing and the temperature of the canopy increasing. However, the magnitude of the decrease in transpiration and the increase of temperature for an actual change of leaf resistance depends upon interrelationships with the atmosphere outside the canopy and the extent of the cropped area. This is particularly important in relation to the use of antitranspirants (cf. p. 180): employed over small areas they may effectively reduce transpiration with little increase in crop temperature; over large areas the decrease in transpiration will be less and the increase in temperature will be greater.

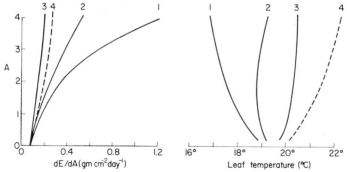

FIG. 13. Rate of transpiration per unit area (dE/dA) and leaf temperature as functions of the leaf resistance and of the cumulative leaf area (A) measured from the soil surface. The data refer to a model canopy, of uniformly distributed leaves, receiving a total net radiation of 0.6 cal cm^{-2} sec^{-1}. Curves 1, 2, and 3 refer to leaf resistance (r_l) of 0 (wet surfaces), 1.2, and 4.8 sec cm^{-1} respectively with values of ρq and $\rho q'$ of 12 and 16 gm m^{-3} at the top of the canopy; curve 4 refers to leaf resistance of 5.2 sec cm^{-1} with $\rho q = 11.1$ and $\rho q' = 18$ gm m^{-3} at the top of the canopy. After Cowan (1968).

Monteith (1963, 1965), using a similar approach to that of Penman and Schofield (1951) and Penman (1956), applied Eq. (38) to a whole crop, defining the external resistance *of the crop* R_a as $\rho(q_0 - q)/E$ and the internal (leaf) resistance of the crop R_l as $[q'(T_0) - q_0]/E$, where E is the rate of transpiration from the crop, q is the specific humidity at a reference height above the crop, and q_0 and T_0 are the values of specific humidity and temperature at wind speed $u = 0$, obtained by extrapolation of the $q(u)$ and $T(u)$ relations above the crop. The rate of transpiration is given by

$$E = \frac{\varepsilon(H - G)/\lambda + \rho(q' - q)/R_a}{\varepsilon + 1 + R_l/R_a} \tag{56}$$

where q' is the saturation specific humidity of air at the reference height. In effect, the crop is treated as a single surface, the crop resistance R_l being in series with the external resistance R_a and the latter being assumed identical with the resistance to transfer of momentum to the crop. The approach is open to criticism since it seems to ignore some of the essential characteristics of canopy transport. The resistance to mass transfer is greater than that for momentum transfer since the dissipation of momentum associated with the form drag of the leaves has no analog in mass transfer theory (see Chamberlain, 1966). Partly for this reason and partly because mass transfer is affected by the radiation profile whereas momentum transfer is not, the distribution of vapor sources in the canopy, in general, differs from that of momentum sinks. Computations (Cowan, 1968) indicate that R_l is a complex function of both the true leaf resistance and weather factors. It is doubtful whether any approach based only on the measurements made above the canopy can lead to a correct estimate of a physiological component of resistance to transpiration. Methods based on measurements within the canopy are becoming established, however. Brown (1964) has used measurements of profiles of radiation, air temperature, air humidity, and leaf temperature to estimate a "leaf-wetness parameter"—essentially a conductance that is the inverse of leaf resistance—in a crop of corn. The method, in essence, is as follows: from Eqs. (52) and (54),

$$E = \frac{\varepsilon(H - G)/\lambda}{\varepsilon + dq'/dq} \tag{57}$$

where dq'/dq is the slope of the relationship between the saturation and actual humidities in a vertical profile within the canopy. From Eqs. (50), (51), and (52)

$$r_l = \rho\left[\frac{q_0' - q}{dE/dz} - \frac{q_0' - q'}{d(H/\lambda)/dz - dE/dz}\right] \tag{58}$$

Substitution of Eq. (57) in Eq. (58) yields a relation that can be used for computing r_l; relations for K and r_a are also easily derived. This method of estimating r_l is difficult in practice since the second differentials with respect to height of q' and q are involved. Table X contains values of the transport characteristics computed from Brown's measurements; the values for r_l are high compared with the minimum values given in Table VIII.

TABLE X

COMPUTED VALUES OF THE TRANSFER COEFFICIENT FOR HEAT
AND WATER VAPOR K, EXTERNAL RESISTANCE r_a, AND INTERNAL
RESISTANCE r_l FOR A CROP OF MAIZE WITH LEAF AREA 3.7 cm^2 per cm^2
SOIL AREA AND HEIGHT 250 cm[a]

Height above ground (cm)	K (cm^2 sec^{-1})	Height interval (cm)	r_a (sec cm^{-1})	r_l (sec cm^{-1})
200	2815			
		150–200	0.30	5.3
150	1180			
		100–150	0.38	7.0
100	1000			
		50–100	—	10.5
50	391			
		0–50	—	14.2

[a] Obtained from the data and computations of Brown (1964).

The usefulness of models, as described in Eqs. (53) and (55), is limited by inadequate knowledge of the diurnal and spatial variation of r_l in field crops. Burrows (1965) has followed the stomatal resistance in crops of potato and sugar beet; generally, these were larger in the upper than the lower layers. Begg et al. (1964) found that the stomatal resistance of leaves in the upper and middle layers of a *Pennisetum* crop were similar throughout a diurnal cycle that included midday closure. Until the urgent need for reliable quantitative data concerning this parameter is satisfied, the only other acceptable information is that of Monteith (1963, 1965). As indicated above, the variations of R_l in his analysis [Eq. (56)] may represent primarily variations of climatic factors and any apparent agreement between R_l, r_l, and leaf area may be fortuitous. With these provisos, some of the conclusions from Monteith's analyses are presented. As a crop consists of a number of leaf surfaces in parallel, if the leaf resistances of the upper and lower surfaces are very similar as in wheat, sugar beet, potato and some other plants, and if these resistances are similar in all layers, then R_l should equal $r_l/2A$, where A is the total leaf area per unit area ground surface (see also Monteith et al., 1965).

Minimum values of R_l found by Monteith are 0.3–0.5 sec cm^{-1}; with $3 < A < 5$, r_l would be expected to vary between 1.5 and 5. At first sight, these agree reasonably well with the values given in Table VIII, but it must be remembered that variation within these limits will have appreciable effects on the transpiration rate.

A number of Monteith's estimates of R_a and R_l are reproduced in Table XI. These indicate that in crops well supplied with water R_a is of the order of 0.1–0.3 sec cm^{-1} and minimum values of R_l are about 0.3–0.5 sec cm^{-1}. In these situations, the evaporation rate is 80–100% of the net radiation. Three entries require special comment. The first, at Davis, from a crop well supplied with water, concerns the excess of evaporation over net radiation due to laterally advected energy despite a reasonably high internal resistance. The second is the sequence at O'Neill in which decreased transpiration was directly associated with increased R_l, both being related to a decrease in soil moisture. The third is the sequence on beans at Rothamsted in which the increased values of R_l following flowering were associated with either internal factors (cf. p. 177) or failure of roots to then extend to absorb sufficient water.

The estimated values of R_a cover a narrow range. This parameter is a function of surface roughness and wind speed, but in many crops the roughness decreases as the wind speed increases; in the higher range of wind speeds the resistance varies little. Bouyancy effects occurring when the air is unstable also tend to give lower resistances than expected (Monteith, 1965). Nevertheless, variation in R_a over the range 0.1–0.5 sec cm^{-1} has an appreciable effect on the proportion of the available net radiation used in transpiration, provided R_l is less than 0.7–0.8 sec cm^{-1}. At higher values of R_l it would have little effect. Monteith also explored the effect of leaf cover on transpiration rate. The transpiration rate increases with the degree of cover up to a leaf area index of about 3 with broad-leafed crops and of about 6 with crops with more upright leaves, providing the soil surface is dry. When the soil surface is wet, variation in the amount of leaf cover has little effect. Empirical evidence concerning the relationship between transpiration rate and degree of cover is conflicting. A number of experiments discussed by Milthorpe (1960) suggest that the transpiration rates of the same crop, and indeed even of different crops, in the same weather vary little with degree of cover—at least, with leaf area indexes greater than 2. On the other hand, Hagan and Vaadia (1960) produce evidence of an appreciable effect of degree of cover. Certainly, changes in temperature and other associated parameters partly offset the decrease in size of R_l with the increase in leaf area. The small leaf area resulting from wide spacing, which is a common feature of crops grown in dry areas, gives lower values of $\lambda E/H$ than found with close spacing; this factor as well as the more extensive root system contributes to the ability of the crop to withstand a period of drought (Milthorpe, 1961b; May and Milthorpe, 1962).

TABLE XI

TRANSPIRATION RATES, HEAT SUPPLY, AND RESISTANCES OF CROPS FROM A NUMBER OF SITES[a]

Surface	Location	E (10^{-2} mm hr^{-1})	H/λ (10^{-2} mm hr^{-1})	$100\lambda E/H$	R_a (sec cm^{-1})	R_l (sec cm^{-1})
Grass	Rothamsted	25	33	76	0.2	0.5
Lawn	Kew	20	41	49	0.5	4.1
Rye grass	Davis	48	60	80	0.3	0.5
		83	60	138	0.1	1.1
Natural prairie	O'Neill	37	55	67	0.3	2.1
		11	58	19	0.2	7.0
		9	51	18	0.3	15
Alfalfa–grass mixture	Hancock	38	42	90	0.2	0.4
Barley	Rothamsted	28	28	100	0.3	0.3
		25	32	78	0.2	0.7
Beans	Rothamsted	27	29	93	0.3	0.5
		25	40	63	0.2	1.1
		15	32	47	0.2	2.3
Pine forest	Munich	60	90	67	0.1	0.9

[a] After Monteith, (1965).

188   I. R. Cowan and F. L. Milthorpe

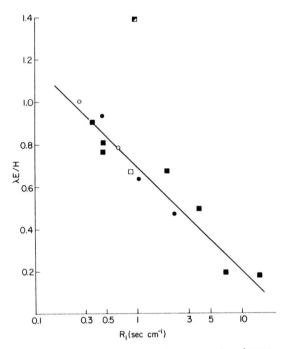

FIG. 14. Fraction of net heat available used for evaporation ($\lambda E/H$) as a function of internal resistance (R_l) of crops. Black squares denote grass, the pied square the value with advected energy at Davis, white square forest, black circles beans, and white circles barley. After Monteith (1965).

There appears to be a close dependence of the proportion of net radiation used in transpiration on internal crop resistance over its entire range (Fig. 14). These values are those given in Table XI and, apart from the anomalous point where advected energy was concerned, were described by the line $\lambda E/H = \log (25/R_l)^{1/2}$. That is, all of the net radiation is used in evaporation with $R_l = 0.25$ sec cm^{-1}. Assuming a maximum leaf resistance (closed stomata) of most crop plants of 50 sec cm^{-1} and a leaf area index of 5, R_l is ≈ 5 and the minimum value of $\lambda E/H$ is 0.35. The largest value of R_l recorded in the table was 15 (with $\lambda E/H = 0.18$); this corresponds to a leaf resistance of 30 sec cm^{-1} with a leaf area index of 1, which is a reasonable value for natural prairie.

Most of the evidence suggests that the transpiration rate is influenced by the internal resistance to diffusion over its entire range. However, knowledge of actual values over a wide range of conditions is still meager and there is real need for much further exploration of leaf resistances to diffusion and their integrated parameter—the internal resistance of the crop to diffusion.

REFERENCES

Altman, P. L., and Dittmer, D. S. (eds.) (1966). "Environmental Biology." Fed. Am. Soc. Exptl. Biol., Bethesda, Maryland.

Bange, G. G. J. (1953). On the quantitative explanation of stomatal transpiration. *Acta Botan. Neerl.* **2**, 255.

Bartholomew, E. T. (1926). Internal decline of lemons. III. Water deficit in lemon fruit caused by excessive leaf evaporation. *Am. J. Botany* **13**, 202.

Begg, J. E., Bierhuizen, J. F., Lemon, E. R., Misra, D. K., Slatyer, R. O., and Stern, W. R. (1964). Diurnal energy and water exchanges in bulrush millet in an area of high solar radiation. *Agr. Meteorol.* **1**, 294.

Brouwer, R. (1965). Water movement across the root. *Symp. Soc. Exptl. Biol.* **19**, 131.

Brown, H. T., and Escombe, F. (1900). Static diffusion of gases and liquids in relation to the assimilation of carbon and translocation in plants. *Phil. Trans. Roy. Soc. London Ser. B* **193**, 223.

Brown K. W. (1964). Vertical fluxes within the vegetative canopy of a corn field, 1962. *Univ. of Arizona, Meteorol. Dept. Interim Rept.* **64-1**.

Burrows, F. J. (1965). The stomatal conductance of sugar beet and potatoes. Ph.D. Thesis, Univ. of Nottingham, England.

Carman, P. C. (1956). "Flow of Gases Through Porous Media." Butterworth, London and Washington, D.C.

Carr, D. J., and Gaff, D. F. (1961). The role of the cell wall water in the water relations of leaves. *Proc. Madrid Symp. Plant-Water Relationships in Arid and Semi-Arid Conditions*, 1959 p. 117. UNESCO, Paris.

Čatsky, J. (1965). Water saturation deficit and photosynthetic rate as related to leaf age in the wilting plant. *In* "Water Stress in Plants" (B. Slavik, ed.), Proc. Symp. Prague, 1963, p. 203. Czech. Acad. Sci., Prague.

Chamberlain, A. C. (1966). Transport of gases to and from grass and grass-like surfaces. *Proc. Roy. Soc.* **A290**, 236.

Copeland, E. B. (1902). Mechanism of stomata. *Ann. Botany* **16**, 327.

Cowan, I. R. (1965). Transport of water in the soil-plant-atmosphere system. *J. Appl. Ecol.* **2**, 221.

Cowan, I. R. (1968). Mass, heat and momentum exchange between plant stands and their atmospheric environment. *Quart. J. Roy. Meteorol. Soc.* (in press).

Cowan, I. R., and Milthorpe, F. L. (1967). Physiological responses in relation to the environment within the plant cover. *Functioning of Terrestrial Ecosystems at the Primary Production Level. Proc. Copenhagen Symp.* UNESCO, Paris.

Cox, E. F. (1966). Resistance to water flow through the plant. Ph.D. Thesis, Univ. of Nottingham, Nottingham, England.

Crafts, A. S., Currier, H. B., and Stocking, C. R. (1949). "Water in the Physiology of Plants." Chronica Botanica, Waltham, Massachusetts.

Dainty, J. (1963). Water relations of plant cells. *Advan. Botan. Res.* **1**, 279.

de Groot, S. R. (1961). "Thermodynamics of Irreversible Processes." North-Holland Publ., North Holland, Amsterdam.

Denmead, O. T., and Shaw, R. H. (1962). Availability of soil water to plants as affected by soil moisture content and meteorological conditions. *Agron J.* **54**, 385.

Dick, D. A. T. (1966). "Cell Water." Butterworth, London and Washington, D.C.

Dimond, A. E. (1966). Pressure and flow relations in vascular bundles of the tomato plant. *Plant Physiol.* **41**, 119.

Dixon, H. H. (1914). "Transpiration and the Ascent of Sap in Plants." Macmillan, New York.

Ehlig, C. F., and Gardner, W. R. (1964). Relationship between transpiration and internal water relations of plants. *Agron. J.* **56**, 127.

Ehrler, W. L., Nakayama, F. S., and van Bavel, C. H. M. (1965). Cyclic changes in water balance and transpiration of cotton leaves in a steady environment. *Physiol. Plantarum* **18**, 766.

Esau, K. (1962). "Plant Anatomy." Wiley, New York.

Fritschen, L. J., and van Bavel, C. H. M. (1964). Energy balance as affected by height and maturity of sudangrass. *Agron. J.* **56**, 201.

Furr, J. R., and Taylor, C. A. (1935). The apparent growth rate of lemon fruits as an index of the moisture supply of the tree. *Proc. Am. Soc. Hort. Sci.* **33**, 70.

Gaastra, P. (1963). Climatic control of photosynthesis and respiration. *In* "Environmental Control of Plant Growth" (L. T. Evans, ed.), p. 113. Academic Press, New York.

Gardner, W. R. (1960). Soil water relations in arid and semi-arid conditions. *In* "Plant-Water Relationships in Arid and Semi-Arid Conditions. Reviews of Research," p. 37. UNESCO, Paris.

Gardner, W. R. (1964). Relation of root distribution to water uptake and availability. *Agron J.* **56**, 41.

Gates, D. M. (1967). Energy exchange in the biosphere. *Proc. 1st Intern Symp. Ecosystems, Copenhagen, 1965.* UNESCO, Paris.

Greenidge, K. N. H. (1957). Ascent of sap. *Ann. Rev. Plant Physiol.* **8**, 237.

Gregory, F. G., Milthorpe, F. L., Pearse, H. L., and Spencer, E. J. (1950). Experimental studies of the factors controlling transpiration. I, II. *J. Exptl. Botany* **1**, 1, 15.

Haberlandt, G. (1914). "Physiological Plant Anatomy," (Translation 4th German ed.). Macmillan, London.

Hagan, R. M., and Vaadia, Y. (1960). Principles of irrigated cropping. *In* "Plant-Water Relationships in Arid and Semi-Arid Conditions. Reviews of Research," p. 215. UNESCO, Paris.

Hayward, H. E., Blair, W. M., and Skaling, P. E. (1942). Device for measuring entry of water into roots. *Botan. Gaz.* **104**, 152.

Heath, O. V. S. (1959). The water relations of stomatal cells and the mechanisms of stomatal movement. *In* "Plant Physiology" (F. C. Steward, ed.), Vol. 2, p. 193. Academic Press, New York.

Heath, O. V. S., and Meidner, H. (1961). The influence of water strain on the minimum inter-cellular space carbon dioxide concentration Γ and stomatal movements in wheat leaves. *J. Exptl. Botany* **12**, 226.

Heath, O. V. S., and Russell, J. (1954). Studies in stomatal behaviour. VI. An investigation of the light responses of wheat stomata with the attempted elimination of control by the mesophyll. *J. Exptl. Botany* **5**, 269.

Huber, B. (1956). Die Gefässleitung. *In* "Handbuch der Pflanzenphysiologie" (W. Ruhland, ed.), Vol. 3, p. 541. Springer, Berlin.

Jenny, H., and Grossenbacher, K. (1963). Root-soil boundary zones as seen in the electron microscope. *Soil Sci. Soc. Am. Proc.* **27**, 273.

Jensen, R. D., and Taylor, S. A. (1961). Effect of temperature on water transport through plants. *Plant Physiol.* **36**, 639.

Jensen, R. D., Taylor, S. A., and Wiebe, H. H. (1961). Negative transport and resistance to water flow through plants. *Plant Physiol.* **36**, 633.

Klemm, G. (1956). Untersuchungen über den Transpirationswiderstand der Mesophyll-membranen und seine Bedeuting als Regulator für die stomatäre Transpiration. *Planta* **47**, 547.

Kohn, P. G., and Dainty, J. (1966). The measurement of permeability to water in disks of storage tissue. *J. Exptl Botany* **17**, 809.

Kozlowski, T. T. (1964). "Water Metabolism in Plants." Harper, New York.

Kozlowski, T. T., Hughes, J. F., and Leyton, L. (1966). Patterns of water movement in dormant gymnosperm seedlings. *Biorheology* **3**, 77.

Kramer, P. J. (1946). Absorption of water through suberized roots of trees. *Plant Physiol.* **21**, 37.

Kramer, P. J. (1949). "Plant and Soil-Water Relationships." McGraw-Hill, New York.

Kramer, P. J., and Bullock, H. C. (1966). Seasonal variations in the proportions of suberized and unsuberized roots of trees in relation to the absorption of water. *Am. J. Botany* **53**, 200.

Kuiper, P. J. C. (1963). Some considerations on water transport across living cell membranes. *Conn. Agr. Expt. Sta. Bull.* **664**.

Lee, R., and Gates, D. M. (1964). Diffusion resistance in leaves as related to their stomatal anatomy and micro-structure. *Am. J. Botany* **51**, 963.

Lemon, E. R. (1963). Energy and water balance of plant communities. *In* "Environmental Control of Plant Growth" (L. T. Evans, ed), p. 55. Academic Press, New York.

Livingston, B. E., and Brown, W. H. (1912). Relation of the daily march of transpiration to variations in the water content of foliage leaves. *Botany Gaz.* **53**, 309.

Macklon, A. E. S., and Weatherley, P. E. (1965). Controlled environment studies of the nature and origins of water deficits in plants. *New Phytologist* **64**, 414.

Maximov, N. A. (1929). "The Plant in Relation to Water." Allen & Unwin, London.

May, L. H., and Milthorpe, F. L. (1962). Drought resistance of crop plants. *Field Crop Abstr.* **15**, 171.

Mees, G. C., and Weatherley, P. E. (1957). The mechanism of water absorption by roots. I. II. *Proc. Roy. Soc.* **B147**, 367, 381.

Meidner, H. (1965). Stomatal control of transpirational water loss. *Symp. Soc. Exptl. Biol.* **19**, 185.

Meidner, H., and Mansfield, T. A. (1965). Stomatal responses to illumination. *Biol. Rev.* **40**, 483.

Mer, C. L. (1940). The factors determining the resistance to the movement of water in the leaf. *Ann. Botany (London)* [N.S.] **4**, 397.

Meyer, B. S., and Anderson, D. B. (1952). "Plant Physiology," 2nd Ed. Van Nostrand, Princeton, New Jersey.

Milthorpe, F. L. (1960). The income and loss of water in arid and semi-arid zones. *In* "Plant-Water Relationships in Arid and Semi-Arid Conditions. Reviews of Research," p. 9. UNESCO, Paris.

Milthorpe, F. L. (1961a). Plant factors involved in transpiration. *Proc. Madrid Symp. Plant-Water Relationships in Arid and Semi-Arid Conditions*, 1959 p. 107. UNESCO, Paris.

Milthorpe, F. L. (1961b). The nature and analysis of competition between plants of different species. *Symp. Soc. Exptl. Biol.* **15**, 330.

Milthorpe, F. L., and Penman, H. L. (1967). The diffusive conductivity of the stomata of wheat leaves. *J. Exptl. Bot.* **18**, 422.

Milthorpe, F. L., and Spencer, E. J. (1957). Experimental studies of the factors controlling transpiration. III. The interrelations between transpiration rate, stomatal movement, and leaf-water content. *J. Exptl. Botany* **8**, 413.

Monteith, J. L. (1963). Gas exchange in plant communities. *In* "Environmental Control of Plant Growth," (L. T. Evans, ed.), p. 95. Academic Press, New York.

Montheith, J. L. (1965). Evaporation and environment. *Symp. Soc. Exptl. Biol.* **19**, 205.

Monteith, J. L., Szeicz, G., and Waggoner, P. E. (1965). The measurement and control of stomatal resistance in the field. *J. Appl. Ecol.* **2**, 345.

Myers, G. M. P. (1951). The water permeability of unplasmolysed tissues. *J. Exptl. Botany* **2**, 129.

Ordin, L., and Kramer, P. J. (1956). Permeability of *Vicia faba* root segments to water as measured by diffusion of deuterium hydroxide. *Plant Physiol.* **31**, 468.

Passioura, J. B. (1963). A mathematical model for the uptake of ions from the soil solution. *Plant Soil.* **18**, 225.

Peel, A. J. (1965). On the conductivity of the xylem in trees. *Ann. Botany* (*London*) [N.S.] **29**, 119.

Penman, H. L. (1942). Theory of porometers used in the study of stomatal movements in leaves. *Proc. Roy. Soc.* **B130**, 416.

Penman, H. L. (1956). Evaporation: an introductory survey. *Neth. J. Agr.* **4**, 9.

Penman, H. L., and Schofield, R. K. (1951). Some physical aspects of assimilation and transpiration. *Symp. Soc. Exptl. Biol.* **5**, 115.

Philip, J. R. (1957). The physical principles of soil water movement during the irrigation cycle. *Trans. 3rd Congr. Intern. Comm. Irrig. Drainage*, Question 8, 8.125.

Philip, J. R. (1958a). The osmotic cell, solute diffusibility, and the plant water economy. *Plant Physiol.* **33**, 264.

Philip, J. R. (1958b). Propagation of turgor and other properties through cell aggregates. *Plant Physiol.* **33**, 271.

Philip, J. R. (1958c). Osmosis and diffusion in tissue: half-times and internal gradients. *Plant Physiol.* **33**, 275.

Philip, J. R. (1966). Plant water relations: some physical aspects. *Ann. Rev. Plant Physiol.* **17**, 245.

Preston, R. D. (1952). Movement of water in higher plants. *In* " Deformation and Flow in Biological Systems " (A. Frey-Wyssling, ed.), p. 257. North-Holland Publ., Amsterdam.

Rawlins, S. L. (1963). Resistance to water flow in the transpiration stream. *Conn. Agr. Expt. Sta. Bull.* **664**.

Ray, P. M. (1960). On the theory of osmotic water movement. *Plant Physiol.* **35**, 783.

Rosene, H. F. (1937). Distribution of the velocities of absorption of water in the onion root. *Plant Physiol.* **12**, 1.

Russell, E. J. (1953). " Soil Conditions and Plant Growth," 8th ed. Longmans, Green, New York.

Scott, F. M. (1950). Internal suberization of tissues. *Botan. Gaz.* **111**, 378.

Slatyer, R. O. (1960). Absorption of water by plants. *Botan. Rev.* **26**, 331.

Slatyer, R O. (1962). Internal water relations of higher plants. *Ann. Rev. Plant Physiol.* **13**, 351.

Slatyer, R. O. (1963). Climatic control of plant water relations. *In* " Environmental Control of Plant Growth " (L. T. Evans, ed.), p. 33. Academic Press, New York.

Slatyer, R. O. (1966). An underlying cause of measurement discrepancies in determination of osmotic characteristics in plant cells and tissues. *Protoplasma*, **62**, 34.

Slatyer, R. O., and Gardner, W. R. (1965). Overall aspects of water movement in plants and soils. *Symp. Soc. Exptl. Biol.* **19**, 113.

Slatyer, R. O., and Taylor, S. A. (1960). Terminology in plant- and soil-water relations. *Nature* **187**, 922.

Spanner, D. C. (1964). " Introduction to Thermodynamics." Academic Press, New York.

Stålfelt, M. G. (1955). The stomata as a hydrophotic regulator of the water deficit of the plant. *Physiol. Plantarum* **8**, 572.

Stamm, A. J. (1946). Passage of liquids, vapors and dissolved materials through softwoods. *U.S. Dept. Agr. Tech. Bull.* **929**.

Strugger, S. (1943). Der aufsteigende Saftstrom in der Pflanze. *Naturwissenschaften* **31**, 181.

Ting, I. P., and Loomis W. E. (1965). Further studies concerning stomatal diffusion. *Plant Physiol.* **40**, 220.

Troughton, A. (1957). The underground organs of herbage grasses. *Commonwealth Agr. Bur. (Gt. Brit.), Commonwealth Bur. Past. Field Crops Bull.* **44.**

van den Honert, T. H. (1948). Water transport in plants as a catenary process. *Discussions Faraday Soc.* **3**, 146.

Visser, W. C. (1964). Moisture requirements of crops and rate of moisture depletion of the soil. *Inst. Land Water Management Res., Wageningen, Tech. Bull.* **32.**

Waggoner, P. E. (1965). Relative effectiveness of change in upper and lower stomatal openings. *Crop Sci.* **5**, 291.

Waggoner, P. E., and Hewlett, J. D. (1965). Test of a transpiration inhibitor on a forested watershed. *Water Resources Res.* **1**, 391.

Waggoner, P. E., and Zelitch, I. (1965). Transpiration and the stomata of leaves. *Science* **150**, 1413.

Weatherley, P. E. (1963). The pathway of water movement across the root cortex and leaf mesophyll of transpiring plants. *In* "The Water Relations of Plants" (A. J. Rutter and F. H. Whitehead, eds.), Brit. Ecol. Soc. Symp., p. 85. Blackwells, Oxford.

Weatherley, P. E. (1965). The state and movement of water in the leaf. *Symp. Soc. Exptl. Biol.* **19**, 157.

Weaver, J. E. (1926). "Root Development of Field Crops." McGraw-Hill, New York.

Wind, G. P. (1955). Flow of water through plant roots. *Neth. J. Agr. Sci.* **3**, 259.

Woolley, J. T. (1965). Radial exchange of labeled water in intact maize roots. *Plant Physiol.* **40**, 711.

Wylie, R. B. (1938). Concerning the conductive capacity of the minor veins of foliage leaves. *Am. J. Botany* **25**, 567.

Zelitch, I. (1965). Environmental and biochemical control of stomatal movement in leaves. *Biol. Rev.* **40**, 463.

Ziegenspeck, H. (1945). Fluoroskopische Versuche an Blättern, über Leitung, Transpiration und Abscheidung von Wasser. *Biol. Generalis* **18**, 254.

Zimmermann, M. H. (1964). Sap movements in trees. *Biorheology* **2**, 15.

Zimmermann, M. H. (1965). Water movement in stems of tall plants. *Symp. Soc. Exptl. Biol.* **19**, 151.

CHAPTER 7

DROUGHT-RESISTANCE MECHANISMS

Johnson Parker

NORTHEASTERN FOREST EXPERIMENT STATION, U.S. FOREST SERVICE,
HAMDEN, CONNECTICUT

I. INTRODUCTION

Plant mechanisms that act as a defense against environmental dehydrative forces might seem simple to study and evaluate. This is not the case. Not only is it difficult to carry out experiments on plant–water relations to obtain clear-cut results, but it is even more difficult to assess these results either by themselves or in the light of other investigators' research. Considering the uncertainties in this field of drought resistance, it is not surprising that some fairly sharp controversies have arisen over experiments. Embarkation, therefore, is made into this *mare seccum* (not to say dry subject) with certain reservations and hopes that the reader will realize that this is a general survey, not a complete compendium.

All land plants in a sense are living either partly or entirely out of their natural original medium: water. In fact, all living things are children of a water environment. In the animal kingdom, which is not usually believed to be aquatic in origin, the ancestral species were either marine or fresh water organisms. The first primitive plants depended on the surrounding water for reproduction. Flagellated gametes are commonly found in the simpler algae; antheridia that bear sperms are found in mosses. All of these male motile bodies must have water for a medium of locomotion. Only in the tracheo-phytes does sexual fertilization become restricted to a kind of self-contained mechanism that is largely independent of the moisture regime in the external environment. Such a fertilization method in itself is a drought-resistance mechanism, since the motile sperm is reduced in the higher plants mainly to a nucleus moving in the confines of a pollen tube.

The plant kingdom, then, was born in the water and only developed a wayward migration to the land as a kind of offshoot of the original marine environment. Once partially removed from water, entirely new adaptations were developed. The mere survival of protoplasm under severe desiccation appears to be a primitive adaptation, whereas the ability to continue meta-bolism during drought is a somewhat advanced characteristic. In the final analysis, all land plants must endure a certain amount of dryness. Even man-groves growing in the mud of a tidal river or cypress trees flourishing in the quiet waters of a Southern swamp put their topmost branches into air that is frequently subjected to drying winds. Drought mechanisms thus can be found in most or all land plants.

II. DROUGHT-RESISTANCE MECHANISMS IN LOWER PLANTS

It is of theoretical as well as of practical interest to examine drought mechanisms in lower plants. Not only is a better understanding of the whole picture of drought resistance thereby developed, but theories found to be applicable in lower plants can sometimes be applied to higher plants.

A. CYANOPHYTA

If bacteria are not considered plants, then the first plants to invade land were probably at least similar to the simplest blue-green algae. Today these organisms may be found invading barren islands in remote corners of the ocean where land vegetation was entirely destroyed by some natural catas-trophe. In such places these algae may merely form a thin coating on the substratum. Layers of slimy material, possibly hemicellulose, surrounding such globular cells as those of *Gloeocapsa*, might appear to retard water loss sufficiently to protect, temporarily at least, some of the cells from desiccation. The hemicellulose appears to delay dehydration, but only for a short time: a matter of a few hours.

Many species of Cyanophyta can become dry as dust and still recover. In Calcutta, for example, species of *Gloeocapsa*, *Nostoc*, and *Oscillatoria* form on roads in rainy weather and make them slippery. As the dry season advances, the mucous sheaths dry up and form an encrustation. This turns to powder under the feet of pedestrians and then blows in the wind to new locations. When some of these cells are wetted, they sometimes begin growth within 5 minutes (Biswas, 1925).

There is evidence of the ability of some blue-green algae to withstand drying for as long as 87 years. A specimen mounted on a herbarium sheet in Germany in 1853 was reported to recover and grow successfully in 1940 (Lipman, 1941). Ray cells of the semidesert plant *Parkinsonia microphylla* have survived 250 years (MacDougal and Brown, 1928), but these cells probably were not subjected to severe internal desiccation.

The physiological cause of such great desiccation resistance as that found in blue-green algae is not understood. The protoplasm of resistant species has long been studied without firm conclusions. Many small vacuoles seem to be characteristic of resistant cells, and the cytoplasm contains granular bodies that appear to be polysaccharides and DNA (Shields and Durrell, 1964).

B. CHLOROPHYTA AND RELATED GROUPS

Various types of specialized cells occur in the single-celled and filamentous green algae, but few studies have been made on actual drought resistance under controlled conditions. Fritsch (1922) and others use the following terms to describe resistant cells: cysts, akinetes, resting cells, and resistant stages. Evans (1958) mentions oospores, zygospores, hypnospores, and akinetes as resting structures that might have drought-surviving capabilities.

Some algae seem to have no resting stages (Rao, cited in Evans, 1958), and investigators did not find any resistant stages in most of the algae studied (Lund, 1942). Petersen (cited in Evans, 1958) held that whereas hydrophytic algae, as opposed to aerial and soil algae, could not survive severe desiccation in the vegetative condition, they could do so in the resting stage as spores. Yet there are vegetative stages of some species that can form thickened cell walls and a fatty pellicle or cuticle to help survive drought. Although some algae rely on early formed zygospores for survival of a drought, other filamentous algae and at least some species of *Cosmarium*, normally aquatic, can survive by some modification of the vegetative stage, such as thickened cell walls, accumulation of oil, or production of mucilage (Evans, 1959).

Algae, including members of Chlorophyceae, Cyanophyceae, and one species of diatom, are known to survive in soils stored for 26 to 73 years (Bristol, cited in Evans, 1959). *Stauroneis*, a diatom, withstood 54 days of dry conditions. *Spirogyra cylindrica* survived severe drying in the zygospore stage. One form of *Mougeotia* died after severe drying, but another, *M. parvula*, survived 19 days of experimental drying, evidently as zygospores. Resting stages (cysts) of *Glenodinium pulvisculus* (Pyrrophyta) survived in the lake's marginal leaf litter and gave rise to motile cells in water (Evans, 1959). It thus appears that some green algae depend on specialized resting cells and others on vegetative forms alone to survive droughts.

C. Phaeophyta and Related Groups

The attaching marine algae, especially the Phaeophyta, are found in a great variety of marine coastal environments throughout the world and are common on rocky shores of relatively cold coastal waters. It was suspected at an early time that survival of littoral marine algae was related to their ability to dehydrate to a low level and still survive. This led to a number of studies that showed that species of algae differed in their ability to resist various osmotic pressures (Osterhout, 1906; Höfler, 1930; Biebl, 1939). Similarly, using different atmospheric relative humidities, desiccation resistance increased with increasing height above mean low tide: those species growing naturally below the ebb tide line could withstand atmospheric relative humidities down to 97% (above this percentage they survived), those enduring the ebb line died at about 94%, and those of the intertidal zone (exposed at low tide) endured down to 88% (Biebl, 1939). Examples of variation in desiccation resistance of marine algae are given in Table I.

Some tendency to retain water in the fronds against a vapor-pressure gradient to the air can also be observed in these attaching marine algae. For example, various algae of Heligoland, rather typical of many of the attaching forms on both sides of the North Atlantic, can continue to photosynthesize over a range of moisture content (expressed as a percent of dry weight) of about 350% down to 100% (Stocker and Holdheide, 1937). Rates of CO_2 absorption by *Fucus vesiculosus* fronds in air were considerably higher than those of oak leaves of comparable fresh weight (Parker, unpublished data). Apparently, then, retention of water plays some role in metabolism of these plants, although as Biebl (1939) stated, their water loss resembles that from a simple gelatin plate. Besides this, the larger attaching algae, with few exceptions, often lie embedded at low tide on top of one another with those underneath retaining water longer than those on top.

Many species of *Fucus* seem to take longer to dehydrate than some of the algae growing normally lower down in the littoral zone. *Fucus* takes up water more slowly from a dry condition than species of *Porphyra* (Rhodophyta) or of *Enteromorpha* (Chlorophyta) (Stocker and Holdheide, 1937). These last two plants could change from a dry condition to full saturation in 30 seconds. But some species may dehydrate more slowly than *Fucus*. On a normal summer day during low tide, *F. vesiculosus* may lose 90% of its saturation water content, whereas a species of *Ulva* may lose 77%, and one of *Chondrus*, 63%

TABLE I

RESISTANCE OF SOME MARINE ALGAE TO DESICCATION[a]

Botanical name	Humidity (%)
INTERTIDAL ZONE	
Porphyra umbilicalis	83.0
Rhodocharton floridulum	88.0
Elachista fucicola	86.0
Ulva lactuca	83.0
Enteromorpha linza	83.0
Cladophora rupestris	83.0
Cladophora gracilis	86.0
AT MEAN LOW TIDE LEVEL	
Polysiphonia nigrescens	86.0
Membranoptera alata	94.6
Plumaria elegans	94.6
Dictyota dichotoma	94.6
SUBLITTORAL ZONE	
Plocamium coccineum	98.8
Antithamnion plumula	98.4
Trailliella intricata	98.4
Halarachnion ligulatum	96.8

[a] Algae were exposed to air of the stated relative humidity for 13 hours. Numbers give minimum humidity tolerated. After Biebl (1952).

(Kanwischer, 1957). Evidently, then, many marine algae can delay water loss for a time, and this period varies with species. But their last line of defense against atmospheric dehydration is within the protoplasm itself.

D. EUMYCETES

In spite of the great economic importance of the true fungi and of the extensive research on these achlorophyllous plants, information is lacking on the mechanisms by which they avoid or endure drought. Many botanists assume that large, thick-walled spores survive for a long time, but there are few definite experiments to prove this. While there are a number of reports of longevity of spores, the conditions (for example, relative humidity) under which they survive are usually not measured in quantitative terms and sometimes are not even mentioned in the papers cited below.

Oospores of certain species of *Phytophthora*, which are known to lie dormant in the soil attached to glass threads for as long as a year, can still germinate and produce sporangia (Legge, 1952). Ascospores of certain species also seem able to tolerate extreme temperature and moisture conditions (Park, 1965). Chlamydospores and conidia of some species of *Fusarium* are fairly resistant to adverse conditions, and conidia in certain Fungi Imperfecti can survive for at least a year (Caldwell, 1958). In some of the Actinomycetes, too, spores may survive long periods of time in the soil (Pfennig, 1958).

Many pathogenic fungi do not produce spores, at least from sexual fusion, but rely on other resistant structures such as sclerotia for survival under adverse conditions. Sclerotia may grow successfully when placed in a favorable environment. Sclerotia of *Rhizoctonia* may be the structures that survive in very dry soil, whereas in *Pythium*, oospores appear to be the surviving structures (Vaartaja, 1964). After 2 years of dark storage, during which time soil moisture approached 0.2% (presumably of the total original soil weight), some species of fungi survived, that is, those of *Pythium* and *Rhizoctonia*. The ubiquitous genera, *Aspergillus* and *Penicillium*, were also found on plates cultured from the same dry soil.

Certain Myxomycetes produced plasmodia from spores that were 32 years old, presumably after being kept under dry laboratory conditions (Smith, 1929). Spores of *Mucor* from old laboratory cultures to which fresh agar had been added survived 2 years; those of *Sclerotium rolfsii*, 5 years (Povah, 1927).

The old question of whether fungi survive in soil as spores or mycelium seems no longer to be controversial, except in a quantitative sense (Park, 1965). Both hyphae and spores seem to survive fairly adverse soil conditions. Rhizomorphs, like sclerotia, may be capable of withstanding severe environmental conditions, and even hyphae can persist for long periods in a dry environment. Certain fungi, present in desert soil as dark, sterile mycelia, will grow after subjection to intense conditions of desiccation and insolation (Nicot, 1960).

In an attempt to study the relationship between bound water and drought in *Aspergillus niger*, Todd and Levitt (1951) found that when the fungus was grown at osmotic pressures exceeding 83 atm, it did not sporulate, although some hyphal growth still occurred even at 132 atm.

Not much is known of the nature of drought resistance of mycorrhizal fungi that would be of considerable interest to physiologists interested in moisture problems in higher plants. It has been found, however, that uninfected *Fagus* roots are more easily injured by desiccation than those with mycorrhizal fungi (Harley, 1940), Just why this is so is not clear, and Harley warned against drawing broad conclusions from this isolated observation. Soil dryness seems to influence development of mycorrhizal fungi. A white fungus, usually found on pine seedlings under high soil moisture conditions, was absent at a low moisture level, whereas a relatively uncommon black-colored fungus was predominant in dry soil (Worley and Hacskaylo, 1959).

Although little is known of desiccation resistance of spores, Loegering and Harmon (1962) found that uredospores of *Puccinia graminis* could be revived after exposure to liquid nitrogen. Since this cold treatment is largely or entirely a desiccation process in this case, severe drying probably could be withstood by such spores.

E. LICHENS

Some of the characteristics of lichens have already been considered since an alga and a fungus are ordinarily combined in the lichen. Most dry site lichens can withstand very severe droughts (Lange, 1953), yet there are many other lichens that are not very drought resistant (Stocker, 1927). Jumelle (cited in Stocker, 1927) found that after 3 months of drought followed by remoistening, *Cladonia rangifera, Ramalina farinaceae,* and *Usnea barbata* were so weakened that practically no respiration could be detected. However, many lichens in the dry state respire nearly 100 times as much as wheat seeds of similar dry weight in the resting condition (Stocker, 1927).

Although a number of worthwhile studies on lichen respiration have been made (for example, Scholander *et al.*, 1952), results are somewhat conflicting and do little to resolve the mechanisms of drought resistance. Differences in photosynthesis among species of lichens of warm and cold climates have been demonstrated (Lange, 1965). Such studies may shed light on causes of geographical distribution, but more needs to be known of water-retentive capacities that might allow lichens to continue metabolism during drought.

The geographical distribution of lichens may depend not so much on the abundance of rainfall as on the frequency of atmospheric moisture such as fog (Stocker, 1927). In other words, it is not only the rainfall per month that counts but the frequent occurrence of moist conditions. This applies especially to epiphytic lichens. In the northern Rocky Mountains *Usnia hirta* occurs on trees only above a certain altitude. This distribution appears to be related to a certain amount of fog, mist, etc., rather than the temperature regime. However, few experiments have been performed on such lichens and no special water-retaining adaptations other than material secreted by cells of the outer cortex appear to be of special significance.

Survival of some tropical species such as *Buellia atrofuscata* may require more than 100 inches of rainfall per year. Other species such as *B. modesta* only occur in rather xeric locations. In tropical countries, too, the precipitation–evaporation index is certainly more meaningful than total rainfall alone for lichen distribution as, for example, in the West Indies (Imshaug, 1955). Unfortunately, precipitation–evaporation data often are not available in tropical countries or at least in the forests or other remote locations where the lichens occur.

F. Bryophyta (Musci and Hepaticae)

The Musci were among the earliest plants investigated in studies of drought resistance. Both Irmscher (1912) and Holle (1915) pointed to the remarkable ability of certain mosses to dehydrate to very low levels and to survive on rehydration.

Many species dry out rapidly at 50% relative humidity and thus possess little tendency to retain water. One liverwort, *Bazzania stolonifera*, mentioned by Biebl (1964), can dry to 6% of the saturation water content within 55 minutes. As might be expected, it also takes up water rapidly. Reabsorption can occur even though cells are dead.

In general, the mechanisms of drought resistance in mosses appear to depend largely on protoplasmic characteristics. Mosses attached to tree branches normally have a higher osmotic pressure than those on the moist forest floor. The former also have lower lethal levels (Table II), as if this were a requirement for that particular habitat.

The percentages given in Table II are lower than those that intertidal algae can withstand when exposed to the air (Table I). In spite of the high protoplasmic resistance to desiccation of some mosses, none of those listed in Table II can survive as low as 29% relative humidity for any length of time. It has been suggested that the great desiccation resistance of such mosses to drying is the result of a lack of plasmodesmata connecting one cell to another. If plasmodesmata were present they would rupture and the cells would die (Levitt, 1956). Probably there are other mechanisms of drought resistance in the Musci; for example, there are definite differences among species in their water permeability (Biebl, 1964).

In some species, such as *Polytrichum commune*, leafy organs undergo a change in position as they dehydrate, so that these organs become appressed against the shoot. Possibly this favors water retention, but the phenomenon could also be related to the ability to escape excessive insolation.

Although relatively little has been written about Hepaticae, Höfler's (1942, 1945) studies have been quite revealing. He found that some liverworts died rapidly after exposure to 95% relative humidity for 48 hours; others withstood 0% over concentrated H_2SO_4 for 48 hours without harm. Some species were capable of hardening, and others were not. Protoplasmic constitution seemed important in drought-resistance of Hepaticae.

G. Pteridophyta

Drought-resistance mechanisms of ferns have not been studied as much as those of higher plants. Nevertheless, organization of the ferns in many cases is as complex as that of many higher plants, in spite of their comparatively low evolutionary status. While some species have fronds that are quite sensitive to

TABLE II

DESICCATION RESISTANCE OF SOME MOSSES AND LIVERWORTS IN THREE DIFFERENT HABITATS[a]

	Desiccation resistance after 24 hours (%) relative humidity								
	96	91	84	75	64.5	52	39	29	
Herberta juniperina	1	1	1	1	1	1	1	d	
Plagiochila sp. 1	1	1	1	1	1	1	i	d	
Omphalanthus filif.	1	1	1	1	1	i	d	d	
Plagiochila sp. 2	1	1	1	1	1	d	d	d	
Rhizogonium spinifor.	1	1	1	1	1	d	d	d	On branches in forest
Thuidium urceolatum	1	1	1	1	1	d	d	d	
Bazzania stolonifera	1	1	1	1	i	d	d	d	
Bazzania cf. *cuneis.*	1	1	1	1	i	d	d	d	
Trichocolea elliottii	1	1	1	i	d	d	d	d	
Metzgeria hamata	1	1	1	1	d	d	d	d	
Moss, undetermined	1	1	1	1	i	d	d	d	
Cyclolejeunea convex.	1	1	1	i	d	d	d	d	Epiphyllous
Bazzania schwanecki.	1	1	1	1	d	d	d	d	
Plagiochila sp. 3	1	1	1	i	d	d	d	d	
Pilotrichidium calli.	1	1	1	i	d	d	d	d	On moist forest soil
Symphyogyna trivitt.	1	d	d	d	d	d	d	d	
Neesioscyphus n. sp.	1	i	d	d	d	d	d	d	

[a] l = living, d = dead, i = intermediate. From Biebl (1964).

drought and frequently die back in early summer to an underground rhizome, a number of "poikilohydrous" ferns tolerate a wide variety of moisture regimes.

As many as 8 species of ferns grow in the extremely dry habitats of certain parts of Arizona (Walter, 1931). One might expect high osmotic pressures in such plants, but OP, as determined cryoscopically, was only 13 to 24 atm. Numerous poikilohydrous ferns have been studied in Africa and Brazil (Oppenheimer, 1960, citing Killian and Morello). One of the most interesting and thoroughly studied of the xerophytic ferns is *Ceterach officinarum*. Its extraordinary ability to dehydrate to low moisture levels and still recover is apparently related to various factors, including longitudinal collenchymatic thickening of parts of cell walls and solidification of vacuoles (Rouschal, 1938). Vacuolar solidification probably results from gelation of catechinlike

compounds during drying. Presumably, gelation prevents distortion or rupture of protoplasmic membranes during dehydration. Rouschal found that
fronds could lose 98 % of their total water without apparent injury. Osmotic
pressure was not especially high in this plant.

   C. officinarum has been further studied in detail by Oppenheimer (1962).
Water retention evidently is of some importance to drought resistance since
the scaly material on the fronds helps to retard water loss during droughts
(Fig. 1). However, as can be seen in the illustration, the drying delay is only
temporary. Fronds with scales dried to the same level as those without scales
in only a few hours.

   Loss of water by *Ceterach* was much more rapid than in many other fern
species, for example, *Polypodium polypoides*, which retained over three fourths
of its water after a week in a desiccator (Pessin, 1924). As *Ceterach* dehydrates,
its transpiration rate progressively decreases (Larcher, cited in Oppenheimer,
1962). Although retention of moisture thus probably plays a role in its
drought resistance, the capacity to survive severe drought depends on its
ability to recover from extremely low moisture levels. When fronds of this

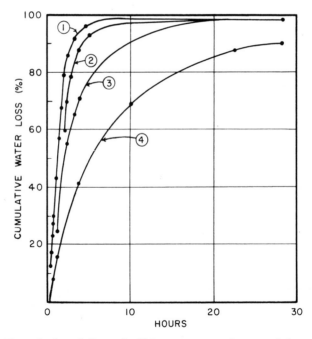

FIG. 1. Transpiration of *Ceterach officianarum* expressed as cumulative water loss in
percent following previous saturation. Fronds 1 and 2 without and fronds 3 and 4 with scales
and sporangia. From Oppenheimer and Halevy (1962), and by permission of the Research
Council of Israel.

species were kept over 90% H_2SO_4 (relative humidity of 0.02% at temperatures used) for 5 days, they still recovered. Some even survived over 100% H_2SO_4 for 5 days (Rouschal, 1937–1938). On the other hand, those kept over concentrated H_2SO_4 for 20 days died. Of course, this study again brings up the question of how viability can be accurately determined. Some fronds appeared alive to the eye after such treatment, but microscopic observations revealed shrunken protoplasts in rehydrated tissues. Using autofluorescence and plasmolysis tests as criteria of life, fronds could be dried in a desiccator over $CaCl_2$ and still revived (Oppenheimer and Halevy, 1962). About 3% of the bound water (on a dry weight basis) still remained and evidently was essential for survival. When fronds were remoistened, respiration immediately began again and was considerably higher than before drying.

A genus physiologically similar to *Ceterach* is *Ramondia*. This can be dried to powder dryness in 12 to 48 hours and will still recover (Koshanin, cited in Oppenheimer, 1962). Detached leaves could withstand desiccation for 2 to 3 years. Strangely, while tops survived, rootlets and root hairs usually died. However, new rootlets could be produced by watering. The hairy coating on *Ramondia* evidently helps in recovering moisture and may also delay desiccation in dry air, but hairs may have other more important functions such as protection against high insolation.

It can be seen from this brief review that very great desiccation resistance is sometimes found in nearly all the main groups of lower plants. In contrast, very few species of higher plants can withstand severe water loss, at least below about 50% of the saturation water content, without injury or death. The higher plants frequently depend on many different adaptations for maintenance of a favorable water balance, so they can usually continue metabolism in dry periods when many lower plants become dormant.

III. DROUGHT-RESISTANCE MECHANISMS IN HIGHER PLANTS

A great deal has been written on drought resistance in higher plants. The following does not attempt, then, even to mention all the various concepts, but what are considered to be the salient ideas are discussed. Historical material can be found in reviews by Stocker (1956), Levitt (1956), and Parker (1956).

A. CLASSIFICATION AND BACKGROUND

One of the first important questions is how to identify drought-resistant plants. In the early part of this century Kearney and Shantz (1911) and Shantz (1927), following a classification proposed by Ten Eyck in 1910, divided plants living in dry habitats into four groups: drought escaping, drought evading, drought enduring, and drought resistant. In one sense, at least, all these plants might be considered "xerophytes," since this word was used originally with a phytogeographical connotation (Schouw, 1822; Clements, 1902). But use of the word "xerophyte" is awkward, since the drought-escaping ephemerals may possess no adaptations to withstand drought other than producing drought-resistant seed. Such plants have been called "pseudoxerophytes" (Henkel, 1946). True xerophytes are usually thought to be plants that can withstand physiological drought of the soil or of high evaporation of the air without cessation of the living process (Huber, 1924, 1935).

The second category mentioned by Shantz, drought-evading plants, was thought to include those that economized on water use. In other words, some plants, such as cereals of semiarid regions, transpired little for a certain amount of unit dry-weight increment, where others transpired a great deal for the same amount. It was probably unknown at the time that since some plants have much larger root-per-leaf surfaces than other plants, their unit transpiration rate is greater than that of certain other plants of similar construction.

Drought-enduring plants were thought by Shantz to include semidesert shrubs that do not conserve water, but lose their leaves, and although drying to low levels, still survive. This property has been termed "desiccation resistance" (Parker, 1956) following the usage of Iljin (1933) and Höfler et al. (1941), or the "plasmatische Dürreresistenz" of Stocker (1956).

Finally, the drought-resistant plants were thought to be the "truly drought-resistant plants," that is, those which held water in leaves and stems in relatively large quantities. The most obvious examples are the succulents. As a matter of fact, some degree of water-retaining capacity is found in all the land-living tracheophytes.

Even before Shantz's time, Schimper (1903) laid much of the foundation for modern ideas of xerophytism, although most of these ideas seem to have evolved from the work of Volkens, Engler, and others. Reduction of transpiration to low levels during drought was emphasized as the important weapon of drought-resistant plants. For example, in tropical areas in which seasonal drought was common, reduction of transpiration by stomatal closure was believed to play an important role. This conclusion seemed supported by experiments of Kamerling (1917), who found that severed leaves of *Philodendron pertusum* lasted 31 days in the shade in a fresh condition, losing only 0.7% of the total leaf weight each day. Yet Kamerling was admittedly at a loss as to how to interpret the word xerophyte.

Many botanists think of a xerophyte as Schimper described typical perennial plants of the Saharan semidesert: "... absence or very weak development of leaf-blades, formation of thorns, felted tomentum, succulence, thick cuticle, coatings of wax, reduced intercellular spaces, protection of the stomata . . . ."

Lundegårdh (1949) considered the common mark of xerophytes to be a "far-reaching resistance to wilting," to translate the German. He cited Stocker's work in the Egyptian deserts that identified plants with frequent water deficits of 50 % of the original water content. This is in contrast to many mesophytes that often wilt when their water content is lowered by as little as 1 %. Lundegårdh also mentioned that high osmotic pressures were frequently associated with xerophytes. For example, Volk (cited in Lundegårdh) measured 102 atm in certain xerophytes near Würzburg. However, Walter (cited in Lundegårdh) felt that some of Volk's measurements may have been in error, and Walter found few plants with OP's of more than 50 atm. Of course, many succulents have very low OP values yet are considered xerophytes. Recently, diffusion pressure deficits (DPD's) at the lethal point of drying were found to be 45 atm for tomato, 90 atm for privet, and at least 130 atm for a species of *Acacia* (Slatyer, 1960). Whether such high DPD's are a real advantage to the plant or are merely a result of their survival when DPD's build up to such high levels is a point of controversy.

Although leaf water maintenance may be the most important factor in many plants for surviving drought, the idea arose early that there were differences among species in moisture levels to which they could be dried and still stay alive (Schröder, 1909). In other words, this was their desiccation resistance, apparently a property of the cells themselves. Also, the tolerance of cells of certain lower plants to solutions of various OP's were known at an early time to be important to survival, and this varied widely in different species.

It is to Maximov's credit (for example, Maximov, 1929a) that he realized the importance of the desiccation-resistance concept. After his travels to North America and to the semideserts of Central Asia, he became convinced of the importance of protoplasmic resistance to drying, or what he called "true xerophytism." Maximov also discovered that xerophytes did not necessarily transpire less than mesophytes, but under humid soil conditions might actually transpire more, at least on the basis of unit leaf area. Oppenheimer (1960), however, believes that most true xerophytes of the semidesert transpire on a whole-plant basis less on the average than mesophytic plants.

Lately the word "xerophyte" has again fallen under criticism. Stocker (1954) felt that Kamerling's question—"Which plants shall we call xerophytes?"—was really obsolete since many species of plants, all growing in one habitat, had so many different adaptations that interblended with each other that it was practically impossible to define the term.

More recently Stocker (1961) referred to "drought resistance strictly speaking," by which he meant the "fundamental drought resistance of the protoplasm." This is reminiscent of Maximov's (1929b) use of "true xero-phytism" to characterize plants with considerable desiccation resistance.

In another recent classification (Levitt *et al.*, 1960), xerophytism was divided into two categories: (1) the ability to stay alive (drought resistance) and (2) the ability to grow and develop (no name [sic]). The former was sub-divided into (a) drought avoidance and (b) drought tolerance (drought hardi-ness was defined differently). Drought avoidance was further divided into ephemerals, water spenders (drought evading), and water savers (drought enduring)—but "evading" was used in a different sense from that of Shantz.

Today many investigators think that these characteristics are determined largely by the plant's genetic constitution and cannot be greatly altered with-out crossing over between two individuals. Although thorns seem to form on certain semidesert plants subjected to drought and "sun leaves" differ from "shade leaves" (for example, Hanson, 1917), most species change dis-appointingly little when subjected to dry conditions and much of the real change may be merely stunting of growth brought on by frequent loss of turgidity (Kramer, 1949), resulting in smaller cells and other characteristics mentioned elsewhere in this review.

B. Moisture Retention

The term moisture retention is used loosely here to include the various means by which moisture is maintained within the plant above levels that might result in its injury or death. Leaves, stems, and roots are taken up in that order.

1. Leaves

Leaves are often the most sensitive part of the plant to drought and at the same time are usually essential for the process of food manufacture. Perhaps largely for these reasons they have been studied more than other parts of the plant. Their various complex characteristics are taken up below.

a. Overall Leaf Character. "Xeromorphic" structures, presumed to be effec-tive in retaining water, frequently are not effective at all in this way (Walter, 1949; Shields, 1950). Many xeromorphic characteristics can be brought on by growing the plant under conditions of bright illumination to enhance rapid transpiration. Under these circumstances they tend to develop the following characteristics (Walter, 1949):

1. Greater thickness of leaf vein per leaf surface
2. Greater number of stomatal openings per unit surface area
3. Smaller size of stomata
4. Smaller size of epidermal and mesophyll cells
5. Greater numbers of hairs per surface, but smaller hairs
6. Thicker outer walls of epidermis and cuticle

Reduction of transpiration often is discussed without particular regard for the basis of the water loss (dry weight, total plant surface area, etc.). Actually, transpiration rate per unit leaf surface is not so much a function of the leaf character (within certain generalized types) as it is of the leaf area per root absorbing surface (Parker, 1949). As gardeners have long believed, some reduction of the top of the plants is an advantage after transplanting when the root surface is reduced by breakage. Probably this increases the amount of water available to the few leaves left. On the other hand a disadvantage of twig pruning is that the photosynthetic surface and food supply for root growth are reduced.

b. *Leaf-Fall and Size Reduction.* Many species of trees possess a mechanism for leaf abscission during drought. Certain semidesert plants are thought to have an advantage by thus reducing transpiration (Runyon, 1934). In some cases, however, it is questionable if this is really an advantage (Ashby, 1932). At least in some semidesert plants, leaf abscission would seem to be an advantage (Oppenheimer, 1960). Leaf shedding, or at least premature autumn defoliation, is also common in deciduous trees of the eastern United States. Usually the trees recover and leaf out the following spring, but even late summer defoliation until about mid-August is harmful to *Acer saccharum* trees and can result in some "dieback" the following year (Houston and Kuntz, 1964). In the Mediterranean region, too, various fruit trees and xerophytic shrubs undergo premature defoliation during an unusually dry period. In Central Asia, species of *Calligonum, Ephedra, Kochia, Artemisia, Salsola,* and *Chondrilla* shed their leaves at the beginning or middle of the summer (Sveshnikova and Zalensky, 1956).

Some Mediterranean species like *Anagyris foetida* are normally leafless in the dry summer and bear leaves and flowers in the rainy season (Evenari, cited in Oppenheimer, 1960). In fact, the rocky heaths of the Mediterranean shores and the Near East abound in low shrubs with superficial root systems, and therefore do not depend on deep soil moisture. These plants possess large leaves in the rainy season and replace them with smaller ones in summer. Examples are *Thymus capitatus* and *Salvia triloba* (Oppenheimer, 1960). Some shrubs replace their leaves with brachyblasts or, in other cases, stipules remain after leaf-fall. These stay alive and turgid under low soil moisture conditions. In *Zygophyllum dumosum* the leaflets are shed and petioles remain attached to the plant (Zohary and Orshansky, 1954). The transpiring surface is thereby reduced by as much as 85%. Zohary and Orshansky concluded that many plants depend on the reduction of leaf number and mass in the rainless season to survive, whereas regulation of water loss by leaves usually plays a minor part in water retention in the semidesert. Both attached to severed branches and detached leaves of *Artemisia tridentata* in Idaho dried from 170 to 60% of the dry weight within only 3 days (Parker, unpublished data).

Other shrubs such as the "switch plant" (*Ephedra trifurca*) of New Mexico
survive as leafless green twigs (Coulter *et al.*, 1911). The structures sometimes
seen on the twigs are reproductive organs. However, Oppenheimer (1960)
points out that little is known of the water economy of the leafless shrubs. In
some cases their unit surface transpiration is very high because of deep
rooting, but other evidence indicates they can reduce transpiration to low
levels. Most plants of the great Indian semideserts also have no leaves, for
example, *Euphorbia royaleana* (Sarup, 1952).

Another peculiarity of leaves adapted to xeric locations is their rolling or
folding (Fig. 2) during a drought. There is evidence that in some plants, such
as *Stipa tenacissima*, rolling reduces transpiration. Grasses in the Mediterranean region and in Auvergne can reduce transpiration as much as 46 to 63 %
by rolling. The effect is even more pronounced with certain grasses of the
Sahara (Oppenheimer, 1960). Specialized cells sometimes called "bulbiform"
cells (*b* in Fig. 2) shrink and cause the leaf to fold or roll (Löv, 1926). In contrast to such reports some investigators were unable to confirm the usefulness
of leaf rolling or folding (Bennet-Clark, cited in Grieve, 1955). In many

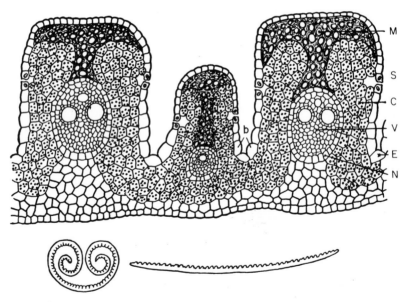

Fig. 2. Cross sections of the leaf of a xerophytic grass, the sea sand reed (*Ammophila
arenaria*). Above: Cross section, highly magnified. c = chlorenchyma, s = stoma, e =
epidermis, b = bulbiform or water-containing cells, v = vascular tissue, n = bundle sheath,
m = mechanical tissue. Below right: Turgid open leaf, low magnification; below left: des-
iccated inrolled leaf, low magnification. From Coulter, *et al.* (1911), by permission of the
American Book Co.

species leaf rolling does not occur until the water content is reduced below the lethal level.

c. Hairs. Hairs are among the most prominent "xeromorphic" structures of leaves and stems. It might be supposed that such hairs decrease transpiration and, in fact, some workers support this idea (Wiegand, 1910; Yapp, 1912). In contrast, Sayre's (1920) experiments suggest that removal of leaf hairs decreases transpiration. Trichomes of such plants as *Crassula* can absorb water readily from droplets on their surface. It would not be too surprising, therefore, if removal of hairs reduced total transpiring surface.

Actually, the situation is more complicated than this. In *A. tridentata* some hairs are alive and filled with protoplasm whereas others are dead and usually filled with air (Diettert, 1937). Furthermore, hairs may serve other purposes, as in scattering incoming radiation or in breaking up soil-reflected radiation, preventing insect attack, and helping to cool the leaf by increasing total radiating surface.

d. Stomata. There is no question that stomatal closure results in some retardation of transpiration in most leaves. A decline in transpiration was related to stomatal closure by F. Darwin (1915) and many subsequent investigators. According to the fundamental investigations of Loftfield (1921) and Stålfelt (1929) on herbaceous plants, and of other workers on woody plants (for example, Pisek and Winkler, 1953), stomatal closure is directly related to a slowing, but not necessarily to a complete cessation of transpiration. In the meantime, photosynthesis may decline at a different rate than does transpiration as stomata close. This may be of great importance to dry matter production and thus to competition and survival in certain xerophytic plants (Larcher, 1965).

In rather drought-resistant crop plants, stomata close more rapidly than in less resistant ones (Stocker *et al.*, 1943). Early stomatal closure helps to maintain a favorable water balance. Even partial closure retards transpiration. The rapid decline in transpiration of a severed leaf can be related to stomatal closure (Huber, 1923; Oppenheimer, 1932; Pisek and Winkler, 1953), and experiments of Satoo and Hakuhara (1953) show that stomatal behavior is directly related to transpiration in *Euonymus japonicus* cuttings.

On the other hand, many drought-resistant plants keep their stomata open longer than some less drought-resistant plants (Shields, 1950). Conifers generally withstand a little more leaf dehydration than broadleaved deciduous species before they begin to close their stomata (Pisek and Winkler, 1953). Stomatal control also has other limitations since cuticular transpiration is very great in some plants. Hence, even if stomata close, some plants soon dehydrate and die.

Whether stomata close completely during dehydration has long been a matter of some doubt. Maximov (1929b) stated that stomatal closure was not complete in many species but that stomatal closure had an advantage for many plants in spite of his criticism of Schimper's concept and his enthusiasm for the idea of desiccation resistance.

Stomatal opening is not as easy to determine as is sometimes supposed, and in conifers with waxy plugs in the stomatal cavities (Fig. 3) it cannot be measured by a surface replica method. This must be done by some other means, such as a dye–penetration method. One procedure for determining stomatal aperture employs Gentian Violet dissolved in ethoxyethanol and

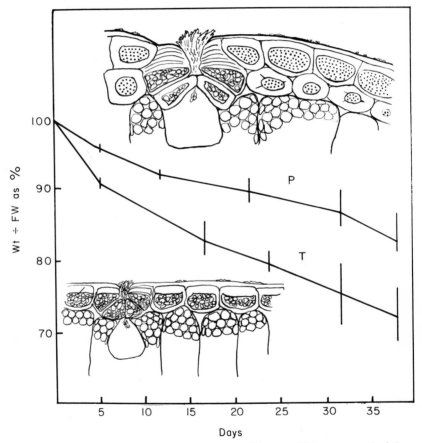

FIG. 3. Upper right: Cross section of epidermal layers of *Picea pungens* leaf. Lower left: Same section of *Tsuga canadensis* leaf. × 500. Graph shows leaf weight as a percentage of fresh weight for *Picea* (P) and *Tsuga* (T) kept as excised, 10-cm-long twigs over 2 *M* sucrose. Vertical lines indicate scatter of data from three samples, each taken from a different tree.

combined with solvents having a low surface tension like chloroform and ether (Oppenheimer and Engelberg, 1962). The solution is placed on the underside of the leaf, and the percentage of surface penetrated is estimated. Such a method showed complete closure of stomata in *Rhododendron, Kalmia,* and *Pinus* leaves throughout the winter in southern Connecticut, even though the surface replica method indicated some stomata open at all times in *Rhododendron* (Parker, unpublished data).

e. Leaf Coatings. Reference is sometimes made to the thickness of the cuticle (Fig. 4) as if this were proportional to the cuticular water loss from the

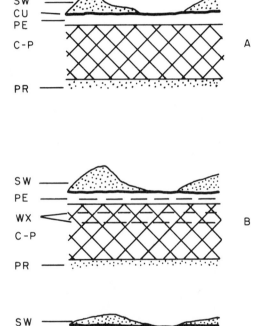

FIG. 4. Diagrams of cuticular development of a cell wall at the leaf surface, seen in cross section (generalized from various species such as corn). A = cell margin of early stage with primary cuticle developing. B + C = stages in impregnation of wax into pectin and cellulose-pectin layer. SW = surface wax, CU = cuticle, PE = pectin layer, C-P = cellulose–pectinlayer, PR = protoplasm, WX = wax. From Schieferstein and Loomis (1958), by permission of The Iowa Academy of Science.

leaf, but this has too often been based on nonexistent evidence. It is questionable if cuticular thickness alone is proportional to the delay in water loss through the cuticle, because the cuticle is complex and varies among species both in fine structure and chemical composition. As the cuticle dries out, submicroscopic channels passing through the cuticle evidently constrict and much less water loss occurs from a dry cuticle than from a moist one (Oppenheimer, 1960). There is no doubt, of course, that water loss is greatly retarded by the cuticle.

Cutin is a fatty material that appears to consist of stearocutic and oleocutic acids in a proportion of 1 : 5 (Meara, in Paech and Tracey, 1955). Lipids also occur in cell walls and can retard water loss. Cuticular transpiration can be one forty-fifth of the total normal transpiration in species of *Kalmia* (Mittmeyer, cited in Oppenheimer, 1960).

Waxes are excreted by submicroscopic pores out to the leaf surface. Such waxes are esters of higher fatty acids and higher fatty alcohols along with free higher acids and higher alcohols. They may be deposited directly on the cuticle and thus retard transpiration. Some workers, however, hold that this external waxy layer is not of much importance in retarding cuticular transpiration (Mueller *et al.*, 1954). Their electron-microscope photographs, made by shadow-casting replicas of the leaf surface of *Picea* leaves, revealed that external waxes were not evenly distributed (Fig. 4) and were readily brushed off. Old leaves generally had less surface wax than younger ones. Apparently, the important controlling factor for cuticular transpiration is the deposition of wax within the cellulose–pectin wall (Fig. 4), not necessarily on top of it (Schieferstein and Loomis, 1958).

The epidermal wax of apples appears to increase in amount as the fruits mature. In some varieties of apple the cutin oil content increases. According to Hall *et al.* (1954) this cutin oil increase causes a decrease in oxygen transfer more than that of CO_2. This follows the laws concerning the behavior of gases passing through lipids.

Resinous exudations that occur on leaves of certain semidesert plants such as *Larrea tridentata* often cover the stomatal surfaces (Runyon, 1934). However, old leaves produce more resin than the young leaves and are generally more drought sensitive than the young ones. This does not by itself disprove the theory that the resin helps to retain water since it may still retard water loss where it does occur.

Volkens (cited in Oppenheimer, 1960) found resinous coatings on leaves of certain plants in the Leguminosae, Saxifragaceae, Anacardiaceae, Compositae, and Zygophyllaceae. He assumed that these coatings had a transpiration-retarding effect. Morello (1955–1956) concluded that various species of *Larrea* could greatly reduce water loss by stomatal closure and such water retention was important to continued metabolism. If this is so, then resinous coatings might aid moisture retention and further some photosynthesis in a period before a dormant condition is attained.

2. Stems

With respect to drought resistance, adaptations of stems can be divided into three categories: (1) adaptations for water storage, (2) prevention of water loss, and (3) lowered resistance to water conduction. There are other adaptations, such as water absorption through the bark, but little is written on these (reviewed by Parker, 1956). Since transpiration and resistance to water transport are considered elsewhere in this book, they will not be discussed here.

Water Storage. It has been known since the writings of Robert Hartig in the mid-1800's that water content of trees may fluctuate seasonally, yet to this day it is not entirely clear what internal or external factors control such variations. It appears from Gibbs' (1958) graphs that there is commonly a decline in the water content of many broadleaved trees during the summer, reaching an annual low in early autumn. One of the curious things about these results is the marked rise in water content in spring. In many trees that undergo a spring rise in water content, a natural positive pressure develops usually before bud-break and leaf expansion. In some species, like *Fraxinus americana*, moisture content increase also occurs, even in those that do not normally exude in spring and thus apparently do not develop positive stem pressures at that time.

If it is assumed that there is little water transpired through the bark, then much of the water in the trunk is available for transpiration in times of drought. Yet when the amount of water used by an average forest tree in 1 day (perhaps 20 gallons) is calculated, it is difficult to see how the tree's water content can act as much of a reservoir. There is little doubt that trunk water content often declines during a drought (Parker, 1956), but how much value the storage water would have in tiding over the period when leaves are lost is an open question.

It has been suggested that some trees can be " leaf seasoned " by felling and leaving them on the forest floor with leaves intact, but there is little difference in trunk water content between felled trees with branches intact and those with branches removed (Smith and Goebel, 1952). On the other hand, experiments with *Pseudotsuga menziesii* branches suggest that some " leaf seasoning " should be possible in this species (Parker, unpublished data).

In some species of plants the water content of the stem appears to play a definite role in maintaining the water content of the photosynthetic cells. Certain succulent desert plants have thick, fleshy stems that can contract or expand, depending on their water content (Coulter *et al.*, 1911).

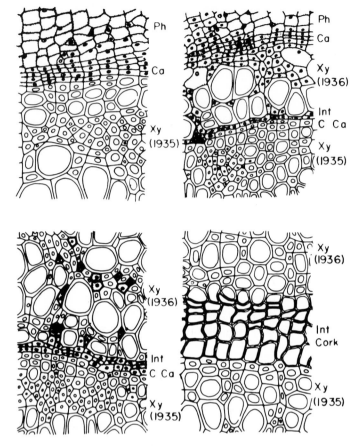

FIG. 5. Cross sections of *Artemisia tridentata* stem. Above left: Collected September 29, 1935. Above right: Collected April 13, 1936. New wood ring about 65 μ wide. Lower left: Collected May 12, 1936. New wood ring about 330 μ wide; only part shown. Lower right: Collected August 1, 1963. Ph = phloem, Ca = cambium, Xy = xylem, Int. C. Ca. = interxylary cork cambium, Int. cork = interxylary cork. All × 365. From Diettert (1937), by permission of *Lloydia*.

Some woody plants in dry regions take on the character of subterranean trees, for example, *Andira humilis* in Brazil (Rawitscher *et al.*, 1943). These trees develop a subterranean trunk and only put out short leafy shoots that emerge just above ground level. In this way, trunk transpiration probably is reduced to low levels.

Stems of some semidesert plants are equipped with corky layers within the xylem, as in species of *Artemisia* (Diettert, 1937). Such layers occur between annual rings (Fig. 5) and possibly help to retain stem moisture and thus to preserve intact the columns of water in the xylary cells.

3. Roots

There are many aspects of roots that relate to drought resistance. Not the least of these is terminal growth, but since this aspect is treated elsewhere in this book it is only mentioned briefly here. Moisture storage and extent and depth of roots are probably also of key importance to survival of dry periods. These are taken up in order.

a. Moisture Storage. Many species of plants store large quantities of water in their roots. This is true not only of semidesert plants, but also of meso-phytic ones of moister environments. All sorts of fleshy roots (consisting mainly of cortex) can be found in biennial plants. However, it should be recalled that many underground storage organs like tubers and bulbs are adaptations of stems and leaves, not roots.

Among semidesert plants, Volkens (cited in Schimper, 1903) was one of the first to describe many remarkable adaptations for storing water in dry regions. In East Africa between Kilimanjaro and the coast, he found many forms that seemed to be literally caricatures, each species having its own grotesque way of surviving in such a climate. Plants with great, bulblike swellings at the root collar, with scraggy, small twigs and extensive roots, with succulent stems and small temporary roots, and so on, were described.

Turning to woody plants of more moist climates, roots seem to have definite limitations in the amount of moisture they can retain above the lethal level in very dry periods. Small roots, and especially root tips, shrink, change color, and may die during a drought. Studies with glass-sided boxes showed that when soil in which *Pinus taeda* seedlings were growing was dried to the wilting point, the roots ceased growth and then turned brownish and shrank somewhat. If the dry condition (approximately the ultimate wilting point) continued for several days, the roots died; but if they were rewatered within about 5 days, new growth began somewhat back from the old growing tip (Parker, unpublished data).

In *P. halepensis*, when growing roots became dormant during drought, the outer 6 to 8 layers of cortical cells collapsed and died as they turned brown. This change was related to total suberization of endodermal cell walls (Leshem, 1965). The color change evidently was not caused by production of suberin, since the brown pigment was bleached out without removing suberin. Even the root tip itself became suberized, judging by Sudan staining of longisections of the root. When growth resumed, a new white root tip burst out from the suberized layers.

In this connection it is difficult to understand how some aerial roots of certain tropical plants can withstand dry air and yet absorb water readily in moist periods. Haberlandt (1928) suggested that "penetration cells" of the root endodermis could allow water to enter; then, when roots shrank with dehydration, such cells could close by shrinkage, something like windows in the side of a building, and thus prevent moisture within the endodermis from escaping.

Roots of most mesophytic woody plants evidently depend largely on retaining moisture above the lethal level for survival during a drought. Smaller roots must suffer keenly from extended periods of drought when soil moisture falls below the ultimate wilting point. Recent studies showed that root cells (mainly bark parenchyma) of *Quercus rubra*, *Fraxinus americana*, and *Acer saccharum* were all about equally resistant to dehydration, the lower limit of survival (lethal level) being about 92% atmospheric relative humidity (Parker, 1968). They thus possess about the same desiccation resistance as tissue sections of oak leaves tested by Sullivan and Levitt (1959; Table III).

Tests of water loss rates from 10-cm-long root segments about 1 cm thick revealed some species differences (Parker, 1968). *Acer saccharum* roots lost

TABLE III

UPPER PORTION: SURVIVAL OF LEAF SECTIONS OF DROUGHTED AND UNDROUGHTED OAK SEEDLINGS AFTER 24 HOURS IN AIR OF RELATIVE HUMIDITIES INDICATED[a]; LOWER PORTION: SURVIVAL OF ROOT BARK SECTIONS FROM MATURE TREES AFTER 24 HOURS IN AIR OF INDICATED RELATIVE HUMIDITIES[b]

	Relative humidity (%)			
	100	96	94	92
Quercus palustris	100	100	33	0
Quercus rubra	100	100	71	16
	Relative humidity (%)			
	99	97	95	86
Quercus borealis	70[c]	72	60	10
Fraxinus americana	40	30	20	3
Acer saccharum	30	18	5	3

[a] From Sullivan and Levitt (1959).

[b] Data represent percentage of living cells in thin slices of root tissue kept in air at relative humidities shown at 22°C. From Parker (1968).

[c] Each number is the average of 9 root sections, 3 roots from each of 3 trees. Statistical analysis did not show significant differences among species at the 5% level in this and 2 similar experiments.

water by bark transpiration about twice as fast as roots of *Fraxinus americana* or *Quercus rubra*. Any injury, such as a cut or gouge in the bark, greatly increased transpiration from the root segment. Whether this difference among species would be of any importance to survival during drought is yet to be demonstrated. Water loss from roots to soil might not only occur as liquid water moving along gradients of tension, but also as vapor into the soil air spaces if the soil were dry enough.

b. Depth and Extent of Roots. Root depth is one of the most important factors, not only in survival of a great many semidesert plants, but of many relatively mesophytic plants including North American forest trees. Although many semidesert species are not deeply rooted, others are. Because of its deep root system, *A. tridentata* is considered more an indicator of moist subsoil conditions than of dry-surface soils.

The problem for such plants is mainly that of establishment; in fact, it might seem a mystery how they can become established at all. Usually there is an enormous quantity of seed produced; then, under just the correct moisture conditions, apparently as controlled by growth hormones (Went, 1948, 1949), these seeds germinate (Walter, 1949). Even then, only rarely are moisture conditions suitable in certain years to allow deep root growth and successful establishment. These plants, including species of *Artemisia* and *Larrea*, are actually poorly adapted for moist conditions and for some reason quickly die if not grown under dry atmospheric conditions (Parker, unpublished data).

Even in mesophytic forests the speed and depth of root penetration are of great importance. Probably the success of *Quercus* seedlings, compared to the frequent failure of other species in forested areas of the eastern United States, is a result of their ability to produce a deep tap root in the first few months of growth. The large seed can nourish a large root extension, and the root penetrates deeper than the general mass of roots of mature trees that are so prolific in the upper soil layers.

In the Rocky Mountains, root development of seedlings is quite important to their withstanding dry periods (Leaphart and Wicker, 1966). In *Pseudotsuga menziesii*, tap roots were found to be well developed in the seedling stage, whereas in *Abies grandis*, *Thuja plicata*, and to some extent in *Pinus monticola*, tap roots were poorly defined.

In the plains areas of the United States, survival of trees has frequently been associated with deep roots developed early in life. *Platanus occidentalis* 6 years old had roots 7 feet deep; *Juglans nigra*, *Quercus rubra*, and *Carya ovata* of similar age (about 6 years old) had roots down to 5 feet in depth (Biswell, 1935). *Populus deltoides* appeared to be intermediate between these two, although depth of roots also was a function of soil conditions. *Robinia pseudoacacia* of undefined age had roots 24 to 27 feet deep in the plains areas of the United States, whereas *Juglans nigra* and *Fraxinus americana* penetrated to a little over 5 feet in similar sites (Weaver and Kramer, 1932).

Quercus macrocarpa is one of the most hardy trees in forest–prairie transition areas, although it also occurs in comparatively wet regions. Probably much of its success, besides a certain resistance to fire, can be traced to its ability to put down a tap root 3 to 5 feet deep in the first summer and to produce extensive laterals at a later age. Roots extending out 55 feet from the bole of the tree are not uncommon (Weaver and Kramer, 1932). Albertson and Weaver (1945) also mentioned the unusual root system of *Q. macrocarpa* and its importance during drought. They described one situation in which species of *Populus* adapted to wet soils died, whereas those adapted to dry sites at higher elevations survived. This occurred because in the drier sites roots had penetrated more deeply than in the wet sites and, as a result, trees in the dry sites did not suffer as much as those in the wet.

Deep roots that allow ample transpiration to occur throughout the year were described for semidesert plants in northwestern Argentina, for example, *Larrea divaricata* and a species of *Acacia* (Morello, 1952, 1955–1956). In the Negev, as a result of deep rooting, certain *Acacias* were able to carry on uninterrupted cambial activity throughout the year in spite of the dry climate (Oppenheimer, 1960). One specimen of *Acacia*, in the vicinity of the Suez canal, was described by Huber (cited in Oppenheimer, 1960) as having roots 30 m deep.

In parts of Brazil where drought is a seasonal occurrence, species of *Andira* have roots penetrating 19 m into the soil (Rawitscher *et al.*, 1943). This allows them to transpire freely throughout the dry season, a situation that seems to allow high CO_2 absorption.

C. Desiccation Resistance

The concept of desiccation resistance was propagated by such investigators as Iljin and Maximov who pioneered much of the field of drought resistance in the earlier part of this century. Iljin (1931) defined *Austrocknungsfähigkeit* as the lowest relative humidity with which a plant can come to equilibrium without injury. This term, as well as *Austrocknungsresistenz* (Höfler, 1942), has been translated and widely used as " desiccation resistance." Höfler *et al.* (1941), following the ideas of Stocker (1928), referred to " critical saturation deficit " as the greatest water loss without injury a plant can withstand, expressed as a percentage of saturation water. This value is very close to, but not quite the same as, Oppenheimer's (1932) " sublethal water saturation deficit," which was based on the moisture content, expressed as a percentage of dry weight, at which dry spots begin to appear on the leaf. Levitt (1956), however, used " tolerance to drought dehydration " and considered it equal to the saturation water content divided by the water content at the critical point of injury. In the meantime, Stocker's (1956) "plasmatische Dürreresistenz" appears to apply to the resistance of the protoplasm itself, rather than to whole tissues or organs.

1. Species Differences

Lethal levels have been determined in plants either on the basis of the relative humidity they can survive or on their own water content. When the latter value is used, there is a problem of the best basis of comparison between species. Use of dry weight, fresh weight, surface area, or even other factors all have their difficulties. In the final analysis, there is no truly valid basis for comparison of different species.

Then, too, the lethal level is very difficult to ascertain, since it is based on various criteria of life, each criterion giving a somewhat different assessment of the lethal point. One of the more satisfactory indicators of life is tetrazolium chloride or one of its closely allied derivatives (Parker, 1953). Nitro blue tetrazolium chloride is a modern improvement. Some investigators believe that the neutral red test is somewhat more precise. This test depends on the ability of the cell to take up and hold the neutral red in its vacuole. Oppenheimer and Shomer-Ilan (1963), for example, felt that this was more precise than the tetrazolium test but that the neutral red test should be coupled with a plasmolysis test as well. In the case of the tetrazoliums, there is a gradual decline in rate of reduction to the colored compound as the leaf or plant organ is increasingly injured. This means that a sharp endpoint is sometimes quite difficult to define (Parker, 1952).

Appearance of the leaf (color, shape, hue of green) would seem a simple and straightforward criterion of life, but partial injury can be difficult to determine since, for example, all the inner cells of the leaf may be dead when necrotic spots begin to appear on the surface (Oppenheimer and Shomer-Ilan, 1963).

While some writers have claimed that there are various levels of injury, it appears difficult in practice to determine a point of "partial injury," since this may become total injury. A study of various native and evergreen conifer leaves (Parker, 1966) showed that values for lethal levels were sufficiently variable within individuals of the same species so that few significant differences among species could be defined. *Juniperus virginiana* and *J. communis*, however, were significantly more resistant to desiccation than other species tested, including many common species of *Pinus*, *Picea*, *Abies*, and several broadleaved shrubs. Varietal differences in desiccation resistance among different geographic origins of Douglas fir are now known (Pharis and Ferrell, 1966).

Assuming that lethal levels can be determined with some accuracy and knowing that frost resistance varies markedly with the season, a seasonal

TABLE IV

DROUGHT RESISTANCE OF CURRENT YEAR'S LEAVES OF *Pinus Cembra* IN A WIND TUNNEL AT DIFFERENT TIMES IN THE GROWING SEASON[a]

Date	Hours since beginning drought												
	24	36	48	60	72	84	96	108	120	132	144	156	168
July 15	1	i	i	d	d	d	d	d					
	1	i	1	d	d	d	d	d					
	1	i	d	d	d	d	d	d					
August 12	1	1	1	1	i	d	d	d					
	1	1	1	i	i	d	i	d					
	1	1	1	1	1	i	d	d					
September 9	1	1	1	1	1	1	i	i	i				
	1	1	1	1	1	1	i	i	i				
	1	1	1	1	1	1	1	i	i				
October 15	1	1	1	1	1	1	i	i	i	i			d
	1	1	1	1	i	1	1	1	i				d
	1	1	1	1	1	1	i	i	1	1			i

[a] The thin line delineates the time when the needles of at least 2 of the 3 test seedlings suffered some injury; the thick line, when they were fully dead. Assessment of the damage made 1 month after the 168-hour period. d = dead, i = intermediate, 1 = living. From Tranquillini (1965).

variation in desiccation resistance in certain plants might be expected. This
has been proven to be the case (Pisek and Larcher, 1954). Also, conifer
seedlings vary considerably in their drought resistance during the growing
season (Table IV), becoming more resistant from summer to autumn (Tranquillini, 1965). The cause of this seasonal change is uncertain. In *Pinus
ponderosa*, 2-year-old leaves transpire more rapidly than the current year's
leaves after they are severed from the branch, and 3-year-old leaves transpire
more rapidly than 2-year-old leaves (Parker, 1954). However, this year-to-year
change is the reverse of what one would expect from the one-season study of
Tranquillini. It could be that the drought-resistance increase during the first
summer is related to an increased desiccation resistance together with the
development of a more impermeable cuticle, whereas the subsequent year-
to-year change is the result of more ineffective stomatal closure. In this
connection it is known that desiccation resistance of certain crop plants,
capable of frost hardening, can be increased by drying treatment (Levitt
et al., 1960).

2. Submicroscopic Factors

In the early part of the present century very little was known about the
submicroscopic structure of protoplasm. In spite of this, a great deal of work
was done in the 1920's and 1930's on the morphology and development of the
microscopically visible parts of cytoplasm, such as mitochondria and other
organelles. Phenomena such as protoplasmic streaming and plasmolysis were
studied in detail. It was revealed at an early time that a dehydrated cell could
almost entirely lose its vacuole; then, on rehydration if cell membranes were
still intact, the vacuole could swell again and assume its original size and shape.
However, if membranes were broken, the vacuole was unable to swell again.

This suggested to Iljin (1931) the so-called mechanical theory of drought
injury. Some workers believed that plasmodesmata, connecting one cell to
another through the cell walls, were stretched during shrinkage and forced to
break, thus tearing the plasma membrane (reviewed by Levitt, 1956). There are
other problems involved here such as ectoplasmic viscosity and adherence of
the cytoplasm to the cell wall (Parker, 1963). In the meantime, in the past two
decades a great deal of energy has been spent on resolving the submicroscopic
character of the nucleus, apparently because of the interest in growth and
genetics. In fact, many reviews on cytology often turn out to be mainly discussions of the condition of the nucleus while the cytoplasm is only briefly
mentioned.

As better information on protein structure became available via classic
molecular chemistry and electron microscope studies, theories could at least be
suggested to explain why protoplasm became "hardy" to drought, heat, and

cold. Stocker (1951) supposed that protoplasm consisted of a latticework of threadlike proteins interspersed with water, salts, sugars, and other kinds of proteins. Points of adhesion in the latticework or fibrils were thought to consist of chemical valence bonds, electrical attractive forces, and adsorptive forces. This is in accord with knowledge that in certain proteins, disulfide, salt, and hydrogen bonds are the major linkages maintaining the structure of the protein (for example, Ling, 1962).

Continuing with Stocker's theory, drought hardening was thought (the evidence was questioned by some) to involve a strengthening of the bonds and thus to an increase in structural viscosity as well as a decrease in pore permeability (to water and urea). Two conditions were believed to occur in sequence during a drought: a reaction and a restitution phase (Stocker, 1951). The first phase consists of disorganization and loosening of the latticework and the second, of reorganization and tightening of this lattice of fibrils.

However, modern experimentation has added many new facts since the early 1950's. First, there are many forms of proteins in the cell, any one of which in theory could be denatured by dehydration. Proteins may act as membranes, fibers, globules, and still other forms. One of the important factors influencing the condition of these proteins is the water bound to them. Also, there are the RNA and DNA complexes associated with proteins that evidently can be influenced by the condition of bound water.

It has become apparent in recent years that protein production by the living cell is dependent on nucleic acids bound to proteins and that injury to this mechanism, as for instance by desiccation, is probably one of the all-important keys to cell injury, since by this means the production of replacement enzymes is destroyed (Webb, 1965).

Working mainly with bacteria and viruses, Webb (1965) gives an insight into the problem of desiccation injury that may be a very long step in ultimate solution of the problem of desiccation injury in living plants. Nevertheless, it should be recalled that higher plants are not bacteria. The large cells encountered in many higher plants frequently contain immense vacuoles, and injury to cell membranes by mechanical tearing may be an important factor in cell injury.

Experiments of Webb and his colleagues suggest that desiccation injury does not take place in the realm of the usual enzymes, such as those of the Krebs cycle, nor does it seem to involve the cell's overall continuity. Rather, injury occurs to a more complex and perhaps more delicate system already mentioned: the process by which new enzymes are manufactured, the RNA–DNA complex. Various protective substances were studied during the process of dehydration. Although some of these substances had a protective effect, many were toxic to bacterial cells. Evidently, the most effective protective substances were the polyhydroxy cyclic saturated hydrocarbons, especially inositol. Not only was inositol nontoxic, but it appeared to replace bound water by hydrogen bonding and to fit in the layer between the nucleic acid and protein to which the nucleic acid was bonded.

The fact that the C-6 sugars are closely allied chemically to inositol, in that they have numerous OH groups and often occur in saturated rings, supports the idea that starch ⇌ sugar shifts, so often observed in plants exposed to cold or drought, are more than just coincidence. Probably certain sugars protect the RNA–DNA complex as well as certain enzymes known to be frost or drought sensitive.

At this point an example might be drawn from the literature to illustrate the importance of bound water in protein spirals (Fig. 6) and to indicate how loss of such water could disrupt the normal structure and function of the protein. Within the protein spiral, linkages with water molecules play a definite role in the protein's reactivity. Part of a protein is shown in Fig. 6 according to Ling (1962) being denatured by the addition of trichloroacetic acid (TCA) or by ammonium chloride (NH_4Cl). It will be seen that the two water molecules (W) provide a stable connection between the positive and negative ions attached to the protein chain. When TCA is added as the sodium salt, Na^+ is weakly adsorbed to the water molecules still attached to the negative point. There is then an uncoiling of the protein and a change in the —SH reactivity. The change consists of a lowering of the electric potential ($\mathscr{E}°$).

In the case of NH_4Cl, the NH^+ is strongly adsorbed and the water molecules are lost. The effect on the —SH group is to raise the $\mathscr{E}°$ value. This change of $\mathscr{E}°$ means that the reactivity of the —SH group and thus of the protein is altered. Possibly something like this occurs during dehydration, in which water molecules are moved out from the positions shown in Fig. 6.

Ling (1962) also discussed the effect of heat that could bring about a removal of the 2 water molecules separating the plus and minus points (for example, in the spiral model shown) and to a drawing together of these two points. Presumably, then, dehydration would affect the protein similarly. A number of botanical workers believe that heat and dehydration have similar effects on the protoplasm. Just how a protecting substance might function has been suggested above. Certain sugars appear capable of replacing the water crystal lattice on the protein. Water evidently occurs around the protein in a hexagonal series (Berendsen and McCulloch, 1960), but whether it is this water or water bound within the protein spirals that is replaced is not known. Webb's suggestion (see above) is therefore of great interest in that it provides a possible location for the protective substance.

Other theories have been suggested to account for the protective action of substances like sugars and certain proteins. Possibly the liquid water–sugar mixture acts as a solvent as the cell dehydrates and prevents "salting out" of the proteins. However, Levitt (1957) has pointed out certain flaws in the theory. For example, Maximov showed that the protective effect could be at least partially achieved by nonpenetrating solutions. In other words, increased resistance to the dehydrating effect of freezing had occurred without the solution having entered the cells.

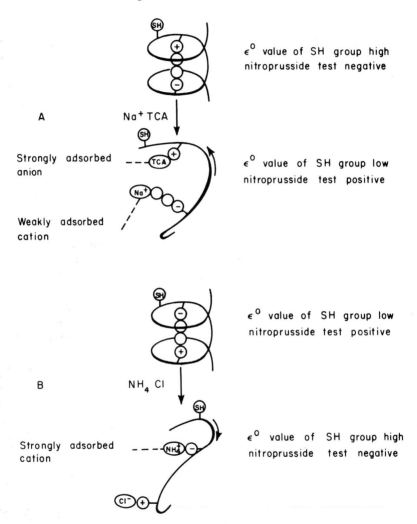

FIG. 6. The effect of the adsorption of a strong anion on the reactivity of the sulfhydryl group of a portion of a protein. A: The addition of trichloroacetate ion leads to its successful competition with a second anion. The adsorption of the stronger anion leads to a decrease of the ε° of the proximal —SH group. B: Introduction of NH_4^+ causes a withdrawal of electrons from the —SH group and increases the ε° value. Empty circles represent H_2O molecules. From Ling (1962), reprinted with permission of Blaisdell Publishing Co.

3. Biochemical Factors

Drought may influence the plant in sequential stages as noted above: reaction and restitution phases. In the first phase, as water is withdrawn, there is probably some interference with enzymatic reactions (Henkel, 1964); phosphorylation is particularly inhibited as viscosity increases. It might also be added that there can be changes in enzymatic reactions to favor one enzyme over another or shifts in pH which could cause, for example, a tendency for starch to be changed to sugar. At least there is little doubt that sugar increases in many plant species subjected to drought (Levitt, 1956, citing others; Kumakhova, 1963). Possibly when sugars did not increase during drought, there was cellular injury.

The biochemistry of hardening has been approached from many sides. Proteins have already been discussed (Section III,C,2). Sugars are known to increase as bound water increases (Todd and Levitt, 1951). Respiration has been related to hardening in certain ways (Parker, 1956). According to Stocker (1956), some authors have measured respiration in the reaction phase and some in the restitution phase so that results of different authors are difficult to compare.

Modern work in Russia suggests that a number of compounds are involved in desiccation and overall drought resistance. For example, in *Helianthus annuus*, an increase in the ratio of organic to inorganic phosphorus, a more "stable" nitrogen metabolism, and an increase in colloidally bound water were found with hardening (Badanova, 1963). Fruit trees have been classified into three types, depending on their drought resistance: (1) the most resistant type (peach), which combines the ability to bind large amounts of water with the ability to reach high osmotic pressures; (2) a less resistant type (apple and pear), which has large amounts of osmotically-active substances (for example, sugars) but small amounts of colloidally-bound water and fairly high osmotic pressures; and (3) a still less resistant type (plum), which binds large amounts of water in association with hydrophyllic colloids and also large amounts of protein nitrogen and hemicellulose (Kushnirenko, 1964).

Much has also been done in Russia in recent years with various minerals as soil additives for increasing drought resistance. Addition of aluminum, cobalt, and molybdenum to soil in which oats and barley were growing, increased drought resistance more than the presowing treatment, which itself had some positive effect (Bozhenko *et al.*, 1963). Dosages were 0.05, 0.17, and 0.75 mg of Al, Co, and Mo per kilogram of soil. The presowing treatment consisted of soaking seeds 16 hours in solutions of salts, for example, a solution containing aluminum nitrate, cobalt nitrate, ammonium molybdate, and copper sulfate in dilute concentration. Under drought conditions these additions made it possible to maintain a high content of foliar protein nitrogen;

they increased amine nitrogen 12 to 20 times, increased amino acids, decreased ammonia content, and increased foliar amine-nitrogen content. These conclusions seem supported by results of Vozhenko and Shkol'nik (1963).

Phosphate fertilizers appear notably successful in increasing hardiness in wheat, beets, and cotton (Badalyan, 1962). Phosphates had the effect of increasing numbers of stomata per unit leaf surface, water-retaining capacity of leaves, bound water, and yield. Increase in sugar content was also reported for wheat and beets. There is, of course, the possibility that phosphorus was low in the soils studied. In fact, the effectiveness of minor elements may also be related to the fact that the crop plants studied were suffering from mineral deficiencies. When provided with a suitable diet they responded favorably. Aluminum and cobalt, however, are not considered essential to a "suitable diet."

Presowing hardening can also be carried out by alternately soaking and drying the seeds, usually a total of 4 times for each drying (Henkel, 1964; Henkel et al., 1964; Adamovitch, 1964). In droughty locations, plant yields from treated seeds were higher than from untreated seeds.

Direct application of various organic compounds to leaves in order to increase hardening has not yet proved practical. Thiouracil and guanine have been reported to produce some frost hardening (Jung, 1962), but the increases reported were very small. Soaking of *Phaseolus* roots in decenyl-succinic acid (DSA) at $1 \times 10^{-3}\,M$ for 2 hours has been effective in increasing desiccation resistance (Kuiper, 1964). When water stress in the plant was severe, survival was markedly increased by the treatment. In artificially cooled substrata, DSA prevented the wilting that usually occurs in the leaves. DSA also had the effect of closing stomata in certain plants and thus curtailed their transpiration and aided in maintaining their water balance in certain circumstances (Zelitch, 1964).

Newman and Kramer (1966) confirmed the increase in permeability in *Phaseolus* roots on application of DSA at $10^{-3}\,M$, but at $10^{-4}\,M$, DSA reduced root permeability. They found that a 1-hour immersion of roots in $10^{-3}\,M$ DSA killed them and new roots formed later. They suggested that DSA is acting as a metabolic inhibitor and that the increase in water permeability was the result of injury to the roots. Kuiper, on the other hand, felt that DSA was being incorporated with the lipids of the cytoplasmic membranes and that it was this that altered permeability. Newman and Kramer suggested that some of the DSA was being carried to the leaves in Kuiper's experiments and thus accounted for stomatal closure that reduced transpiration and enhanced the maintenance of a favorable water balance.

Finally, certain growth retarding or stimulating substances have had some effect in improving tolerance of plants to dry soils (for example, Halevy, 1964; Leibundgut and Dafis, 1964). But the cause of this effect remains unknown.

Drought resistance is a plant characteristic that is the sum of the many parts of the plant from whole organs to the fine structure of the cytoplasm, from the seed to the mature plant. Compounds can be applied that reduce transpiration, encourage root growth, or protect the cytoplasmic proteins or protein–nucleic acid combinations. As time goes on these methods will be improved, but it is difficult to see how most of these compounds can greatly aid the plant without also causing a state of at least partial dormancy or inducing injury to some degree.

REFERENCES

Adamovitch, A. A. (1964). An increase in the drought resistance of a spring wheat variety. *Fiziol. Rast.* **11**, 743.

Albertson, F. W., and Weaver, J. E. (1945). Injury and death or recovery of trees in prairie climate. *Ecol. Monographs* **15**, 393.

Ashby, E. (1932). Transpiratory organs of *Larrea tridentata* and their ecological significance. *Ecology* **13**, 182.

Badalyan, V. S. (1962). The drought resistance of plants and ways to increase it. *Sb. Nauchn. Tr. Armyansk. Sel'skokhoz. Inst.* **12**, 365.

Badanova, K. A. (1963). The effect of soil dryness and hot wind on the metabolism of plants hardened to drought. *Akad. Nauk SSSR* p. 230.

Berendsen, H. J. C., and McCulloch, W. S. (1960). Structure of water in biological tissue. *Neurophysiology Quart. Prog. Report.* Res. Lab. Elec., M.I.T. Jan. 15, 1960.

Biebl, R. (1939). Über Temperaturresistenz von Meeresalgen verschiedener Klimazonen und verschiedenen tiefer Standorte. *Jahrb. Wiss. Botan.* **88**, 389.

Biebl, R. (1952). Ecological and non-environmental constitutional resistance of the protoplasm of marine algae. *J. Marine Biol. Assoc. U.K.* **31**, 307

Biebl, R. (1964). Austrocknungsresistenz tropischer Urwaldmoose auf Puerto Rico. *Protoplasma* **59**, 277.

Biswas, K. P. (1952). Road slimes of Calcutta. *J. Dept. Sci. Calcutta Univ.* **7**, 1.

Biswell, H. H. (1935). Effect of environment upon the root habits of certain deciduous forest trees. *Botan. Gaz.* **96**, 676.

Bozhenko, V. P., Nazarenko, A. M., and Momot, T. S. (1963). The action of aluminum, cobalt, molydbenum, and copper on the physiological processes determining drought resistance and on the production of plants. *Gessel'-Khozizdat Ukr. SSR, Kiev* 168.

Caldwell, R. (1958). Fate of spores of *Trichoderma viride* Pers. ex Fr. introduced into soil. *Nature* **181**, 1144.

Clements, F. E. (1902). A system of nomenclature for phytogeography. *Engler's Botan. Jahrb.* **31b**, 70.

Coulter, J. M., Barnes, C. R., and Cowles, H. C. (1911). "A Textbook of Botany," Vol. II, "Ecology." American Book Co., New York.

Darwin, F. (1915). On the relation between transpiration and stomatal aperture. *Phil. Trans. Roy. Soc. London. Ser. B* **207**, 413.

Diettert, H. (1937). The morphology of *Artemisia tridentata* Nutt. *Lloydia* **1**, 3.

Evans, J. H. (1958). The survival of freshwater algae during dry periods. (I). An investigation of the algae of five small ponds *J. Ecol.* **46**, 149.

Evans. J. H. (1959). The survival of freshwater algae etc. (II & III). *J. Ecol.* **47**, 55.

Fritsch, F. E. (1922). The moisture relations of terrestrial algae. I. Some general observations and experiments. *Ann. Botany (London)* **36**. 1,

Gibbs, R. D. (1958). Patterns in the seasonal water content of trees. *In* " The Physiology of Forest Trees " (K. V. Thimann, ed.), Ronald Press, pp. 43–69, New York.

Grieve, B. J. (1955). The physiology of sclerophyll plants. Presidential Address, 1953. *J. Roy. Soc. W. Australia.* **39**, 31.

Haberlandt, G. (1928). " Physiological Plant Anatomy ", Trans. by M. Drummond. Macmillan, London.

Halevy, A. H. (1964). Effect of hardening and chemical treatments on drought resistance of Gladiolus plants. *Intern. Hort. Congress 1962, 16th, Brussels* **4**, 252.

Hall, E. G., Huelin, F. E., Hackneys, F. M. W., and Bain, J. (1954). Gas exchange in granny Smith. *Intern. Congr. Botan. 1954, 8th, Paris, Sects. 11 and 12*, p. 405.

Hanson, H. C. (1917). Leaf structure as related to environment. *Am. J. Botany* **4**, 533.

Harley, J. L. (1940). A study of the root system of the beech in woodland soils with species reference to mycorrhizal infection. *J. Ecol.* **28**, 107.

Henkel, P. A. (1946). The resistance of plants to drought and how to increase it. *Tr. Inst. Fiziol. Rast. Akad. Nauk SSSR* **5** (1).

Henkel, P. A. (1964). Physiology of plants under drought. *Ann. Rev. Plant Physiol.* **15**, 363.

Henkel, P. A. Mart'yanova, K. L., and Zubova, L. S. (1964). *Fisiol. Rast.* **11**, 538.

Höfler, K. (1930). Das Plasmolyse-Verhalten der Rotalgen. *Z. Botan.* **23**, 570

Höfler, K. (1942). Über die Austrocknungsfähigkeit des Protoplasmas. *Ber. Deut. Botan. Ges.* **60**, (94).

Höfler, K. (1945). Über Trockenhärtung und Härtungsgrenzen des Protoplasmas einiger Lebermoose. *Akad. Wiss. Wien, Math.-naturw. Kl. 1945.* 5.

Höfler, K., Migsch, H., and Rottenburg, W. (1941) Über die Austrocknungsresistenz landwirteschaftlicher Kulturpflanzen. *Forschungsdienst* **12**, 50

Holle, H. (1915). Untersuchungen über Welken, Vertrocknen und Wiederstraffwerden. *Flora (Jena)* **108**, 73

Houston, D. R., and Kuntz, J. E. (1964). Pathogens associated with maple blight. Part III of studies of maple blight. *Wisconsin Univ. Agr. Expt. Sta. Res. Bull.* **250**, 59.

Huber, B. (1923). Transpiration in verschiedener Stammhöhe. I. *Sequoia gigantea. Z. Botan.* **15**, 425.

Huber, B. (1924). Die Beurteilung des Wasserhaushaltes der Pflanzen. *Jahrb. Wiss. Botan.* **64**, 1.

Huber, B. (1935). Xerophyten. *In* " Handwörterbuch der Naturwissenschaften," 2nd ed., Vol. 10, pp. 702–720, Fischer, Jena.

Iljin, W. S. (1931). Austrocknungsresistenz des Farnes *Notochlaena marantae* R. Br. *Protoplasma* **13**, 322.

Iljin, W. S. (1933. Über Absterben der Pflanzengewebe durch Austrocknung und ihre Bewahrung vor dem Trockentode. *Protoplasma* **19**, 414.

Imshaug, H. A. (1955). The lichen genus *Buellia* in the West Indies. *Farlowia* **4**, 473.

Irmscher, E. (1912). Über die Resistenz der Laubmoose gegen Austrocknung und Kälte. *Jahrb. Wiss. Botan.* **50**, 387.

Jung, G. A. (1962). Effect of uracil. thiouracil, and guanine on cold resistance and nitrogen metabolism of alfalfa. *Plant Physiol.* **37**, 768.

Kamerling, Z. (1917). Welche Pflanzen sollen wir Xerophyten nennen? *Flora (Jena)* **106**, 433.

Kanwischer, J. (1957). Freezing and drying in intertidal algae. *Biol. Bull.* **113**, 275.

Kearney, T. H., and Shantz, H. L. (1911). The water economy of dry land crops. *Yearbook Agr. U.S. Dept. Agr.* **1911**, 331.

Kramer, P. J. (1949). "Plant and Soil-Water relationships." McGraw-Hill, New York.

Kuiper, P. J. C. (1964). Inducing resistance to freezing and desiccation in plants by decenyl-succinic acid. *Science* **146**, 455.

Kumakhova, T. A. (1963). Physiological changes in the root system of wheat under drought conditions. *Notes 4th Sci. Conf. Graduate Students Rostov Univ.* 237 (*Biol. Abstr.* 88435, **45**, 1964).

Kushnirenko, M. D. (1964). Water metabolism and the degree of drought resistance of some fruit trees. *Fiziol. Rast.* **11**, 487.

Lange, O. W. (1953). Hitze- und Trockenresistenz der Flechten in Beziehung zu ihrer Verbreitung, *Flora (Jena)* **140**, 39.

Lange, O. L. (1965). Der Gaswechsel von Flechten bei tiefen Temperaturen. *Planta* **64**, 1.

Larcher, W. (1965). The influence of water stress on the relationship between CO_2 uptake and transpiration. *In* "Water Stress in Plants" (*B. Slavik, ed.*), *Proc. Symp. Prague, 1963*, pp. 184–193 Junk, The Hague.

Leaphart, C. D., and Wicker, E. F. (1966). Explanation of pole blight from responses of seedlings grown in modified environments. *Can. J. Botany* **44**, 121.

Legge, B. J. (1952). Use of glass fibre material in soil mycology. *Nature* **169**, 759.

Leibundgut, H., and Dafis, S. (1964). De l'influence de croissance synthétique sur la germination, le dévelopement des racines à la résistance à la sécheresse de quelques essences forestières importantes pour les régions à climat sec. *Schweiz. Z. Forstwesen* **115**, 454.

Leshem, B. (1965). The annual activity of intermediary roots of the Aleppo pine. *Forest Sci.* **11**, 291.

Levitt, J. (1956). "The Hardiness of Plants," 278 pp. Academic Press, New York.

Levitt, J. (1957). Mechanism of freezing in [plant or animal?] living cells and tissues. *Science* **125**, 194.

Levitt, J., Sullivan, C. Y., and Krull, E. (1960). Some problems in drought resistance. *Bull. Res. Council Israel Sect. D* **8**, 173.

Ling, G. N. (1962). "The Physical Theory of the Living State: the Association-Induction Hypothesis." Ginn (Blaisdell), Boston, Massachusetts.

Lipman, C. B. (1941). The successful revival of *Nostoc commune* from an herbarium specimen 87 years old. *Bull. Torrey Botan. Club* **68**, 664.

Loegering, W. O., and Harmon, D. L. (1962). Effect of thawing temperature on urediospores of *Puccinia graminis* f. sp. *tritici* frozen in liquid nitrogen. *Plant Disease Reptr.* **46**, 299.

Loftfield, J. V. G. (1921). The behavior of stomata. *Carnegie Inst. Publ.* **314**. Cited by Lundegårdh (1949), p. 201.

Löv, L. (1926). Zur Kenntnis der Entfaltungszellen monokotyler Blätter. *Flora (Jena)* **120**, 283.

Lund, J. W. G. (1942) The marginal algae of certain ponds with special reference to the bottom deposits. *J. Ecol.* **30**, 245.

Lundegårdh, H. (1949). "Klima und Boden," 484 pp. Fischer, Jena.

MacDougal, D. T., and Brown, J. G. (1928). Living cells two and a half centuries old. *Science* **67**, 447.

Maximov, N. A. (1929a). Internal factors of frost and drought resistance in plants. *Protoplasma* **7**, 259

Maximov, N. A. (1929b). "The Plant in Relation to Water." Allen & Unwin, London.

Morello, J. (1952). El bosque de algarroba y la estepa de Jarilla. *Darwiniana* **9**, 315.

Morello, J. (1955-1956). Estudios botanicos en las regiones aridas de la Argentina. *Rev. Agron. Noroeste Arg.* **1**, 301, 385; **2**, 79.

Mueller, L. E., Carr, P. H., and Loomis, W. E. (1954). The submicroscopic structure of plant surfaces. *Am. J. Botany* **41**, 593.

Newman, E. I., and Kramer, P. J. (1966). Effect of decenylsuccinic acid on the permeability and growth of bean roots. *Plant Physiol.* **41**, 606.

Nicot, J. (1960). Some characteristics of the microflora in desert sands. *Proc. Symp. Ecol. Soil Fungi.* p. 94. (Cited by Park, 1965.) Liverpool Univ. Press, Liverpool.

Oppenheimer, H. R. (1932). Zur Kenntnis der hochsommerlichen Wasserbilanz mediterraner Gehölze. *Ber. Deut. Botan. Ges.* **50A**, 185.

Oppenheimer, H. R. (1960). Adaptation to drought: xerophytism. *In* "Plant-Water Relationships in Arid and Semi-Arid Conditions. Reviews of Research," p. 105. UNESCO, Paris.

Oppenheimer, H. R., and Engelberg, N. (1962). Anciennes et nouvelles méthodes de mesure de l'ouverture stomatique des conifères. Colloq. *Intern. Methodol. l'ecophysiol. végétale.*, Montpelier, April (Mimeograph).

Oppenheimer, H. R., and Halevy, A. H. (1962). Anabiosis of *Ceterach officinarum* Lamm. et DC. *Bull. Res. Council Israel* Sect. D **11**, 127.

Oppenheimer, H. R., and Shomer-Ilan, A. (1963). A contribution to the knowledge of drought resistance of Mediterranean pine trees. *Mitt. Florist-soziol. Arbeitsgemeinschaft* **10**, 42.

Osterhout, W. J. V. (1906). The resistance of certain marine algae to changes in osmotic pressure and temperature. *Univ. Calif. (Berkeley) Publ. Botany* **2**, 227.

Paech, K., and Tracey, M. V. (1955). "Modern Methods of Plant Analysis," Vol. II. Springer, Berlin.

Park, D. (1965). Survival of microorganisms in soil. *In* "Ecology of Soil-borne Plant Pathogens." (K. E. Baker and W. C. Snyder, eds.), pp. 82-98. Univ. of California Press, Berkeley, California.

Parker, J. (1949). Effects of the variation in the root-leaf ratio on transpiration rate. *Plant Physiol.* **24**, 739.

Parker, J. (1952). Desiccation in conifer leaves: anatomical changes and determination of the lethal level. *Botan. Gaz.* **114**, 189.

Parker, J. (1953). Some applications and limitations of tetrazolium chloride. *Science* **118**, 77.

Parker, J. (1954). Differences in survival of excised ponderosa pine leaves of different ages. *Plant Physiol.* **29**, 486.

Parker, J. (1956). Drought resistance in woody plants. *Botan. Rev.* **22**, 241.

Parker, J. (1963). Cold resistance in woody plants. *Botan. Rev.* **29**, 123.

Parker, J. (1966). Leaf water retention versus desiccation resistance as the cause of drought resistance in leaves of woody evergreens. *Advan. Frontiers Plant Sci. (India,* **15**, 157.

Parker. J. (1968). Drought resistance of roots of white ash, sugar maple, and red oak. *U.S. Dept. Agr. Forest Service Northeast. Forest Expt. Sta., Sta. Paper* (in press).

Pessin, L. S. (1924). A physiological and anatomical study of the leaves of *Polypodium polypodioides*. *Am. J. Botany* **11**, 370.

Pfennig, N. (1958). Beobachtungen des Wachstumsverhaltens von Streptomycetes auf Rossi-Cholodny-Aufwuchsplatten im Boden, *Arch. Mikrobiol.* **31**, 206.

Pharis, R. P., and Ferrell, W. K. (1966). Differences in drought resistance between coastal and inland sources of Douglas fir. *Can. J. Botany* **44**, 1651.

Pisek, A., and Larcher, W. (1954), Zusammenhang zwischen Austrocknungsresistenz und Frosthärte bei Immergrünen. *Protoplasma* **44**, 30.

Pisek, A., and Winkler, E. (1953). Die Schliesbewegung der Stomata bei ökologisch verschiedenen Pflanzentypen in Abhängigkeit vom Wassersätigungszustand der Blätter und vom Licht. *Planta* **42**, 253.

Povah, A. (1927). Notes upon reviving old cultures. *Mycologia* **19**, 317.

Rawitscher, F., Ferri, M. G., and Rachid, M. (1943). Profundidade dos solos e vegetacão em campos cerrados do Brasil meridional. *Annals Acad. Brasil. Cienc.* **15**, 267.
Rouschal, E. (1938). Zur Ökologie der Machien. *Jarhb. Wiss. Botan.* **87**, 436.
Rouschal, E. (1937-1938). Eine physiologische Studie an *Ceterach officinarum. Flora (Jena)* **132**, 305.
Runyon, E. H. (1934). The organization of the creosote bush with respect to drought. *Ecology* **15**, 128.
Sarup, S. (1952). Plant ecology of Jodhpur and its neighborhood. A contribution to the ecology of north-western Rajasthan. *Bull. Natl. Inst. Sci. India* **1**, 223.
Satoo, T., and Hakuhara, N. (1953). Water relations of cuttings shortly after planting. *Tokyo Daigaku Nogakubu Enshurin Hokaku (Bull. Tokyo Univ. Forests)* **45**, 89.
Sayre, J. D. (1920). The relation of hairy leaf coverings to the resistance of leaves to transpiration. *Ohio J. Sci.* **20**, 55.
Schieferstein, R. H., and Loomis, W. E. (1958). Growth and differentiation of the epidermal wall. *Proc. Iowa Acad. Sci.* **65**, 163.
Schimper, A. F. W. (1903). Plant Geography Upon a Physiological Basis, Trans. by W. R. Fisher. Oxford Univ. Press (Clarendon), London and New York.
Scholander, P. F., Flagg, W., Walter, V., and Irving, L. (1952). Respiration in some arctic and tropical lichens in relation to temperature. *Am. J. Botany* **39**, 707.
Schouw, J. F. (1822). Grundträk till en almindelig plantegeografi. Copenhagen. Cited by Oppenheimer (1960).
Schröder, D. (1909). Über den Verlauf des Welkens und die Lebenszähigkeit der Laubblätter. Dissertation. Göttingen.
Shantz, H. L. (1927). Drought resistance and soil moisture. Ecology **8**, 145.
Shields, L. M. (1950). Leaf xeromorphy as related to physiological and structural influences. *Botan. Rev.* **16**, 399.
Shields, L. M., and Durrell, L. W. (1964). Algae in relation to soil fertility. *Botan Rev.* **30**, 92.
Slatyer, R. O. (1960). Aspects of the tissue water relationships of an important arid zone species (*Acacia aneura* F. Muell.) in comparison with two mesophytes. *Bull. Res. Council Israel Sect. D* **8**, 159.
Smith, E. C. (1929). The longevity of Myxomycete spores. *Mycologia* **21**, 321.
Smith, W. R., and Goebel, N. B. (1952). The moisture content of green hickory. *J. Forestry* **50**, 616.
Stålfelt, M. G. (1929). Die Abhängigkeit der Spaltöffnungsreaktion von der Wasserbilanz. *Planta* **8**, 287.
Stocker, O. (1927). Physiologische und ökologische Untersuchungen an Laub- und Strauchflechten. *Flora (Jena)* **121**, 334.
Stocker, O. (1928). Das Wasserhaushalt der ägyptischen Wüsten- und Salzpflanzen. *Botan. Abstr.* **13**.
Stocker, O. (1951). Kälte- und dürrefeste Pflanzen. *Umschau* **22/20**, 1.
Stocker, O. (1954). Die Trockenresistenz der Pflanzen. *Congr. Intern. Botan. 1954, 8th, Paris, Sects. 11 and 12* p. 223.
Stocker, O. (1956). Die Dürreresistenz. *In* "Handbuch der Pflanzenphysiologie" (W. Ruhland, ed.), Vol. 3, p. 696. Springer, Berlin.
Stocker, O. (1961). Contributions to the problem of drought resistance of plants. *Indian J. Plant Physiol.* **4**, 87.
Stocker, O., and Holdheide, W. (1937). Die Assimilation Helgoländer Gezeitenalgen während der Ebbezeit. *Z. Botan.* **32**, 1.
Stocker, O., Rehm, S., and Schmidt, H. (1943). Der Wasser- und Assimilationshaushalt dürreresistantes und dürreempfindlicher Sorten landwirtschaftlicher Kulturpflanzen. *Jahrb. Wiss. Botan.* **91**, 278

Sullivan, C. Y., and Levitt, J. (1959). Drought tolerance and avoidance in two species of oak. *Physiol. Plantarum* **12**, 299.

Sveshnikova, M. V., and Zalensky, O. V. (1956). Water regime of plants of arid territories in Central Asia and Kazakstan. *18th Intern. Geogr. Congr. Moscow. 1956*, p. 227. USSR Academy of Sciences, Leningrad.

Todd, G. W., and Levitt, J. (1951). Bound water in *Aspergillus niger*. *Plant Physiol.* **26**, 331.

Tranquillini, W. (1965). Über den Zusammenhang zwischen Entwicklungszustand und Dürreresistenz junger Zirben (*Pinus cembra* L.) im Pflanzengarten. *Mitt. Forstl. Bundes-Vers. Mariabrunn. Beitr. Subalpinen Waldforsch.* **66**, 241.

Vaartaja, O. (1964). Survival of *Fusarium*, *Pythium*, and *Rhizoctonia* in very dry soil. *Can. Dept. Forestry, Forest Entomol. Pathol. Branch Bi-monthly Progr. Rept.* **20**, 3.

Vozhenko, V. P., and Shkol'nik, M. Ya. (1963). The water balance of plants as related to metabolism and productivity. *Akad. Nauk SSSR* p. 275.

Walter, H. (1931) "Hydratur der Pflanze und ihre physiologisch-ökologische Bedeutung." Fischer, Jena.

Walter, H. (1949). "Einführung in die Phytologie," Band III: Grundlagen der Pflanzenverbreitung, Teil I: Standortslehre. Ulmer, Stuttgart.

Weaver, J. E., and Kramer, J. (1932). Root system of *Quercus macrocarpa* in relation to the invasion of prairie. *Botan. Gaz.* **94**, 51.

Webb, S. J. (1965). "Bound Water in Biological Integrity." Thomas, Springfield, Illinois.

Went, F. W. (1948). Ecology of desert plants. I. Observations on germination in the Joshua Tree National Monument, California. *Ecology* **29**, 242.

Went, F. W. (1949). Ecology of desert plants. II. The effect of rain and temperature on germination and growth. *Ecology* **30**, 1,

Wiegand, K. M. (1910). The relation of hairy and cutinized coverings to transpiration. *Botan. Gaz.* **49**, 430.

Worley, J. F., and Hacskaylo, E. (1959). The effect of available soil moisture on the mycorrhizal association of Virginia pine. *Forest Sci.* **5**, 267.

Yapp, R. H. (1912). *Spirea ulmaria*, L. and its bearing on the problem of xeromorphy in marsh plants. *Ann. Botany* **26**, 815.

Zelitch, I. (1964). Reduction of transpiration of leaves through stomatal closure induced by alkenylsuccinic acids. *Science* **143**, 692.

Zohary, M., and Orshansky. G. (1954). Ecological studies in the vegetation of the Near East deserts. V. The *Zygophylletum dumosi* and its hydroecology in the Negev of Israel. *Vegetatio* **5-6**, 341.

CHAPTER 8

DETERMINATION OF
WATER DEFICITS IN PLANT TISSUES

H. D. Barrs

C.S.I.R.O. DIVISION OF IRRIGATION RESEARCH, GRIFFITH, N.S.W., AUSTRALIA

I. INTRODUCTION: THE NATURE OF
PLANT WATER DEFICITS (WD)

Plant water deficits (WD) are primarily described by two basic parameters, the content of water θ or the energy status of the contained water, usually expressed as the total water potential ψ (Slatyer and Taylor, 1961). Consequently, WD may be recognized and directly quantitatively assessed by measuring either of these basic components, although the determination of both components is necessary to describe any water deficit completely. Therefore, discussion will center mainly around the determination of these two attributes.

Other plant attributes are associated with θ and ψ and so may be used to give indirect estimates of WD. The accuracy of the estimate will depend on the degree of correlation of the measured attribute with θ or ψ. Examples of relatively accurate indirect estimates are the measurement of a component of ψ. The components generally recognized in a plant cell are osmotic potential π, arising from the presence of solutes, especially in the vacuole; turgor pressure P, the hydrostatic pressure developed in the cell in response to π and the tensile strength of the cell wall; and the matric potential (ψ_m) arising from the imbibitional forces of colloids in the cell and forces of capillarity in the cell wall. These components combine to give the total potential as shown in Eq. (1).

$$-\psi = -\pi - \psi_m (\pm) P \tag{1}$$

The algebraic signs indicate the normal condition of each term when referred to a zero reference of pure free water. It will be seen that with the exception of P all components normally are negative. In this chapter the convention will be adopted that a fall or lowering in energy status means a shift to a more negative value. Thus, a change of ψ from -5 to -7 bars is described as a fall, lowering, or decline of 2 bars. P normally is positive. However, it is possible in some species that P may decline to a negative value when ψ is very low. The water in the cell is then in a state of tension instead of compression. The osmotic and matric components can only vary between zero and negative values. Total water potential is also normally zero or some negative value, but it could conceivably become positive under the influence of root pressure, although this would be a very unusual condition. Little is known about the magnitude and contribution of ψ_m to ψ, although Wiebe (1966) has shown it to be negligible in tubers, roots, and stems. If this component is ignored, the relation of ψ, π, and P to water content or cell volume may be described by means of a Höfler-type diagram, as shown in Fig. 1. Clearly, variations in ψ may be inferred from observations of changes in P or π, but a quantitative estimate of ψ is only possible if the sum of P and π is known. Figure 1 also

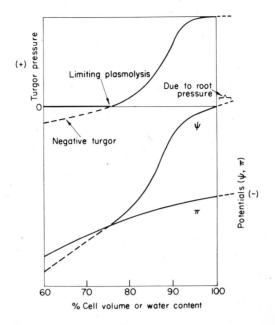

FIG. 1. Diagrammatic relationships between cell volume or water content and total water potential or components thereof for a single cell.

shows that quantitative relationships should exist between ψ, π, or P and cell volume or cell water content.

The above components are uniquely related to ψ. Other plant attributes also vary with WD and, therefore, have been suggested as useful guides to the condition of water within the plant. Chief among these is stomatal aperture. In general, stomatal aperture declines with decreasing θ. However, stomatal aperture is also affected by a wide range of other factors (Heath, 1949) and is not uniquely related to WD; hence, alterations in stomatal aperture should only be used with caution as a guide to WD—often the relation may be no more than semi-quantitative. Other indirect criteria of WD that have been suggested from time to time include leaf temperature (Tanner, 1963) and transpiration. The relation of these criteria to WD is probably even more indirect than that of stomatal aperture. Thus, both leaf temperature and transpiration rate are markedly affected by transient changes in the plant's aerial environment, while WD may show little corresponding variation. If such criteria are considered, the only safe approach seems to be an empirical one, such as that adopted by Palmer et al. (1964), in which transpiration of stressed plants was referred to that of unstressed controls, as a relative transpiration ratio.

However, in defense of indirect criteria it must be pointed out that they may more readily increase our understanding of how WD affects plants than may direct measurements. For example, stomatal aperture may represent plant responses interpretable in terms of growth. Direct measurements of WD, on the other hand, do not always give such valuable information. A plant is a complexity of interlocking systems; the unravelling of the effect of WD on them and their relationships can be understood only by adopting the widest possible approach. Certainly, no one plant attribute can be singled out as a comprehensive criterion of WD.

II. DIRECT MEASUREMENT OF WATER CONTENT (θ)

A. Evaluation of Water Content as a Measure of Water Deficit

It often is maintained that plant or plant organ θ does not provide a satisfactory measure of water stress (Kramer and Brix, 1965; Weatherley, 1965) and that the only true criterion is ψ. This latter quantity has been suggested as particularly useful because knowledge of ψ gradients between the soil and plant, or between different parts of a plant, gives information leading to valid assessments of the direction and magnitude of water movement. However, recent work (Macklon and Weatherley, 1965a; Barrs, 1966a) suggests that this may not always be so when overall gradients are the only factors considered.

It also is often suggested that ψ provides a better basis than θ for comparing the degree of water deficit between plants. Slatyer (1960) showed, however, that when $\psi = -20$ bars, relative water content (RWC) was about 50% in tomato leaves but about 90% in *Acacia aneura* phyllodes. Tomato plants had a large water deficit but *Acacia* did not. Slatyer's example, although an extreme case, showed RWC was better than ψ as a measure of WD. Further research is needed to establish whether it is water shortage per se or the energy status of plant water that is more important in affecting plant growth and performance. Ultimately, measurement of WD is most meaningful in terms of the effect of stress on plant growth. Meanwhile, it is suggested that both RWC and ψ are important measures of WD. In fact, studies of the relation between the two quantities may reveal information useful in assessing plant responses to environment.

Slatyer and McIlroy (1961) suggested that RWC may be a relatively insensitive measure of WD at high ψ values. This would be true if the relation between the two (plotting ψ on the X axis and RWC on the Y axis) were convex at high water contents. This type of relation has been found by Weatherley and Slatyer (1957), Slatyer (1960), Jarvis and Jarvis (1963b, 1965),

Begg *et al.* (1964), Taylor (1964), and Lemée and Gonzalez (1965). However, a linear or concave relation has also been found (Cornejo and Vaadia, 1960; Carr and Gaff 1962; Todd *et al.*, 1962; Wiebe and Wihrheim, 1962; Whiteman and Wilson, 1963; Ehlig and Gardner, 1964; Taylor, 1964; Macklon and Weatherley, 1965b; Weatherley 1965). Hence, the insensitivity of RWC as a measure of WD in highly turgid plants is not firmly established. The form of the relation may vary among species and probably depends on the techniques used to measure these quantities. Further refinement of techniques is needed before this point can be definitely established.

It may be concluded that measurement of θ continues to be one useful criterion of WD.

B. BASES FOR THE EXPRESSION OF WATER CONTENT

1. Dry Weight and Derivatives Thereof

Superficially, determination of θ for plant tissues would appear to be simple and straightforward. By analogy with measurement of soil water content, it would appear adequate to determine (1) the field fresh weight of a sample, and (2) the dry weight after heating the sample in an oven at about 85°C to constant weight. The difference between these two weights is θ. However, the quantity so obtained is only useful if it can be compared with others; comparisons may be required between different species or cultivars or between different times of the day or over a growing season in the same plant or species. Therefore, some basis for the expression of θ must be adopted. It is here that difficulties arise.

Again by analogy with soils, the most obvious basis would be the dry weight, water content being expressed as a percentage of dry weight. Typical values on this basis are leaves about 400%, roots about 800%, stems of annuals about 400%, and tree trunks about 100%. Many workers have used this basis in the past (Livingston and Brown, 1912; Miller, 1917; Kramer, 1937; Wilson *et al.*, 1953), and some continue to use it (Rahman *et al.*, 1959; Totsuka and Monsi, 1959; Krayevoi, 1962; Satoo, 1962; Moiseev, 1963; Parker, 1963a; Tranquillini, 1963; Önal, 1964a,b; Startseva, 1964; Bobkova, 1965; Hatakeyama and Kato, 1965). However, dry weight is unsatisfactory since it may not remain constant. This is particularly true of leaves, the plant organ whose water content is most commonly measured, where both a diurnal variation and a long-term increase in dry weight can occur. As shown in Chapter 1, total dry weight is an unsatisfactory basis for the expression of diurnal changes in water content, and curves such as those of Wilson *et al.* (1953) purporting to show the pattern of diurnal fluctuations in organ water content on this basis must be interpreted with caution. Mason and Maskell

(1928), recognizing that diurnal fluctuations in total dry weight were largely due to labile carbohydrates, suggested that the difficulty could be overcome by the use of residual dry weight, that is, dry weight after extraction of the tissue in dilute HCl. Denny (1930) found both this and total nitrogen satisfactory bases on which to express changes in chemical constituents over short time intervals. In principle, there is no reason why such bases should not be satisfactory for expressing diurnal variations in θ. However, they have not proved popular, partly because of the added tedium of their determination, and also because, like total dry weight, they may show a large increase with time. Continual increases in total dry weight of leaves have been reported by Miller (1917) in maize and sorghum, by Ackley (1954) in pear, and by Gej (1962) in wheat. Although common, such increases are not universal. Hewlett and Kramer (1963) found only a small initial increase in dry weight of four broadleaf forest tree species; thereafter, it remained stable for several months. Kozlowski and Clausen (1965), however, found that dry weight of oak leaves increased progressively for at least a month. In cotton, Weatherley (1950), has shown that various derivatives of total dry weight (residual dry weight, protein nitrogen and cellulose), increased considerably with time, even though the leaves sampled were of the same physiological age. His data for residual dry weight are reproduced in Fig. 2, which also shows that θ per sample remained rather constant as the season progressed but that θ referred to residual dry weight decreased continually and considerably.

Total dry weight is usually not a suitable basis for expressing θ, and derivatives of total dry weight, whilst they may be satisfactory for short-term studies, are not suitable bases for following long, seasonal trends.

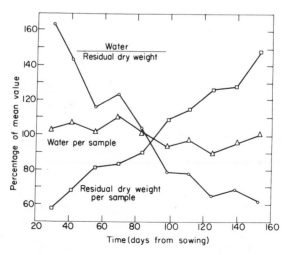

Fig. 2. Water content per sample, water referred to residual dry weight, and residual dry weight per sample as a function of crop age in cotton leaves. From Weatherley (1950).

2. Fresh Weight

Fresh weight has been widely used as a basis for θ (Livingston and Brown, 1912; Miller, 1917; Iyama and Murata, 1961; Zholkevich *et al.*, 1962; Marinchink *et al.*, 1964; Shou-Ju, 1963; Popova and Matveeva, 1964; Rastorgueva, 1964; Zemlyanukhin, 1964; Amanov, 1965; Kharanyan, 1965; Letey *et al.*, 1965; Samuilov, 1965; Sveshnikova, 1965; Routley, 1966). However, this basis suffers from two disadvantages: (1) the errors due to changes in dry weight are still present and, (2) the extent of changes in water content, especially large ones, tends to be reduced. The first point is illustrated in Fig. 3, in which a spurious decline in water content on a fresh weight basis is apparent at 2 AM because of a concurrent increase in dry weight. The second point is shown in Fig. 4, in which water content on a fresh weight basis declined by only a few percent whereas water content on the basis of water content at full turgor (discussed in Section II,B,4), declined by some 30% or 6 times as much. Hence, fresh weight is no more satisfactory a basis than is dry weight. Indeed, it may be less satisfactory because of its inherent tendency to minimize large changes in water content.

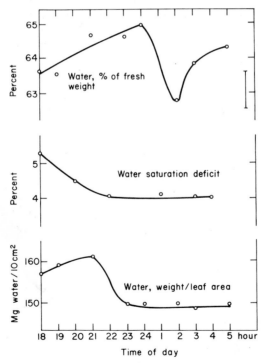

FIG. 3. Comparison of time trends in water content expressed as a percent of fresh weight, water saturation deficit, and per unit area in sweet-lime leaves. From Halevy and Monselise (1963).

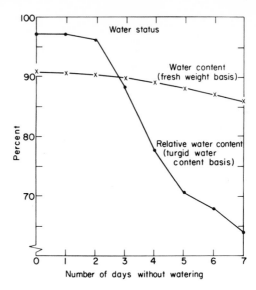

FIG. 4. Comparison of time trends in water content expressed as percent fresh weight and as relative water content in corn. From Mattas and Pauli (1965), courtesy *Crop Science*.

3. Area

Although not as popular as dry weight or fresh weight, leaf area has been used to express θ of leaves by various workers (Miller, 1917, 1924; Totsuka and Monsi, 1960; Totsuka *et al.*, 1960). It appears to be satisfactory provided fluctuations in θ are not large. This is the case in Fig. 3, in which on the basis of leaf area the spurious decline in leaf θ at 2 AM, which has already been noted on dry and fresh weight bases, no longer occurs. However, leaf area does not remain constant when large changes in θ occur (Thoday, 1909), and as θ falls, leaf area may also decline, leading to an underestimate of the decline in water content if a constant area is sampled.

4. Water Content at Full Turgor

a. Explanation of Basis. In essence, this approach consists simply in comparing θ of a sample immediately after collection with that after the same sample has been rendered fully turgid by allowing water uptake until ψ has risen to zero. This procedure is somewhat more demanding than the techniques previously discussed since a minimum of three determinations is required; field fresh weight, turgid fresh weight, and dry weight. Also, as will be shown, a number of complicating factors arise during the course of determination of θ at full turgor. However, at present an approach along these lines is widely accepted, and fully turgid water content seems to be the best available basis for expressing plant organ water content.

b. *Use of Whole Leaves*. Stocker (1928, 1929a,b) was the first to use this basis. His method was to cut off a whole leaf or, when working with conifers, a small branch, weigh it immediately (fresh weight), stand it in a little water in a closed container for 48 hours, weigh it again (fully turgid weight) and finally weigh it after oven drying (dry weight). These three weights were then used to determine the WD as shown Eq. (2):

$$\text{WD} = \frac{(\text{fully turgid weight} - \text{fresh weight})}{(\text{fully turgid weight} - \text{dry weight})} \times 100 \tag{2}$$

WD is thus the water uptake expressed as a percentage of θ at full turgor. More recently, many workers have replaced the term WD by water saturation deficit (WSD), (Halevy, 1960a,b; Halevy and Monselise, 1963; Larcher, 1965; Natr and Kousalova, 1965; Polster, 1965; Slavik, 1965, 1966; Solarova, 1965). The latter term seems preferable because of its wide acceptance and because it describes the basis used, thus avoiding confusion with WD measured on any other basis. However, Hewlett and Kramer (1963) prefer the retention of WD on grounds of priority. Figure 3 shows that WSD as defined above is a reliable basis on which to express leaf water content, since WSD remained constant, as one would expect, during the late evening and early morning, despite fluctuations in dry weight.

Unfortunately, some investigators did not realize the importance of using fully turgid water content as the basis for θ; thus, Stefanoff (1931) reverted to a dry weight basis and calculated a quantity he also called water deficit, as shown in Eq. (3):

$$\text{``WD''} = \frac{(\text{fully turgid weight} - \text{fresh weight})}{\text{dry weight}} \times 100 \tag{3}$$

Other investigators sought to avoid determining dry weight by using the fully turgid weight instead of the fully turgid water content as the basis. The resulting quantity has been termed relative saturation deficit (RSD) (Halma, 1933; Compton, 1936) or "déficit de saturation hydrique" (DSH) (Mouravieff, 1959, 1964), as shown in Eq. (4):

$$\text{RSD} = \text{DSH} = \frac{(\text{fully turgid weight} - \text{fresh weight})}{\text{fully turgid weight}} \times 100 \tag{4}$$

Stålfelt (1955, 1961) used Eq. (4) but equated it with water deficit. Hewlett and Kramer (1963) incorrectly state that Mouravieff (1959) attributed this basis to Stocker. Mouravieff's text shows he was aware that Stocker's basis was the water content at full turgor. Mouravieff erroneously attributed Eq. (4) to Killian, since the latter (1947) in fact used Stocker's basis. The confusion probably arose because Killian equated DSH with WSD.

It is obvious from the foregoing that complete chaos can arise unless a standard basis and nomenclature characterizing water deficits are adopted. Furthermore, the use of any basis other than the fully turgid water content is invalid. Equation (2) should be used, WD being replaced by WSD. WD should be reserved as a generic term including either θ or ψ or both.

c. Use of Leaf Discs. In 1950 Weatherley made an important modification to Stocker's technique by using discs punched from leaves, which were floated on water for 24 hours in diffuse daylight to obtain full turgor, instead of standing whole leaves in water. This procedure was advantageous since it was more sparing of material, permitted standardization of the sampling procedure, and allowed the same leaf to be sampled more than once. Weatherley's expression of water content differed from Stocker's and was termed relative turgidity (RT), as shown in Eq. (5):

$$RT = \frac{\text{(fresh weight } - \text{ dry weight)}}{\text{(fully turgid weight } - \text{ dry weight)}} \times 100 \tag{5}$$

Thus, the field water content, rather than the amount of water taken up, was referred to the water content at full turgor [cf. Eq. (2)]. RT and WSD are simply related: $100 - RT = WSD$,

As with Stocker's basis [Eq. (2)] and with Weatherley's, some workers have departed from the original equation. Relative turgidity has been erroneously expressed as (fresh wt $\div$ turgid fresh wt) $\times$ 100 by Meyer and Gingrich (1966) and Wager (1957). Letey *et al.* (1965) apparently calculated water content on a fresh weight basis and called this "turgidity." Again, the use of such variants is deplored because they are confusing and often unsound.

A discing technique has proved popular with many investigators (Basler *et al.*, 1961; Begg *et al.*, 1964; Bliss *et al.*, 1957; Box, 1965a; Čatsky, 1959, 1960, 1963; Dale, 1961a; Dancer, 1964; Ehlig, 1962; Ehrler, 1963; Farbrother, 1957; Fischer and Kohn, 1966; Gale and Poljakoff-Mayber, 1965; Gardner and Ehlig, 1965; Janes, 1964, 1966; Jarvis and Jarvis, 1963a,b; 1965; Jarvis and Slatyer, 1966b; Lebedev, 1963; Lee, 1965; Mederski, 1961, 1963, 1964; Macklon and Weatherley, 1965a,b; Mattas and Pauli, 1965; Millar, 1964, 1966; Nakayama and Ehrler, 1964; Namken, 1964; Namken and Lemon, 1960; Natr, 1965; Natr and Kousalova, 1965; Nezgovorov and Solovev, 1965; Oppenheimer, 1954; Post, 1962; Rychnovska-Soudakova, 1963; Shepherd, 1964; Sing and Alderfer, 1966; Slatyer, 1955, 1957, 1960, 1961; Slavik, 1963a,b; Werner, 1954; Whiteman and Wilson, 1963; Wormer and Ochs, 1959). However, the term "relative turgidity" has not been readily accepted on the ground that it suggests some connection with turgor pressure (Slavik, 1966; Walter, 1963b), although no such relation actually exists. The possibility of confusion is further increased since Soviet workers (Petinov, cited in Slatyer, 1965) recognize a relative turgor scale. Also, Virgin (1955) has used the term relative turgor to describe actual turgor when referred to full turgor. In fact, some workers have been deceived by the phrase "relative turgidity" into thinking turgor pressure is implicated in the measurement. Thus, Weatherley's relative turgidity measurements (1950, 1951) have been described as "leaf studies of turgor pressure in cotton" by Box and Lemon (1958). Namken and Lemon (1960) again make this inference. Weatherley (1965) supported the suggestion made to him by the author, that relative water content (RWC) would be a preferable term to RT. RWC describes the quantity being measured, has recently been used by various workers (Ehlig and Gardner, 1964; Jarvis and Slatyer, 1966b; Mederski, 1963), and has no confusing implication of a relation with P. Jarvis and Jarvis (1965), however, defined RWC differently [RWC = (fresh wt − dry wt)/dry wt as a percentage of a control water content]. If it is desired to calculate this parameter, it should be called something else to distinguish it from RWC. Many European workers do not calculate RWC but prefer WSD. Neither term seems to have any decisive advantage, and both will probably continue in use. If the multiplicity of terms used is reduced to either of these two, much existing confusion will be eliminated.

d. Sources of Error and a Comparison of RWC Values from Intact Leaves and Leaf Discs. Possible sources of error have been evaluated more fully in discs than in whole leaves. Two classes of error are common to both procedures. First, water uptake may continue after full turgor has apparently been attained. Second, dry weight may change while water uptake occurs.

Continued uptake of water is well documented in leaf discs (Barrs and Weatherley, 1962; Čatsky, 1959, 1965; Weatherley, 1950). The typical pattern is an initial relatively rapid uptake completed in two to four hours, followed by a slower uptake that persists at a constant rate as long as the floated discs remain healthy. These have been termed phases I and II, respectively (Barrs and Weatherley 1962). Stocker (1929b) was apparently aware that this phenomenon also occurs in intact leaves, since he recommended the leaves be stood in water for as long as 48 hours. Weatherley (1950) showed that water uptake by intact cotton leaves may be divisible into these two phases. Yemm and Willis (1954) also found these two phases present in chrysanthemum leaves. Čatsky (1959) found phase II absent from old leaves of tobacco, but it was very marked in young leaves. Later (1963) he showed that phase II was present even in old leaves of rape and cabbage and that it was again very pronounced in young leaves. Hewlett and Kramer (1963) found negligible phase II uptake in leaves of broadleaf forest trees after 4 hours, but when equilibration was allowed to continue for 3 days the leaves often became visibly infiltrated with additional water. In general, both discs and whole leaves showed phase I and II components.

Work with leaf discs has given information about these two components. Weatherley (1950) suggested that phase I represented uptake in response to tissue water deficiency, and that phase II was due to growth. Barrs and Weatherley (1962) confirmed that phase II was due to growth since it could be inhibited by various metabolic inhibitors, although this was not considered practicable on a routine basis. Their results also showed that phase II follows phase I. Therefore, they concluded that fully turgid θ would be obtained at the point on the water uptake curve where phase I was just completed, but phase II had made no contribution. They suggested a 4-hour floating period as usually adequate, but urged pilot experiments to check this where its suitability had not previously been established. Čatsky (1960) arrived at a similar conclusion, recommending a 3-hour saturation period. Later (1963) he modified this procedure for use with young leaf discs, where phase II is particularly pronounced, by determining θ after 3 hours and again after 6 hours of floating. Assuming that phase I is completed after 3 hours, this enables a correction for the linear phase II uptake to be applied by extrapolating to zero time, using Eq. (6):

$$\text{WSD} = \frac{(2 \times \text{fresh wt after 3 hours}) - (\text{wt after 6 hours}) - \text{initial wt}}{(2 \times \text{fresh wt after 3 hours}) - (\text{wt after 6 hours}) - \text{dry wt}} \times 100$$

$$(6)$$

Yemm and Willis (1954), working with whole leaves, also applied an extrapolation procedure, first determining the form of the uptake curve directly, usually by four weighings. Čatsky's extrapolation procedure [Eq. (6)] seems now to be applied indiscriminately to young and mature leaf discs alike by some workers (Solarova 1965). Čatsky (1963) showed that this procedure is useful in estimating WSD of young tissues and that phase II uptake can otherwise cause spuriously large WSD's in young leaves, even when intact tissue is used. However, if phase II follows phase I, as Barrs and Weatherley (1962) suggest, there is a risk of a small overcorrection since part of phase I will also be removed during the extrapolation to zero time. This effect is in fact shown in Čatsky's (1965) data, although he does not comment upon it. The increase in experimental labor and computation when fresh weights after both 3 and 6 hours are determined, may be considerable when the technique is used routinely on a large number of samples. This, together with the above possibility of overcorrection, suggests that a single fresh weight, taken after 3 or 4 hours, as recommended by Barrs and Weatherley (1962) would be a preferable procedure when working with mature or nearly mature leaves. Millar (1966) considers that phases I and II are concurrent since leaves normally grow at less than full turgor. However, he offers no direct experimental evidence. The matter perhaps should be reinvestigated.

Hewlett and Kramer (1963) have suggested that leaf discs, when compared with intact leaves, may take up excessive quantities of water, thereby giving spuriously low RWC's. They stated that most workers have been unable to obtain values as high as 98%. However, the papers they cite (Fraser and Dirks, 1959; Slatyer, 1955; Vaadia et al., 1961; Weatherley, 1951) do not support this statement well. Thus, Slatyer (1955) found maximal values of 98% in peanuts and 100% in grain sorghum—only in cotton did RWC's fail to exceed 95%—but Weatherley (1951) found maximal RWC's of 98 to 99% in cotton. Vaadia et al. (1961) in fact do not present data on this point, nor do they discuss it. Finally, as Hewlett and Kramer themselves point out, the basis used by Fraser and Dirks (1959) may have been incorrect; hence, their data are inadmissible. Other workers have also reported high values, for example, 99% in corn at 6AM (Namken and Lemon, 1960).

Hewlett and Kramer (1963) go on to point out that they obtained RWC's very close to 100% using whole leaves, but Ackley (1954), also using whole leaves, comments on the failure of his RWC's to approach 100% very closely. Hewlett and Kramer (1963) presented data showing that discs cut out from leaves of a broadleaf tree species previously brought to full turgor gave RWC values of 92.5 and 94.5%. However, other workers have not found this. Thus, Weatherley (1950) punched and floated discs from fully turgid cotton leaves and showed that the subsequent uptake of the discs had only a phase II component and that this was virtually identical with that of a parallel sample of intact leaves standing in water under a bell jar. As already noted, Čatský (1965) found agreement between RWC using leaf discs and RWC calculated from loss in weight of intact, previously fully turgid leaves; in fact, his data show a slight trend in the opposite direction to that of Hewlett and Kramer, as discussed earlier. Barrs (unpublished) found for pepper (*Capsicum frutescens*) that leaf discs punched from large pieces of leaf previously floated on water for 6 hours to render them fully turgid gave a mean RWC of 100.2%. It appears that although the disc technique may not be readily applicable to some broadleaf tree species it works well with herbaceous species.

Hewlett and Kramer (1963) attributed excessive water uptake by leaf discs to infiltration and injection of the cut edges and release of lateral pressure on discing. Data of Barrs (unpublished), Čatský (1965), and Weatherley (1950), discussed above, show that these errors are not always present. Indeed, no quantitative data seem to be available from which any effect solely attributable to release of lateral pressure can be evaluated, apart from Ernest's early observation (1934b). There is no doubt, however, that injection and infiltration can be sources of error. It is essential that the leaf punch be kept as sharp as possible. Even so, some tissues still become injected when floated on water, for example, leaves of *Sambucus nigra* (Barrs and Weatherley, 1962). In this species the middle of the disc may show considerable injection although the region nearer the edges may not. Čatsky (1960) suggested that injection can be minimized by supporting leaf discs in holes in soaked spongy polyurethane, so that only their edges receive water. Barrs and Weatherley (1962) also found an effect of disc size on injection, small discs having lower RWC's than large ones. This error appears to be due to injection of the cut edges. It is minimized by using discs not smaller than 8 mm in diameter. Carr and Gaff (1962) found a small and apparently constant injection error in discs of *Eucalyptus globulus*. They allowed for the error by subtracting 0.4 mg from the uptake of each 8 mm leaf disc.

Errors due to change in dry weight (usually loss) during floating have been reported for discs by Weatherley (1950). Dale (1961a) found such a loss could cause RWC's to be 2.5% too low when a 22-hour floating period was used. Weatherley (1950) corrected for this error by collecting a duplicate sample that was oven dried immediately after determining its fresh weight. He showed (1954) that solute leakage was not responsible for loss in dry weight, although Wormer and Ochs (1959) and Shepherd (1964) attributed error to this source. Barrs and Weatherley (1962) showed that gain or loss in dry weight of discs depended on the light intensity they were exposed to during floating, with an intensity of 65 footcandles corresponding approximately to the compensation point. They also showed that error due to dry weight loss was not significant, provided floating was limited to 4 hours. Čatsky (1965) reached a similar conclusion for a 6-hour floating period.

Dry weight losses also occur in intact leaves while they attain full turgor. Wilson and Huffaker (1964) found an 8% loss in dry weight of clover leaves when floated for 24 hours. Virgin (1965), using Stocker's technique with a 24-hour exposure, found a dry weight loss of 5.8% in wheat leaves due to respiration, calculated on a fresh weight basis, for which he applied a correction. Hewlett and Kramer (1963) do not consider this source of error specifically when advocating use of intact leaves. It is likely that it will be small if time for full turgor to be attained is limited to "a few hours," but if, as Čatsky's (1963) curves show, phase I in whole leaves with only petioles standing in water is not completed for 24 hours, considerable dry weight losses may be expected. The rapid water uptake of leaf discs enables completion of phase I before significant dry weight loss occurs. This may not always be true of whole leaves. Thus, unless a correction for dry weight loss is applied, which would be difficult for whole leaves, discs may be preferable to whole leaves.

Turgid water content of leaf discs is affected by both the temperature at which they are floated (Werner, 1954) and the humidity (Phillis and Mason, 1945; Weatherley, 1947; Werner, 1954). Discs therefore should be floated at constant temperature in closed petri dishes. When whole leaves are used, they too should be equilibrated at constant temperature, although this practice does not seem to have been general. Ackley (1954) is a notable exception. Millar (1966) reported that for needles of *Pinus radiata*, when water uptake is determined at a temperature widely different from the temperature (T_0) of the needles before sampling, RWC values may be considerably in error. He therefore recommended water uptake should be determined at a temperature approximating T_0. Similar data for broadleaf species were not presented; hence, it is not known how far these are affected. However, Carr and Gaff (1962), using leaf discs of *Eucalyptus globulus*, found RWC's differed by less than 1%, when they were floated at 16° or 23°C.

Dew can interfere with the measurement of RWC (Weatherley, 1950; Werner, 1954), but it is the writer's experience that it can be satisfactorily removed *before* sampling, using facial tissues. This procedure is somewhat tedious, but when the number of discs per sample is kept to a minimum of 12, it is not too onerous.

Milthorpe and Spencer (1957) suggested that RWC values could be in error due to irreversible contraction of the cell walls on wilting, but Barrs and Weatherley (1962) showed that this did not occur in castor bean leaves. They also pointed out that if it were to occur, the RWC technique would correctly indicate a reduction in turgid water content.

Gaff and Carr (1961) suggested that cell wall water can, within limits, buffer the protoplast from short-term dehydration. They speculated that RWC's as low as 90% in potato and coffee leaves mainly represented variations in cell wall water content, provided weather conditions were changing fairly rapidly during the day. However, Slatyer (1955) reported that growth was reduced when RWC fell to 90% in cotton, sorghum, and peanuts, so any buffering was far from complete. Čatsky (1965) found an exact and meaningful relation between RWC and photosynthetic rate, a reduction of RWC from 95 to 90% causing a 50% reduction in photosynthesis. There is little evidence here for any buffering action of the cell walls. Ehrler *et al.* (1965) have shown that an autonomic cycle of leaf water content with a period of 20 to 30 minutes can be induced in cotton under constant environmental conditions. This is accompanied by correspondingly large fluctuations in transpiration and leaf diffusive resistance. Barrs (unpublished) found similar effects were also associated with large fluctuations in photosynthetic rate in pepper. Clearly, even when leaf water content is varying cyclically, the postulated mediation of cell wall water is ineffective. It may well be negligible.

Weatherley (1965) reported apparently abnormally large water uptake by discs from young leaves of a plant that previously was exposed to prolonged water deficit. The prolonged stress prevented these leaves from attaining maximum size, but the potential for expansion remained and was manifest when the discs were floated on water. This possible source of error has yet to be evaluated fully, however; if the phase II component is unduly large, Čatsky's extrapolation technique [Eq. (6)] should allow for this.

e. Use of Needle Leaves and Leaf Segments. In conifers and some grasses, the punching of discs is not practicable. As previously discussed, Stocker (1929a,b) saturated small branches of conifers, but this approach was not adopted by later workers. Jarvis and Jarvis (1963b, 1965) worked with needle segments of *Pinus sylvestris* and *Picea abies*. Segments 7 mm long and cut at both ends were floated for 5 hours to bring them to full turgor. However, there is evidence that a floating procedure may not be acceptable in some conifers, and most workers have favored the use of intact or bisected needles brought to full turgor by standing them in a little water in a closed container. Thus, Harms and McGregor (1962) found that ½-inch-long segments of needles of *Pinus taeda* become waterlogged on floating, giving spuriously low RWC values. Clausen and Kozlowski (1965) found that floated needles or needle segments of *P. resinosa*, *P. strobus*, and *Abies balsamea* usually became waterlogged and sank. Rutter and Sands (1958) and Harms and McGregor (1962) brought needles to full turgor by standing them in a little water in a closed chamber for 24 hours. For the long needles of *P. resinosa*, Clausen and Kozlowski (1965) also found this procedure satisfactory, but for short needles (*Abies balsamea, Tsuga canadensis*) they recommended that instead of standing in water the needles be pushed into a layer of saturated sand deep enough to support them. The basal ends of whole needles (Clausen and Kozlowski, 1965; Sands and Rutter, 1958), or bisected needles (Harms and McGregor, 1962), when placed in water become injected, so the layer of water should be kept as shallow as possible. Sands and Rutter (1958) found that this effect could cause a bias when needle length varied in response to nutritional treatments. In 1-year-old needles of *P. sylvestris* RWC was lowered by about 1% for every centimeter of reduction in needle length. All the above workers found that dry weight losses of whole or bisected needles were negligible, even though a 24-hour saturation period was used.

Segments have been used satisfactorily for determining RWC in phyllodes of *Acacia aneura* and grass laminae. Slatyer (1960) used 10 phyllode segments, each 1.5 cm long, floated for 24 hours at 5° to 7°C to minimize phase II effects. However, these low temperatures may also reduce phase I uptake (Barrs and Weatherley, 1962), so this procedure cannot be universally recommended. Rychnovska and Bartos (1962) used 26-mm-long segments of grass leaves that were saturated by applying strips of water-saturated foam polyurethane to the edges of the segments. Full turgor was obtained after 1 hour in the dark. Rychnovska-Soudkova (1963) used a similar procedure but increased saturation time to 2 hours.

C. Summary and Final Recommendations

Dry weight, fresh weight, and area are all unsatisfactory bases on which to express water content because they are not stable. Dry weight fluctuates diurnally and shows permanent increases over longer periods. The fresh weight basis minimizes large changes in water content and is also affected by dry weight changes. Area declines when water stress is high.

Water content at full turgor is the only satisfactory basis so far devised. To this may be referred either the amount of water taken up as tissue becomes turgid, giving the water saturation deficit [see Eq. (2)], or the initial water content, giving the relative water content [see Eq. (5)]. Either floating leaf discs or whole leaves with their petioles standing in water in a closed container may be used. In each case, constant temperature is necessary. Leaves take up water slowly, so a correction for dry weight loss may be necessary, and it must be ensured that the water deficit is fully satisfied. Discs take up water more quickly so that full turgor is usually attained with negligible dry weight loss. A sharp punch, preferably honed before each sampling, will minimize errors resulting from injection and water logging of the cut edges of leaf discs.

Figure 5 shows two suitable punches: one a tube with a piston ejector, the other a modified sheep's earmarker. With the former, leaf discs are punched out against a rubber bung or softened polyvinyl chloride sheet and then injected into a tared weighing bottle immediately after a sample has been collected. In the latter, each disc drops into the bottle as it is punched. Twelve discs usually comprise an adequate sample. The polyvinyl chloride sheet is crumbled less than a rubber bung by the repeated action of the punch (Bartos et al., 1960). The sheet therefore is preferable to the bung for routine use since the error due to collection of crumbled particles in the bottles is minimized. Sampling should be restricted to reduce variability, for example, to mature but not senescent leaves, say between the third and fifth from a shoot apex. Samples should be replicated once.

In very young tissues fresh weights should be determined after 3 and 6 hours of floating to correct for uptake due to growth of discs [Eq. (6)]. In older tissues one determination of turgid fresh weight just after the water deficit is satisfied, normally after 3 to 4 hours of floating, is adequate [Eq. (2)]. The needle leaves of many gymnosperms will not float, so they must be stood in a shallow layer of water or wet sand to attain full turgor with minimum injection. Here, 24 hours exposure is recommended, dry weight losses being negligible. Segments of grass leaves are satisfactory substitutes for discs, a cutter comprising two parallel safety razor blades attached to a block permits rapid sampling in the laboratory from previously collected leaves.

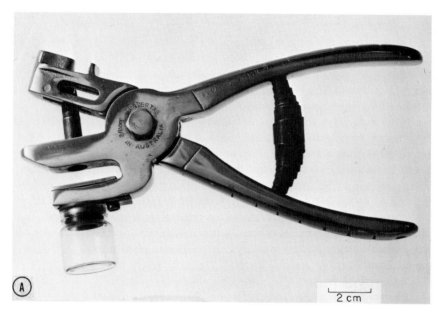

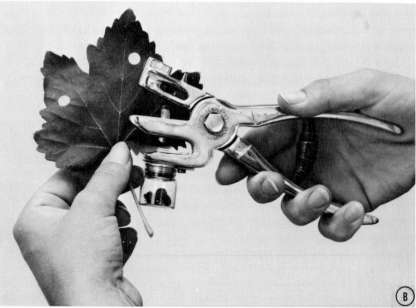

Fig. 5. Leaf disc punches used for sampling for relative water content measurement, A, modified from sheep's ear marker; B, sampling a leaf (leaf detached for clarity only; veins should be avoided). See also Fig. 5C, p. 253.

Fig. 5C. Leaf disc punch for relative water content sampling, fitted with piston ejector.

As various tissues have different requirements, pilot experiments should be performed to determine the best approach when this has not been previously established.

Direct determinations of θ have the merit of simplicity and readily lend themselves to field use. Their main disadvantage is that they are destructive. Discing permits sampling the same leaf more than once, but it would be unwise to take more than two or three discs from a leaf.

III. INDIRECT MEASUREMENT OF WATER CONTENT

A. EVALUATION OF INDIRECT MEASUREMENTS

The principal advantage of indirect methods over direct ones is that the former may be nondestructive and therefore permit more than one sampling of the same leaf or plant. In some cases, even continuous monitoring may be possible. A further important advantage is that the transducers used often lend themselves to automatic reading and recording. Apart from freeing the experimenter for other activities, automatic reading and recording are important in their own right since information that might otherwise not have been collected will be retained. When continuous data are available, mathematical analysis of the dynamics of the system being studied becomes possible, and the intensity and depth of the investigation may be considerably increased.

However, some extra labor will be involved, in construction and in calibrating the technique in terms of θ. It is precisely at this latter point that many indirect techniques fail. They give results that obviously are related to θ, but in many cases a quantitative relation is not established, principally because the particular method involved responds to other factors as well as θ. Not only must the technique be capable of calibration, but this calibration should be reasonably stable and, if possible, not too closely related, for example, to one particular spot on one particular leaf. Furthermore, the use of the technique must not alter θ, for example, by shading or altering the angle of the leaf.

Of the indirect methods presently available, the beta gauging technique comes closest to realizing these requirements.

B. Direct Measurement of Size in Relation to Water Content

1. Measurement of Leaf Thickness

It is essential that leaf thickness measurement be of adequate sensitivity to follow *changes* in leaf thickness accurately. From data given by Linacre (1964) and Meidner (1952) the thickness of leaves of 20 species varied between 100 and 750 μ. This gives the range of absolute measurements required. Meidner's results show that on the average a change in leaf thickness of about 10% was the maximum that was correlated with change in leaf water content; for thin leaves this represents a change of only 10 μ. If this method is to be used to follow changes in θ with an accuracy of only 10% (not a stringent requirement), then it will be necessary to measure leaf thickness for thin leaves to better than 1 μ. Direct measurements of this order of magnitude on living leaves are not easily made, especially under field conditions. It is not surprising, therefore, to find that this direct approach has been attempted by only a few workers. One of the earliest was Bachmann (1922), who used an assembly of levers. Meidner's results, mentioned above, were obtained with a system of gear wheels, and his instrument seems to have been reasonably successful. The standard error of thickness measurements was 0.05 μ, sufficient to detect a change of about 1% of the range of θ that was correlated with leaf thickness. In practice, accuracy would be somewhat less than this since the standard error quoted is for measurements of thickness of a feeler gauge, rather than of a leaf. Meidner did not take the calibration of the instrument sufficiently far to determine the exact form of the relation between leaf thickness and θ.

Recent interest in directly measuring leaf thickness has been slight. One important reason for this is the advent of the considerably more sensitive and amenable beta ray gauging system, discussed in Section III,C,1. However, Gardner and Ehlig (1965) showed that "relative leaf thickness" measured as RWC per unit area is a function of RWC. Brun (1965) has measured leaf thickness (1) by the change in focus of a microscope necessary to refocus it onto a securely clamped leaf and (2) by modifying an automatic balance to read thickness instead of weight. The sensitivity of the measurements was not as high as Meidner's, but the changes in leaf thickness under study were far greater (about 5 times as much). Change in leaf thickness was not calibrated in terms of θ, but there was evidence that the large and rapid changes induced by cutting in his experiments were not due solely to changes in leaf θ. Brun suggested these changes were largely the result of elimination of root pressure rather than of change in θ. Such an observation points up a common danger in all indirect methods of assessing water status: The measurement made may alter in response to a change in some factor other than the one under study. Unless one is aware of this, indirect measurements may lead to invalid results.

2. Measurement of Fruit Size

It has long been recognized that fruit size and plant water status may be closely related. Bartholomew (1926) obtained interesting curves of change in diameter of lemon fruits measured with an "auxograph," which was a modified thermograph. This instrument enabled him to obtain continuous records, and the results were obviously qualitatively related to environmental conditions. The lemon fruit was particularly suitable since irreversible increases due to growth were absent for at least the final month before harvest. Furr and Taylor (1939) measured the circumference of lemon fruits with a steel tape and converted their values to volume, using a previously established relation. They recognized "apparent growth rate" as the volume increase over short time intervals and "true growth rate" for intervals from one period of full turgor to the next. These investigators considered changes in apparent growth rate to be an excellent index of relative WD of trees in the field. They also concluded that the magnitude of the difference in apparent growth rate just before and just after irrigation was an index of the WD to which the trees were subjected just before irrigation. However, they made no direct measurements of water status and did not develop a numerical index based on fruit size.

Oppenheimer and Elze (1941) measured circumference of orange fruits with a steel tape and converted this to volume, since this gave them constant volume increments with increasing fruit size, although the corresponding diameter increments declined. At the same time they measured soil water content, stomatal aperture, and leaf WSD. They concluded that WSD measurements were insensitive criteria of water deficit and thought the latter was better characterized by stomatal aperture early in the season and by fruit growth rate later, when conditions were cloudier. They determined WSD by Stocker's (1929a,b) method [see Section II,B,4,b] and found for a mean WSD = 8% a standard error of 2.9, which was high. However, in a later experiment in which irrigation was based on stomatal aperture, their results seem to show that WSD was as well correlated with fruit growth rate as was stomatal aperture. Both a steel tape and a modified thermohygrograph were used by Hendrickson and Veihmeyer (1941) in measurements on pears and apples. Their results showed that changes in the size of pears would need to be corrected, even on a diurnal basis, for irreversible increases due to growth. However, no attempt in this direction has yet been made, and this outstanding problem is one of the drawbacks of the method.

Anderson and Kerr (1943) illustrated additional difficulties in the use of fruit size as a criterion of water status. Again using modified thermographs as auxographs, they measured both diurnal and long-term changes in the diameters of cotton bolls. In young bolls, effects of WD were completely masked by effects of temperature, since boll diameter not only continually increased, but did so at a higher rate during the day than during the night. This pattern of behavior persisted even when the leaves of the parent plant were wilted. Measurement of the diameter of young bolls did not reflect the overall water status of the plant. Mature bolls were somewhat more satisfactory because they usually shrank during the day and recovered at night. However, during 7 consecutive days of severe drought, mature bolls showed a considerable overall shrinkage superimposed on the diurnal fluctuations. After rain the mature bolls increased in size again over several days, but diurnal fluctuations in diameter were absent. It is apparent that in cotton at least it would be very difficult to establish a quantitative relation between fluctuations in plant water status and fruit diameter.

Cockcroft (1963) considered it should be possible to time irrigations by measuring the circumferences of peaches and pears, but he found the technique was lacking in sensitivity, permitting too great water stresses to develop. Tukey (1959) found hand measurements with a vernier caliper were not very precise and that the periods of fruit contraction and expansion were not readily determinable. Therefore, he measured changes in fruit size (1963, 1964) with a linear voltage displacement transformer put into the tube of an old microscope; the fruit, still attached, rested on the stage of the microscope. This transducer had the advantage of giving an electric signal, which with suitable circuitry gave a continuous and sensitive record. This setup, although still somewhat cumbersome, is preferable to Bartholomew's (1926), already considered, in which it was necessary to enclose the branch to which the fruit was attached in a Stevenson screen, thereby considerably altering the micro-climate. Till (1965) suggested that measurements of fruit size were only useful when referred to a control that was kept free of soil water stress.

Despite considerable research, measurements of fruit size provide only qualitative data on water stress. This approach has probably been over-emphasised since fruit is frequently the final yield.

3. Measurement of Trunk Diameter in Trees

MacDougal (1921, 1925, 1936, 1938) frequently demonstrated the presence of diurnal fluctuations in the diameter of tree trunks. His results show that diameter may decline by 1% during the day, swelling again during the late afternoon and evening. He considered these changes to be mainly due to fluctuations in the xylem tension with changes due to growth being relatively insignificant over 1 day. If this view is broadly correct, such diurnal fluctuations in diameter would be expected to be a useful measure of plant water status, as tension in the xylem should be related to transpiration rate and evaporative power of the air. More recent work has supported this possibility. Kuroiwa *et al.* (1958), using a very sensitive mirror dendrometer, observed expansions and contractions of diameter within 10 minutes after the sun was obscured by, or emerged from, a cloud. Kozlowski and Winget (1964) found that diurnal shrinkage increased with canopy development in *Populus tremuloides* and that stem diameter increased within 30 minutes of a cloudburst. Impens and Schalk (1965) briefly reported a correlation of -0.99 between shrinkage and potential evapotranspiration estimated by Penman's method. However, comparisons of decapitated trees, or those given two overlapping sawcuts, with controls, showed practically no changes in diametral fluctuation patterns (Greenidge, 1962). These results are not so readily equated with the concept of the development of high tensions in the xylem and thus cast some doubt on how far diametral fluctuations really do relate to plant water status.

It is desirable that dendrographs (which record diameter) rather than dendrometers (which do not record) should be used for these studies in order to characterize the pattern fully. The former are also preferable because they are more accurate. Descriptions of various versions of each class of instrument may be found in Kramer and Kozlowski (1960). Bormann and Kozlowski (1962) refer to papers using band dendrometers, which measure change in circumference, and various dendrometers that measure change in a single radius. They found the latter class of instrument considerably more accurate; the former were too insensitive to show diurnal fluctuations. These workers also describe in detail the construction and positioning of a dial gauge dendrometer, using a template. Impens and Schalk (1965) described an exceptionally sensitive dendrograph based on the linear voltage displacement transformer, having an output of 1.3 mV/μ. This transducer has been considered in more detail in Section III,B,2, where its application to the measurement of fruit size was discussed. The writer is unaware of the development of any quantitative relation between diurnal fluctuation in tree trunk diameter and plant water status. However, the continued interest in this sphere may establish such a relation. As with fluctuations in fruit size, corrections will have to be made for interference from other factors such as growth. In trees growth seems to be less of a problem, over a few days at least, than in fruit.

C. INDIRECT MEASUREMENT OF SIZE IN RELATION TO WATER CONTENT

1. By Beta Ray Gauging

a. Beta Ray Gauging of Leaf Thickness. This comparatively recent technique is the most successful indirect method of estimating θ from size of plant organs. Unlike most indirect methods, it permits the establishment of quantitative relationships between these two properties. The technique has been used in industry for some time; its principles are well established and have been discussed by Siri (1949) and Pollard and Davidson (1951). The physics of its application to leaves is discussed by Nakayama and Ehrler (1964). The technique was apparently first applied to plants by Yamada *et al.* (1961). Mederski (1961, 1963, 1964) demonstrated the efficacy of this approach, and his reports encouraged others to improve the method.

The technique consists of measuring the mass of a leaf by placing it between a source and a detector of beta radiation. The count rate varies inversely with the mass of the leaf, and over short periods of time (for example, 1 day), fluctations in leaf mass are almost entirely due to changes in θ, so count rate is inversely related to leaf θ. Although various beta sources have been tried, the detector system favored by most workers (Ehrler *et al.*, 1965, 1966; Mederski, 1961, 1963; Nakayama and Ehrler, 1964; Gardner and Niemann, 1964), has been a thin-window Geiger tube connected to a scaler or via a ratemeter to a recorder. Mederski (1964) briefly describes a further refinement for field use in which a cam timer is used to switch one of several beta gauges in turn to a distantly located ratemeter and recorder.

The beta sources that have been used include ^{35}S (Yamada *et al.*, 1961), ^{14}C (Mederski, 1961, 1963, 1964; Skidmore and Stone, 1964; Whiteman and Wilson, 1963), ^{99}Tc (Gardner and Niemann, 1964) and ^{147}Pm (Ehrler *et al.*, 1965, 1966; Nakayama and Ehrler, 1964). The last-mentioned authors present a useful discussion on the selection of a source and conclude that ^{14}C is suitable for absorber thicknesses (that is, fresh weight divided by area of leaf sampled) from 5 to 20 mg cm^{-2}; ^{147}Pm and ^{99}Tc, from 10 to 40 mg cm^{-2}; and ^{204}Tl, from 15 to at least 70 mg cm^{-2}. Jarvis and Slatyer (1966a) used ^{147}Pm of 0.3, 0.6, and 3 mc for leaves of density thickness 10–30 mg cm^{-2} and ^{204}Th of 1 mc for thicker leaves. Figure 6 shows construction details for a beta ray

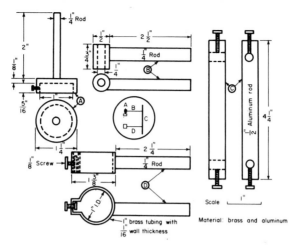

FIG. 6. Construction details of a β-ray gauge. From Nakayama and Ehrler (1964).

gauge, and Fig. 7 shows results obtained with an intact, attached cotton leaf. Inspection of the latter figure shows that the basic data (counts per minute) are well correlated with RWC and leaf ψ.

A common calibration procedure has been to measure the decline in count rate as originally fully turgid leaf discs progressively lose water. By this means, Mederski (1961) and Nakayama and Ehrler (1964) established that a logarithmic relation exists between count rate and RWC. However, Jarvis and Slatyer (1966b) pointed out that this tedious process may be considerably quickened and simplified by first calibrating the beta gauge in terms of absorber thickness (or "effective leaf thickness"), since the relationship between count rate and absorber thickness is linear. This relation is established using discs of aluminum foil of varying thickness. Subsequently, only the count rate for fully turgid leaf discs (floated after punching from the monitored leaf at the end of the run) together with their water content and dry weight are required to fix the slope and intercept of the relation between effective leaf thickness and RWC. Counts on both the aluminum discs and the leaf discs should be made at the end of each run. By these means, Jarvis and Slatyer (1966b) clearly demonstrated a large shift in intercept but not in slope of the relation between effective leaf thickness and RWC in progressively older leaves of cotton. Mederski (1964) found that young soybean leaves showed appreciable shrinkage of surface area with loss of turgor. Such shrinkage compensated for reduction in mass per unit area as the leaf lost water and resulted in small, variable absorption coefficients.

Careful calibration is essential to the success of the beta gauging technique. The distance between source and detector must be kept constant during a run, and accuracy is further improved by keeping the gauge in one position on the

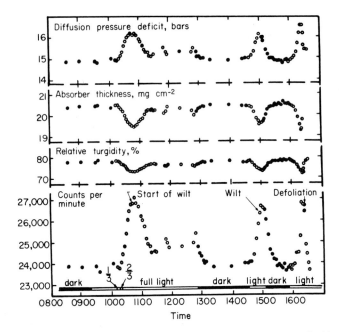

FIG. 7. Effects of different light intensities on leaf thickness as measured with a beta ray gauge and on associated measurements of water potential (DPD) and relative water content (RT). From Nakayama and Ehrler (1964).

leaf, thus eliminating variability due to sampling different areas. However, such precautions must not jeopardize the validity of the measurements. Packing the spaces between source, detector, and leaf with felt (Skidmore and Stone, 1964) may well have detrimental effects on the sampled area. Similarly, source and detector should be as small as possible to minimize effects on the microclimate of the leaf. Shading could otherwise conceivably increase the turgor of the monitored portion above that of the bulk of the leaf. Jarvis and Slatyer (1966a) describe a very small beta source–detector system.

Some workers (Gardner and Niemann, 1964) have proceeded, via a previously established relation between RWC and ψ, to calibrate beta ray counts indirectly in terms of ψ. As they recognized, this is somewhat hazardous, a direct calibration in terms of ψ is preferable. Perhaps the chamber sample changer of Campbell et al. (1966) for psychrometric measurement of ψ for leaf subsamples might be useful in this connection. However, the conclusion of Whiteman and Wilson (1963) that beta ray absorption cannot be used to estimate leaf ψ seems extreme and has not been supported by other investigators. Nor has their suggestion of the use of "relative absorption," that is, count rate corrected for absorption of dried material, been adopted. Indeed, as they point out, the destructive sampling necessary to apply this correction eliminates the principal advantage of beta gauging.

Progress made so far suggests that the beta gauge technique for measuring leaf thickness may well become one of the most useful tools in assessing plant water status.

b. Beta Ray Gauging of Whole Plants. In principle, if a relation can be established between thickness of an individual leaf and absorption of beta rays, it should also be possible to correlate the mass of all the aerial portions of a number of plants with beta ray count rate, at least with reasonably small plants such as those in many pastures or row crops. As yet little progress in this direction has been made; indeed, the feasibility of this approach remains to be demonstrated. However, Mott *et al.* (1965) constructed an instrument for estimating pasture yield, using beta gauging, which apparently reflected the water content of the sample.

Such an instrument should permit rapid, nondestructive estimates of θ on a large number of samples, thereby appreciably decreasing the error of the mean. Limited destructive sampling at various stages of crop growth would be necessary for calibration purposes.

2. By Gamma Ray Gauging

Compared with the use of beta rays, the gamma ray gauging technique has received scant attention. Klemm (1959) followed diurnal variations in tree trunk moisture content using ^{137}Cs as a gamma source since it has a long half-life. The rays were collimated by lead shielding and detected by a Geiger–Mueller tube connected to a counter in the laboratory. His data show that the reciprocal of the count rate increased after rain, as did relative humidity. The data also illustrate a diurnal pattern of reciprocal count rate, increasing at night and decreasing during the day, in a way very similar to the dendrograph records discussed earlier [Section III,B,3]. The final conversion from count rate to θ was not made.

Although soil scientists successfully used gamma ray gauging for determining soil water content (Danilin, 1955; Ferguson and Gardner, 1962; Gurr, 1962, 1964; Mukhin and Chistotinov, 1961), and the possibility of defining the area to be investigated by collimation makes the technique attractive, few other workers have applied it to living plants. Indeed, Hinsch and Niemann (1964) stated that the error caused by the fact that the gamma rays measure total hydrogen, including organic compounds, is too large to be ignored. Therefore, they used a capacitance technique (see the next section) to measure θ of living tree trunks, although they measured trunk density by gamma attenuation using backscattering and a gamma-scintillation spectrometer. A useful discussion of the physics of the application of gamma ray gauging is given by Wilkins *et al.* (1964), although they were primarily concerned with measurement of silage density. Woods *et al.* (1965) investigated gamma ray attenuation in pine wood using an integral counting technique.

3. By Measuring Capacitance

This technique involves comparison of capacitance of a suitable condenser when airfilled with that when the air is largely replaced by a representative portion of a crop, typically a pasture. The measurement is carried out *in situ* in the field with intact, undisturbed samples. Data obtained so far have been used mainly to estimate pasture yields. However, the original paper on this subject by Fletcher and Robinson (1956) pointed out that the method essentially measures θ since the capacity measured increases almost entirely because of the high dielectric constant of water compared with the low dielectric constant of air or plant dry weight. The change in capacitance of the probe condenser is converted to an audio frequency that in effect is the difference in frequency between an oscillator attached to the probe and an oscillator held by the operator.

The method has been improved subsequently by a number of workers. Campbell *et al.* (1962) modified the condenser from the three parallel plate arrangement of Fletcher and Robinson (1956) into a matrix of vertical rods. This arrangement reduces error due to the clumpiness of the pasture. Campbell *et al.* (1962) also found it important to insulate the plates of the condenser from the grass and ground. Alcock (1964) found readings were much more closely correlated with θ of the area sampled than with dry weight, r^2 values being 0.974 and 0.389, respectively. A detailed technical description of his apparatus is given by Hyde and Lawrence (1964). Johns *et al.* (1965) modified the equipment to permit rapid field adjustment of instrument zero. They also noted that pasture lowers the resistance across the capacitor and pointed out that this effect must cause an additional change in frequency. Johns and Watkin (1965) found dew caused 6% overestimation of dry weight. In Australia, Jones (1963, 1964, 1965, 1966) produced a model that is now commercially available, and Dowling *et al.* (1965) also produced an improved model. The instruments are calibrated by comparing meter reading with dry weight or θ of the same sample determined after its removal by clipping. Calibrations are necessary for different pastures and even for the same crop at different growth stages.

As mentioned earlier, these devices are used to estimate yield rather than θ. However, Hinsch and Niemann (1964) successfully used the modification of frequency induced by a change in capacitance to measure θ of living tree trunks with a specially devised probe inserted into the trunk. Thomas (1966) described determination of soil θ by using the "fringe" capacitance of a suitably designed probe electrode system.

D. Miscellaneous Properties Associated with Water Content

1. Electrical Resistance

Box and Lemon (1958) and Namken and Lemon (1960) attempted to modify techniques used in the lumber industry to measure resistance of living plants directly. Two hypodermic needles mounted in lucite blocks were inserted longitudinally into stems of cotton, corn, or grain sorghum, and the electrical resistance between them was measured with a 90-cycle ac ohmmeter. In cotton, the resistance readings increased during rainless periods and declined after rain or irrigation, but in grain sorghum, no useful relationship could be established. In corn, RWC was determined simultaneously, and a qualitative relationship between this and electrical resistance was established. However, as Mederski (1961) pointed out, the method lacks sensitivity and the correlation between resistance and RWC is not high. Kreeb (1966) measured conductivity of leaves using "Argentol" ring electrodes painted onto them. His data show smooth changes in conductivity as evaporative conditions are changed. A continuous record can be obtained. Results look promising and may subsequently prove to be quantitatively related to leaf θ. The measurement may reflect the degree of hydration of the cell walls and cuticle rather than the protoplasts.

Commercially available instruments for measuring resistance of seeds, dried fruit, or dried apple have been described and evaluated by Joffe (1964), Joffe et al. (1964), and Sykes and Coote (1962). These methods appear reasonably accurate but have not been modified for use with intact plant material. Thus, they offer no advantage over conventional methods of determining θ.

2. Infrared Spectrophotometry

This technique involves determination of θ by measuring the amount of absorbance of infrared radiation by a sample, generally at a wavelength of 1.94 μ. The technique is quite accurate (to about 0.01%) but unfortunately is destructive. It is used in determination of the θ for seeds, which are either extracted with methanol (Hart et al., 1962) or ground and dispersed in methanol (Norris, 1964). Again, the need to destroy the sample cancels out its advantages.

IV. MEASUREMENT OF TOTAL WATER POTENTIAL (ψ)

A. Liquid Phase Methods

1. Introduction—The Isopiestic Principle

Apart from a few miscellaneous techniques considered later, all methods for the determination of ψ carried out in the liquid phase are similar in principle. Parallel samples of cells or tissues are immersed in a range of concentrations of a nonpenetrating solute in order to find that concentration of solution in which no net exchange of water occurs between sample and solution. The osmotic potential of this isopiestic solution is assumed to be equal to the ψ of the sample.

In practice, the range of solutions chosen often does not include the isopiestic solution. Hence, it often is necessary to estimate the isopiestic concentration. This is achieved by observing the direction and often also the extent of change in some property of either the solution, such as density or refractive index, or of the tissue such as size or weight. In those methods where only the sign of the change is observed, the isopiestic solution can only be said to be between an upper and a lower limit, for example, between solutions Nos. 3 and 4 in Fig. 8A. Provided the sensitivity of the method is adequate, precision may be increased by decreasing the concentration difference between

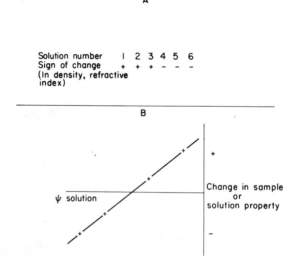

FIG. 8. Use of the isopiestic principle, A, without graphical interpolation; B, with graphical interpolation.

the solutions. When the extent of the change is also measured, graphical interpolation may be used to estimate the isopiestic solution, Fig. 8B. The linear relation of Fig. 8B is idealized. In practice, a curvilinear relation is typical. This can sometimes be converted into a linear form, thereby aiding interpolation of the isopiestic potential. The data are also often normalized, for example, by expressing the change at each point as a percentage of the initial value. The graphical method succeeds best when the amounts of solution and of plant sample are kept constant throughout an experiment.

The methods used are described briefly before proceeding to their evaluation.

2. Methods Based on Change in a Property of the Plant Sample

a. The Cell Method. The isopiestic solution is determined by finding the solution concentration that causes no change in the size of a cell or cell group in a fragment of tissue observed under the microscope. Before immersion of the sample in a test solution, it is mounted in liquid paraffin and cell size is assessed by drawing the outline of the cell with a *camera lucida*. The sample is transferred to an osmotic solution for a time, remounted in paraffin, and the new cell size is compared with the original. This process is repeated with different solution concentrations until the new cell size corresponds to the original, indicating immersion in the isopiestic solution. The method was suggested by De Vries (1884), but was first used by Ursprung and Blum (1916). Ernest (1931) reexamined the technique critically and suggested that if cells were not visible in intact specimens, for example, leaf mesophyll cells, they should be made visible by stripping rather than sectioning since this would avoid errors arising from release of cell sap from injured cells. She modified the technique (1934a) by using a fresh piece of tissue for each solution and making the second measurement of cell size directly in the sugar solution to which it had been transferred. This procedure could conceivably increase error since it introduces the natural variability existing between samples. There is also the risk that solution π may decline by evaporation during examination of samples under the microscope. Ernest (1934a,c) also stressed the importance of mounting a specimen in sufficient fluid to avoid distorting cells by the weight of the cover slip.

Oppenheimer (1936) argued that released cell sap does not cause an error since it may be removed from the section or strip surface when it is immersed in paraffin. He also queried Ernest's results on the grounds that after transfer from liquid paraffin to sugar solutions, residual paraffin drops can magnify, thereby interfering with accurate observation of cell size.

As cell size is generally only assessed qualitatively, results usually have the form of Fig. 8A. Graphical interpolation (Fig. 8B) requires quantitative measurement of projected cell area for each solution. This is usually too time-consuming to be practicable. Even a qualitative assessment of cell size is tedious, so the method is generally only used when no other method is available, for example, in the determination of ψ for guard cells. An experienced observer often can avoid using extreme solution concentrations, thus saving time. The cell method has the disadvantages of additional errors discussed in Section IV,A,4.

b. The Simplified Method. Ursprung (1923) introduced this simplification of the cell method. The isopiestic solution is equated with that which causes no change in the length of tissue strips. The procedure (Molz, 1926a) is to immerse samples in paraffin oil immediately after collection and in the laboratory to cut and trim strips, still under paraffin oil, measure their length microscopically while mounted in paraffin oil, and then transfer them to a suitable range of solutions for $\frac{1}{2}$–2 hours. The strips are then remeasured in the solutions. When working with delicate tissue the weight of the cover slip is borne by supporting particles of glass. When necessary, the isopiestic solution may readily be found by graphical interpolation using normalized data, as shown in Fig. 9. The final leveling off of the curves commences at a solution concentration that represents an approximation of π for the strips at incipient plasmolysis. This point is taken up again in Section V,C,4.

The simplified method gives best results with pieces of tissue that are reasonably thin and soft. Two variants, described below, increase the range of material with which it may be used.

c. Change in Thickness of Tissue Strips. In some cases, for example, sclerophyllous leaves, changes in length of tissues may be too small to be measurable. Crafts *et al.* (1949) reported that strips of some leaves, for example, *Sedum nicaense*, may distort when volume change is induced by immersion in solutions, so that even though volume may increase, both length and width may decrease. In both these cases, the detection of the isopiestic solution by measurement of sample thickness, first suggested by Ursprung and Blum (1927), may be advantageous. These workers later (1930) described the microscopic observation of the movement of a jewel-mounted lever for this purpose.

d. Change in Length of Massive Tissues. This modification of the simplified method was described by Pringsheim (1931) and used by Lyon (1936, 1940). The latter measured change in length of either cylinders cut with a cork borer

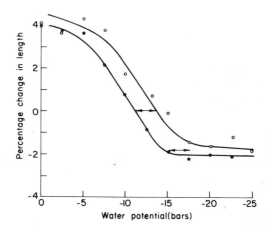

Fig. 9. A determination of leaf water potential by the simplified method. From Brouwer (1963).

or of square sticks cut with a double-bladed knife. The technique is useful for potato tissue and the like.

e. Change in Curvature of Tissue Pieces. Shaw (1933) used this method to ascertain isopiestic solutions for rings of cortical and phloem tissues of apple and pear shoots. Earlier, De Vries (1884) used the method with longitudinal stem sections. This technique is limited in the range of tissues to which it may be applied and has received little further attention.

f. The Gravimetric Method. The originator of this technique does not seem to be known (Meyer and Wallace, 1941). The isopiestic solution is that which causes no change in weight of the sample. Graphical interpolation may be used since change is measured quantitatively, preferably with normalized data. Ashby and Wolf (1947) standardized the surface drying procedure necessary before weighing the tissue. They used a 50-gm weight applied without shearing for 5 seconds. Heavier weights squeezed water out of the tissue, causing a spurious overestimate of weight loss. Manohar (1965) has also reported errors arising from drying difficulties.

g. Change in Volume. The most convenient method is to measure volume by liquid displacement. This limits the technique to massive tissues, since only in these is volume change large enough to be accurately measured. Currier (1943) used beetroot cylinders and determined their volume by liquid displacement in closely fitting calibrated glass tubes. These tubes contained small quantities of the same range of solution concentrations as subsequently used (in larger quantities) for equilibration of tissue samples. After 8 hours, the cylinder surfaces were dried and their volumes were remeasured. Graphical interpolation may be used to estimate the isopiestic solution if necessary.

3. Methods Based on Change in a Property of the Solution

a. Change in Density. The isopiestic solution is that which undergoes no change in density after immersion of tissue in it. As usually carried out, density change is only assessed qualitatively so that data of the form shown in Fig. 8A are obtained. Consequently, unless one of the solutions used happens to be exactly isopiestic, ψ can only be estimated between an upper and lower limit. These limits correspond to the π difference between the two solutions most nearly equivalent to the sample.

   The determination is carried out by duplicating a suitable range of solutions in test tubes and adding subsamples of tissue, for example, leaf discs to one set of tubes. After allowing time for water exchange to occur, a concentrated drop or a small crystal of methylene blue or Gentian Violet is added to the control solution (Kozlowski, 1964; Mouravieff, 1959), the tissue is removed from the test solution and, from a special dropper, a drop of the control solution is injected below the surface of the test solution. The dye colors the drop so that one can observe the density change of the test solution by seeing whether the control drop rises or falls. An alternative procedure (Slatyer and McIlroy, 1961) is to add the dye to the test solution with the tissue still in place. This obviates the need to remove the tissue and facilitates time studies of changes in ψ. However, some tissues tend to absorb the dye, reducing the intensity of coloration (Schläfli, 1964). Mouravieff (1959) considers that direct contact between the tissue and dye may alter tissue permeability. Till (1966) describes a third variant in which the colored solution is poured into and layered underneath the other solution. Till's method would seem to be less sensitive than that of Mouravieff since it only permits the detection of solutions that have been diluted.

Although this simple technique has correctly been attributed to Shardakov by subsequent writers (Kozlowski, 1964; Kramer and Brix, 1965; Slatyer and McIlroy, 1961; Walter, 1963b), various papers between 1948 and 1956 being cited, it does not seem to be generally appreciated that Shardakov first described his method as early as 1938. It is in fact a modification of Arcichovskij's (1931) technique.

Suitable equipment is illustrated in Fig. 10. Accuracy and ease of observation are increased if the dropper is easily controllable, permitting gentle extrusion of a single drop. The end of the dropper should be bent through 90° so that no vertical movement of the drop occurs when it is extruded.

b. Change in Refractive Index (RI). This technique was devised by Maximov and Petinov (1948). The isopiestic solution is that which undergoes no change in RI after immersion of tissue in it. RI is measured quantitatively with a refractometer and graphical interpolation of the isopiestic solution therefore may be employed. One difficulty is that RI changes much more for tissues in hypertonic than in hypotonic solutions, giving a markedly curvilinear plot (Ashby and Wolfe, 1947). Gaff and Carr (1964) point out that this may lead to bias in the estimate of the isopiestic point in favor of those points close to it. They show that the data may be linearized by converting values of Δn to $\Delta n/M$. This permits the statistical fitting of a line based on all the data, thereby increasing accuracy in determining the null point. $\Delta n/M$ should be plotted against π rather than M, so as to avoid including effects due to curvilinearity arising from nonideal behavior of the solution.

c. Rate of Uptake of Solution. This approach has been used by Brouwer (1953) to estimate ψ of intact roots. His results showed that the steady state rate of water uptake fell linearly with decrease in π of the solution. He assumed that extrapolation of plotted data to zero uptake would indicate the isopiestic solution. This is a modification of techniques involving decapitation of plants

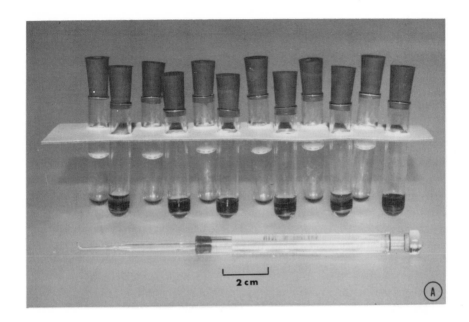

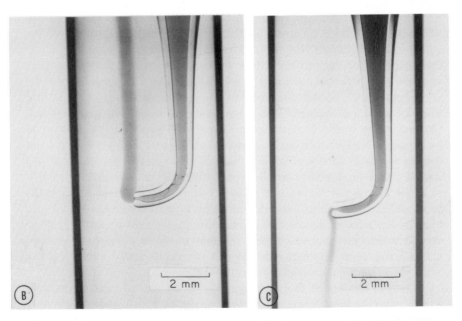

FIG. 10. A, Equipment for the determination of leaf water potential by the Shardakov technique; B and C, comparisons of test and reference solutions; test solutions colored by Gentian Violet. The colouration is exaggerated in the photographs.

to study rates of water movement through them (Sabinin, 1925; van Over-beek, 1942). As Crafts *et al.* (1949) point out, this approach may yield results confounded by root pressure effects.

4. Sources of Error in Liquid Phase Methods

a. Errors Peculiar to Methods Involving Measurements on Plant Tissue. In these techniques the volume of solution can be kept large compared to sample volume. Hence, errors arising from effects of the sample on the solution usually are sufficiently small to be negligible. However, any anomalous effects of the solution on the tissue are likely to be important.

Two such effects have been reported: injection of the intercellular spaces and infiltration of plasmolyzed cells. Ashby and Wolf (1947) investigated the former by comparing results from the gravimetric and the refractometric methods, the latter method of course, being unaffected by this error. In tissues having large intercellular spaces, such as carrot and leaf of iris, they found injection caused a large spurious weight gain, which in turn caused an overestimate of ψ by 100% or more. The error was considerably smaller in potato tissue, where intercellular space also was smaller. Ashby and Wolf found that uptake due to injection was constant for each tissue, and when weight change was corrected by the appropriate amount, the refractometric and gravimetric methods agreed well. They also showed, as expected, that error caused by injection was eliminated if the tissue was first equilibrated with a sucrose solution, since the intercellular spaces were now injected before the determination commenced. Under these conditions, they stated that both methods gave a ψ equal to π of the solution initially used for equilibration.

Slatyer (1958) compared a modified gravimetric method (to be described in detail later) that is carried out in the vapor phase with the simplified and the gravimetric methods. His results (Fig. 11) showed that the two liquid phase methods gave spuriously depressed ψ at values below -10 bars in tomato and -20 bars in privet, and at even lower ψ values no estimate was possible since the liquid phase samples always showed some gain in weight or length over the whole range of solutions tested. He attributed these results to two effects. First, a wilted cell will not become smaller when placed in a hypertonic solution. Hence, such cells cannot lose weight or shrink further. Second, since only positive changes in weight could be obtained in severely wilted tissue, some solute penetration into the vacuole must have occurred. Solute penetration is considered later.

Figure 11 also shows that in moderately wilted tomato these errors were equally present in both the liquid phase methods; hence, a comparison of these two methods alone would not have revealed the error. Therefore, it is not surprising that Meyer and Wallace (1941) previously reported good agreement between the gravimetric and simplified methods, the latter being modified for use with potato. This led them to conclude erroneously that both

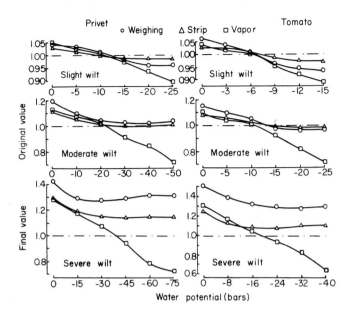

FIG. 11. Comparison of two liquid phase methods (the gravimetric and simplified methods) with a gravimetric vapor phase technique for determining leaf water potential. From Slatyer (1958).

methods were correct. In general it seems preferable, when seeking to evaluate ψ measurement techniques, only to compare methods that are likely to be affected by dissimilar errors. A final check of measured tissue ψ against π of a solution initially used to equilibrate the tissue should also be made when possible (Ashby and Wolf, 1947; Ordin et al., 1956).

Despite Slatyer's criticism of the gravimetric and simplified methods on the above grounds, earlier workers apparently succeeded in obtaining ψ values, using these methods with tissues having severely depressed water potentials.

Molz (1926b) used the simplified method to measure ψ down to -66 bars in the perianth of *Helleborus foetidus*, and Ursprung (1929) found ψ values of -34.5 bars in the vexillum of *Lotus corniculatus*. More recently, Plaut and Ordin (1961) measured ψ values down to -18 bars in sunflower leaves and found the values they obtained were well correlated with the θ of the soil in which the plants were growing. Ordin et al. (1956) considered the simplified method satisfactory for oat coleoptile sections at least down to -15 bars. They also showed that for sections preequilibrated in solutions of known π value, the method gave tissue ψ values in close agreement with these π values, at least over the range from -6 to -15 bars. Indeed, Crafts et al. (1949) criticized the technique on the grounds that potato tissue continued to shrink after all cells were plasmolyzed. Meyer and Wallace (1941) also found this. These liquid phase techniques may be more suitable for some tissues than for others. It seems prudent not just to assume the validity of measurements based entirely on only one of these techniques.

b. Errors Peculiar to Methods Involving Measurements on the Solutions. In these techniques the volume of the solution must be small so that changes in its properties due to water exchange with the immersed tissue remain sufficiently large to be measurable. Hence, although these techniques are free from the injection errors considered above, they are affected by transfer of solute from the tissue to the solutions or by nonosmotic water exchange.

The principal source of solute is from cut cells in the tissue sample, although Gaff and Carr (1964) reported a small contribution even from intact immersed leaf tissue. Ashby and Wolf (1947) found a small constant increase in RI that they attributed to solute release from cut cells. They concluded this was negligible, but Gaff and Carr (1964) pointed out that the increase was of the same order as the critical values of the change in RI near the isopiestic point and that the isopiestic concentration therefore could be overestimated by 100%. Although this may be a valid criticism, it must also be remembered that Ashby and Wolf were able to check the accuracy of their results by comparison with the gravimetric method and by a preequilibration technique (see the previous section). Release of cell sap will affect the refractometric method in two ways: first, the solution may be diluted by water in the cell sap; second, the cell sap solutes may appreciably increase the solution RI if they are organic but not if they are largely inorganic. The densimetric technique of Shardakov will be similarly affected, but here the solution density will be altered by the cell sap solutes, regardless of their chemical composition. Gaff and Carr (1964) found the Shardakov method gave a slightly higher ψ than did the refractometric method, which they attributed to differential effects of released cell solutes. They pointed out, however, that the effect could equally well be in the opposite direction. Schläfli (1964) presented evidence that release of cell sap from cut cells may continue, although at a reducing rate, for some hours. Rehder (1961) found that initially ψ values using the Shardakov technique were very low. He showed that this could not be due to the high density of released cell sap on cutting the tissue, since the density of the cell sap was less than that of the solution.

The possibility of nonosmotic exchange of water between sample and solution must also be considered. Gaff and Carr (1964) suggested that cell walls may be a major source of such water, since they earlier found (Gaff and Carr, 1961) that up to 40% of leaf water content at full turgor may be held in cell walls. They considered that this water would be freely available to dilute the surrounding solution, the cell walls presumably then becoming fully imbibed with the resultant diluted solution. This would have two consequences. (1) Only the ψ of the protoplast would be estimated. This would not matter greatly provided ψ in the cell wall, and in the protoplast had initially been equal. However, *if* as Gaff and Carr (1961) claimed, the cell wall ψ often is considerably *below* that of the protoplast, because of the former acting as a buffer, then (2) it is necessary to decide whether ψ of the cell wall or of the protoplast is the more meaningful. For most investigations, the latter is preferable since it is more directly related to biochemical activity and growth potential of the protoplast, but for studies of water movement in the plant, the former may be preferable if, as Weatherley (1965) has suggested, water movement is mainly through the cell walls. The possibility of any such buffering action has been critically considered in Section II,B,4,d.

The second consequence of solution dilution by cell wall water will be a spurious lowering of the isopiestic solution concentration, since the apparent isopiestic concentration is that at which water loss by osmotic uptake by the protoplast is balanced by water gain from the cell wall. This will be a more dilute solution than the one actually isopiestic with the protoplast. The latter solution would have shown a decline in RI or density due to dilution by cell wall water, even though this would have been partially offset by subsequent uptake of water by the protoplast. This error is illustrated in Fig. 12.

The water normally held to the cell wall by capillary matric forces is released when the cell is immersed in solution and so is available to cause these dilution effects. If this were a large source of error, then it should become apparent when liquid phase methods dependent on change in density or refractive index are compared with liquid phase methods permitting the use of relatively large volumes of solution or with vapor phase methods. Such comparisons would be expected to show *higher* ψ values for results from the first group of methods. However, this has not been generally reported. Indeed, Carr and

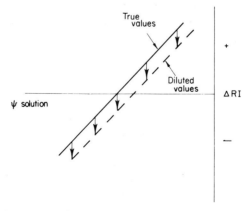

Fig. 12. Schematic representation of possible error in the refractive index (RI) method for determining water potential due to dilution of test solutions by water from the cell walls.

Gaff (1962) themselves found *higher* ψ values at the same leaf RWC, using a vapor phase technique, than the refractometric method. This is a surprising result. The opposite would have been expected both on grounds of cell wall dilution, if it were important, and buffering effects of the cell wall that they postulate. Carr and Gaff (1962) do not appear aware of the anomalous nature of their finding. It certainly offers no support for the existence of errors from either of these sources.

Weatherley (1965) reported broadly similar results. He showed that leaf discs floated on mannitol solutions of the same ψ as the discs (determined by a vapor phase technique) took up liquid. He attributed this to imbibition by cell walls, and this seems reasonable. However, a survey of the literature does not support his statement: "The fact that the classical method of measuring water potential by immersion in graded osmotica gives different results from vapor equilibration methods." Thus, Grieve (1961) checked the Shardakov and a vapor phase method and found reasonable agreement between them; Knipling (1965) found the Shardakov method agreed with a vapor phase method to within 15% and explained the discrepancy in terms of factors other than dilution by cell wall water. Kramer and Brix (1965) found the Shardakov and a vapor phase method in agreement for tobacco and tomato leaves, except for small differences at low ψ values in tomato. Lemée and Gonzalez (1965) found excellent agreement between the Shardakov and a vapor phase method, and Rehder and Kreeb (1961) found that differences between the Shardakov and a vapor phase method either were small or in the opposite direction to that expected as a result of dilution by cell wall water.

Comparisons with liquid phase methods involving measurements on the tissue sample in general also fail to support this view. Shardakov (1938) reported coincidence of ψ values determined by his and by the simplified methods. Lemée and Laisné (1951) reported good agreement between the simplified method and the refractometric method, at least for fleshy tissue. Manohar (1965) found the Shardakov method superior to the gravimetric technique.

Little direct evidence is available that dilution by cell wall water is a source of error in liquid phase methods. Indeed, some workers suggested that the relatively dry cell walls of the epidermis of leaves may cause an initial concentration of the surrounding solution by preferentially taking up water (Rehder, 1961; Schläfli, 1964; Walter, 1963b). However, it is difficult to see how this can be so. There is no semipermeable membrane between the cell walls and the solution, so the latter should be taken up in its entirety by the matric forces of the cell wall, which should not differentiate between solute and solvent. Provided sufficient solution is available, the cell walls should become fully imbibed and their ψ_m should rise to zero; at the same time solution π should increase by the amount of water originally held in the cell wall. Table 1 shows that in experiments using cellulose dialysis membranes

TABLE I

EFFECT OF ADDITION OF PARTIALLY IMBIBED DIALYSIS MEMBRANE OF KNOWN WATER CONTENT AND POTENTIAL (ψ INIT.) ON THE MEASURED (ψ FINAL OBSERVATION) AND CALCULATED (ψ FINAL CALCULATION) WATER POTENTIALS OF KNOWN SODIUM CHLORIDE SOLUTIONS, ASSUMING THE IMBIBED WATER IS FREELY AVAILABLE TO DILUTE THE SALT SOLUTIONS PRESENT IN EXCESS[a,b]

$\psi_{initial}$:	-1.8	-2.0	-2.8	-3.3	-3.3	-3.3	-3.4	-3.8	-6.2	-7.2	-13.2	-14.0	-26.1	-29.0
$\psi_{final\ observation}$:	-0.8	-1.5	-2.6	-3.0	-3.0	-2.0	-1.6	-2.5	-3.4	-5.9	-10.0	-11.0	-23.7	-20.2
$\psi_{final\ calculation}$:	-0.5	-1.4	-3.2	-2.4	-2.8	-2.5	-2.7	-3.3	-4.0	-6.7	-9.6	-12.2	-21.8	-21.6

[a] From Barrs (unpublished).
[b] ψ measured in bars.

wetted to various degrees, the ψ increased more or less as predicted by this hypothesis when known amounts of salt solution of known π were added to the membranes. Had the membranes preferentially absorbed water, salt solution concentration would have risen and an overall fall, rather than the observed rise in ψ, would have been expected.

c. Errors Common to All Liquid Phase Methods

i. Solute penetration. A basic assumption of liquid phase methods is that the only transfer between solution and sample is osmotic movement of water. If the solute can penetrate into the protoplast, then errors will arise because the protoplast π will be lowered, in turn lowering the tissue ψ and raising the π of the solution. The latter will be more important in techniques where solution volume is kept low; the former will affect all liquid phase methods.

It is likely that solute penetration has been a source of error in much of the published work (Slatyer, 1966). Sucrose solutions have traditionally been used as the standard osmotic agent, for example, by Ursprung and Blum (1916), Molz (1926a,b) Ernest (1931), and more recently by Manohar (1965), Louie (1963), and by many workers in the Soviet Union where the refractometric method is widely accepted (Kharanyan, 1965; Samuilov, 1965; Petinov and Shaidurov, 1964). Weatherley (1954) has shown that in all nine species he studied, leaf discs floated on sucrose solutions actively accumulated sucrose to varying degrees. Using the refractometric method Goode and Hegarty (1965) concluded that spuriously low ψ values of apple leaves were the result of the active uptake of sucrose. For leaf tissue at least, sucrose solutions should be used as osmotic agents with the greatest caution. How far other tissues are able to accumulate sucrose actively is largely an open question, which perhaps could be answered by use of radioactive tracers. However, Ordin *et al.* (1965) found sucrose was absorbed from solution by *Avena* coleoptile sections, depressing tissue π. They also demonstrated that mannitol was a satisfactory osmotic agent, although there was evidence of slight uptake after 20 hours of exposure. The behavior of coleoptiles in Carbowax solution was identical to that in mannitol solution, so presumably Carbowax was also satisfactory. Some reservations concerning the usefulness of mannitol were expressed by Goode and Hegarty (1965) since Trip *et al.* (1964) reported that it is absorbed and respired. However, the response is variable and does not occur in all species. In *Avena* coleoptiles no appreciable dissimilation of mannitol was found in the first nine hours after addition of this compound. In potato leaves 99% of the mannitol supplied was absorbed, it did not readily leave, and it gave rise to $^{14}CO_2$. This latter finding is in contrast to the results of Thimann *et al.* (1960), who found ^{14}C-labeled mannitol entered mostly the free space of potato tuber; after one day in 0.3 M mannitol a maximum of 0.008 M had entered the cells. Such a difference could reflect a greater metabolic activity in leaves and, in general, problems of active solute uptake may be greatest in leaf tissue. Thimann *et al.* also considered Carbowax 1500 was a satisfactory osmotic agent. However, Burström (1953) considered it likely that mannitol penetrated *Helianthus* tuber. This probably was not an active accumulation since the tubers had previously been stored at 3°C and were exposed to the mannitol solutions at the same temperature. Manohar (1966a) has reported the penetration of the seed coat of pea by sodium chloride, glycerol, and mannitol, but not by Carbowax.

The relative merits of different osmotic agents are further discussed in Section V,D,2.

ii. Effects of cutting tissues. There is no doubt that cutting plant tissue has many disturbing effects. Tensions that presumably existed in the veins prior to their severance may be expected to decline markedly, permitting a subsequent general rise in ψ as the cells of the tissue absorb this water. Ernest recognized this source of error as early as 1931, but it has still to be quantitatively assessed. Rehder (1961) speculated that such an error might be responsible for a rise in ψ in his samples with time.

A second effect of cutting is a progressive reduction in the tissue component of P (arising from mutual pressure between the cells) as the sample is cut into smaller pieces, depressing tissue ψ. This effect would be expected to be maximal in methods dealing with very small pieces of tissue, such as the cell method. Ernest (1934b) stated that she demonstrated this effect by measuring ψ of mesophyll cells from leaves previously floated intact on water for 3 days. She considered the value obtained, -8 bars, to be a maximum since the tissue originally should have been at full turgor. Lemée and Gonzalez (1965) found, like Rehder (1961) and Schläfli (1964), that ψ rises as the period of immersion of tissue samples is increased. Lemée and Gonzalez attributed this effect to gradual restoration of tissue pressure that was temporarily lost in the cut portions of the samples. However, Schläfli (1964) showed that the effect persists in tissue first killed by heating. Here tissue pressure would be completely and permanently eliminated, so its restoration could not have been responsible for gradual rises in ψ. In general, loss of tissue pressure after cutting does not seem to have been regarded as an important source of error, provided tissue pieces are not excessively small.

Cutting will also release cell sap. The effect of this on properties of the solution has already been considered. However, released cell sap may also affect intact cells. Ernest (1931) demonstrated this by comparing ψ values for strips of intact cells from *Crocus* leaves ($\psi \sim -7$ bars) with values for sections including cut cells ($\psi \sim -10$ bars). She therefore recommended separation of cells by stripping as preferable to sectioning in the cell method. It seems likely that this source of error will be reduced in techniques where tissue pieces are not too small and also where properties of the tissue pieces rather than of the osmotic solutions are measured.

A further effect of isolating tissue is that all ψ gradients previously existing in it will gradually approach a mean value. Hence, ψ measurements will always be mean values provided they are taken when equilibrium has been established between solution and sample. It is not possible at present to assess the importance of this effect. It could lead, for instance, to a spurious depression of ψ in leaf mesophyll cells because of removal of water from them by drier epidermal cells. If Gaff and Carr (1961) are correct in their postulate that leaf protoplasts often are at a higher ψ than their surrounding cell walls, then this effect must disappear when tissue is isolated, and again ψ for protoplasts will be spuriously depressed. Such effects will be particularly important in the cell method, if attempts are made to follow ψ gradients in the same section as Ursprung (1929) has done. Ernest (1931) has rightly pointed out that adjacent cells in the same section must all come to the same ψ value rather rapidly.

Weatherley (1965) raised the possibility that cell walls may become infiltrated with the solution, thereby relaxing them, reducing P and so depressing ψ. If this were so the vapor phase techniques should give higher ψ values than liquid phase methods as they would be free of this source of error. Weatherley's data support this view but, as we have already seen, other comparisons generally do not.

A final source of error in liquid phase methods is that there will inevitably be differences between the subsamples that have to be taken. Such differences may be increased by the preparation of subsamples, but in some tissues, notably leaves, they will always be present to some extent prior to sampling. This was demonstrated by Campbell et al. (1966) in leaves of maize and chestnut, using a vapor phase technique, in which only a small quantity of tissue was needed for each sample, Slavik (1963a) has shown that leaf θ may also vary similarly within the area of one leaf blade.

5. Final Recommendations and Comments

To minimize drying effects, preparation of subsamples should be carried out as quickly as possible in a humid cabinet. All tissue should be thoroughly randomized. Where a cutter is employed, it should be sharp to minimize cell damage. Schläfli (1964) found that samples could be prepared more quickly with scissors than with a leaf punch. Kramer and Brix (1965) recommend that cutting be kept to a minimum. Ashby and Wolf (1947) pointed out that discrepancies between the gravimetric and refractometric methods disappeared if the tissue was first equilibrated with a solution. Lemée and

Laisné (1951), investigating the refractometric method, recommended giving tissues a preliminary rinse in the same concentration of solution as that to which they were subsequently exposed. Gaff and Carr (1964) recommended such exposure for 30 to 40 minutes, stating that only 25% of the total exchange occurs in this period. They also recommended that samples be left for several hours in fresh solutions before finally taking measurements. Lemée and Gonzalez (1965) recommended a similar procedure for the Shardakov technique, that is, a 1-hour preliminary exposure followed by a change of solution and an additional 6-hour exposure. All these investigators found that accuracy was increased by this simple precaution (which minimizes errors resulting from effects of cell wall water or sap from cut cells on the solutions); it will apply particularly to methods where solution properties are measured. Errors of this nature will be less important where tissue properties are measured, since solution volume may be relatively large. However, results would be improved if the solutions were stirred or at least shaken occasionally to reduce concentration gradients.

The use of short equilibration times, 30–45 or even 5–10 minutes (Crafts *et al.*, 1949) and 20–30 minutes (Shardakov, 1938), seems now to have been generally abandoned (Schläfli, 1964, Kramer and Brix, 1965, Walter, 1963b), although Walter has also pointed out the danger of solute penetration if the equilibration period is unduly extended. This applies particularly to leaves in sucrose solutions.

Liquid phase methods can be surprisingly laborious and time-consuming, particularly when the approximate isopiestic concentration is not known and a wide range of solutions must be used to ensure its inclusion. This applies especially to studies of diurnal variation in leaf ψ, which often varies widely. It sometimes is worthwhile to make short preliminary tests with a few widely spaced solution concentrations. Or it may be possible to obtain a rough estimate of the isopiestic solution simply from the fresh weight of the sample.

Although considerably more work is needed before the absolute accuracies of the various liquid phase methods can be stated, their relative sensitivities are known. In methods that depend on change in size of samples, measurement of volume is more precise than measurement of area, and this in turn is more accurate than change in length or thickness. Thus, Ernest (1934a,b,c) determined isopiestic values to 0.001 *M* sucrose or about -0.03 to -0.04 bars, using the cell method. Ursprung (1929) gives results to the nearest half bar for the simplified method, and Ordin *et al.* (1956) considered its accuracy to be approximately ± 1 bar. Data of Meyer and Wallace (1941) suggest a sensitivity of about ± 0.5 bar for the gravimetric method. Shardakov (1938) considered his technique could differentiate between sugar solutions differing by a few hundredths in molarity, and it is certainly possible to differentiate between two solutions only 0.5 bar apart giving a sensitivity of ± 0.25 bar. Inspection of the results of Ashby and Wolf (1947) and Gaff and Carr (1964) suggest a sensitivity for the refractometric method of slightly better than ± 1 bar, although Petrov (1962) found the technique relatively insensitive. Maximov and Petinov (1948) give the accuracy as ± 0.2 bar under the most favorable conditions and as 1.5 to 2 bars in normal use. Due to the possibility of active sugar uptake, the refractometric method should be used only with caution, especially for leaves. The use of sucrose should be avoided where possible in liquid phase methods—mannitol or, better still, Carbowax being preferable.

6. Miscellaneous Liquid Phase Methods

Spomer (1964) tried to measure ψ in woody stems by inserting Fiberglas, nylon, or gypsum blocks into them. His preliminary report showed that only gypsum blocks were effective. Nieman and Poulsen (1964) measured ψ values varying between 3 and 13 cm of mercury in cotton stems, using a mercury water manometer applied over a cut in the stem.

Useful descriptions of three methods for estimating ψ in stems have been given by Scholander et al. (1962), although, as these workers point out, the techniques are at best semiquantitative. In the closed burette technique the lowest pressure is determined against which the xylem can absorb water. This method is limited to positive pressures. Where tensions exist, they are indicated by the removal of all the water from the burette. In the delta pressure technique, the sensitivity of the absorption rate to changes in burette pressure is measured and extrapolated to zero rate. In Renner's (1911) potometer technique, a capillary burette is connected to an attached twig and the water absorption rate is reduced by compressing the xylem with a screw clamp. The twig is detached and a note is made of the rate at which a moist vacuum can draw water through the resistance. Assuming simple filtration, the sap pressure can be calculated from the ratio of the flow rates.

B. Vapor Phase Methods

1. Introduction

According to Bennet-Clark (1959) measurements of ψ for plant parts, in the vapor phase, were made as early as 1915 by Ursprung on the fern annulus and by Renner on elaters of liverworts. The possibility of such measurements therefore existed contemporaneously with liquid phase measurements. However, liquid phase techniques dominated the field from 1916 (when the cell method was first used) until 1930, when Ursprung and Blum published a modified version of Ursprung's vapor phase technique. This was probably because liquid phase measurements were much easier to make and possible errors associated with immersion were largely overlooked or ignored.

Some of the more recent vapor phase techniques, although feasible for many years, require familiarity with precise electrical measurements and have therefore regrettably been foreign to many plant physiologists. Furthermore, advances in related fields, such as the development of vapor pressure techniques for π measurement in the biomedical field (Hill, 1930; Baldes, 1934), were not carried over into plant physiology as early as might have been expected, for example, van Andel's (1952) apparatus.

Some vapor phase techniques (Ursprung and Blum, 1930; Slatyer, 1958) retain the isopiestic principle common to most liquid phase methods. Advantage is taken of the fact that a definite quantitative relation exists between ψ of a solution and the relative vapor pressure above it:

$$\psi = (RT/M)(\ln p/p^0) \tag{7}$$

Subsamples of tissue are held in small enclosed spaces just above each solution instead of being immersed in the solutions. Since the solute is not volatile it does not escape into the air above the solutions, which therefore acts like a semipermeable membrane. The relative vapor pressure above the solution therefore becomes equal to solution π. Hence, the samples are exposed to a range of known ψ values without being immersed in solutions, and the isopiestic value is obtained from observations on the tissue samples or on the solutions.

A more direct approach is to isolate the sample in a sealed chamber in the absence of a salt solution. A measurement of relative vapor pressure, or of some related property, then gives the ψ of the sample directly, provided the sample and the space in the equilibration chamber have first come to equilibrium. Suitable transducers are the thermocouple psychrometer (Spanner, 1951; Richards and Ogata, 1958) or the vapor pressure instrument of Macklon and Weatherley (1965b).

This more direct approach is preferable to an isopiestic one since the time and labor of preparing and measuring subsamples are saved and the error arising from variability between subsamples is eliminated. A return to an isopiestic technique in thermocouple psychrometry, although avoiding the use of subsamples, was advocated by Boyer and Knipling (1965) on the grounds of error elimination. However, the weight of available evidence suggests that this approach may not be necessary (Barrs, 1965a; Manohar, 1966c; Zollinger et al., 1966). Techniques using electrical transducers, for example, thermocouple psychrometry, offer an important advantage in that they may readily be fully automated (Lang and Trickett, 1965) with a final output as punched paper tape (Lang and Trickett, 1966).

The methods are described before discussing and evaluating them.

2. Simple Isopiestic Methods

a. Measurement of Change in Solution Volume. This method was originally proposed by Ursprung and Blum (1930) for π (expressed sap) or ψ (soil samples). It is illustrated in Fig. 13. In this form it is a modification of Halket's (1913) adaptation of Barger's (1904) method for determining molecular weights. Change in solution volume is indicated by change in the liquid-filled lengths of the capillaries as observed by a micrometer with a reticle eyepiece. Water distills to or from the capillaries, depending on the direction of the ψ gradient between the sample and solutions. Graphical interpolation of the isopiestic value is feasible, although the plot is not linear. Ursprung and Blum (1930) recommended immersion of the chamber and capillary tubes in a stirred water bath at room temperature to provide some measure of temperature control. They either removed the chambers from the bath to measure capillary lengths or preferably measured these *in situ*, using a stilling tube projecting from the objective into the water above the chamber. Effects resulting from curvature of the menisci in the capillaries are negligible, provided diameters of 0.1 mm or greater are used. A diameter of 0.3 mm and a length of 6 mm were convenient. The distance of the meniscus from the capillary rim affects the rate of movement of the meniscus. Hence, this

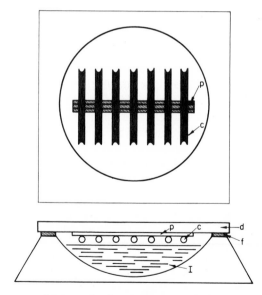

Fig. 13. Water potential determinations by the method of Ursprung and Blum (1930). The capillary tubes c contain standard reference solutions and are attached to a cover glass d by plastic cement p. The cover glass is sealed to a shallow dish by grease f. The dish content, I, is intact leaf.tissue or expressed sap. From Crafts *et al.* (1949).

distance must be standardized if graphical interpolation is used. Corrections to shifts in meniscus position resulting from temperature effects were hopefully applied using a control capillary in a second chamber containing a solution approximately of the same π as the isopiestic capillary. In an alternative technique (Levitt, 1964), the capillaries are replaced by a range of solutions on filter paper pieces and the changes in weight of the pieces are noted. Bennett-Clark (1959) pointed out that by replacing the expressed sap (Fig. 13) with intact plant tissue, for example, a large leaf disc, ψ can be measured. However, few such measurements have been made.

b. Measurement of Change in Sample Weight. This is another straightforward transference of a liquid phase method, the gravimetric method, to the vapor phase. Measurement of changes in weight of subsamples are made after they have stood over a range of solutions for some time. The method was first proposed by Arcichovskij and Arcichovskaja (1931). An important advantage of this approach lies in the sensitivity of weighing methods compared with microscopic determination of linear dimensions used in the preceding method. Slatyer (1958) showed that previous lack of success with vapor phase methods by early workers was largely due to failure to control temperature accurately. Slatyer's successful technique consisted essentially in immersing special microdesiccators, each containing a sample of 10–12 leaf discs 0.7 cm in diameter supported over a salt solution, in a water bath controlled to $\pm 0.001°C$. Each sample is weighed before and after 24 hours exposure to the vapor above each solution. Barrs and Slatyer (1965) later reported 8 hours of exposure as sufficient. Slatyer found only 40 seconds were necessary for transferring a sample from a microdesiccator to a weighing bottle. Erroneous change in weight therefore would be restricted to this period, even though the weighing bottles were not subsequently temperature controlled, since the total weight of discs and air in the bottle must remain constant. This is a further advantage over the previous method in which change in solution volume will continue during the whole of the period between withdrawal and determination. The need for precise temperature control in vapor phase techniques apparently was not recognized for a long time by most plant physiologists, but it was appreciated early by animal physiologists. For example, a water bath controlled to $\pm 0.001°C$ was described by Hill as early as 1930.

Slatyer's (1958) microdesiccators were unsatisfactory in some respects. The sample was supported only 5 mm above the liquid and could easily be splashed by the salt solution. This was especially true because screw-top jars were used. These had to be screwed up tightly to ensure a seal, and they were easily jerked during unscrewing after the equilibration period. Although close to the liquid, the leaf discs were not ideally exposed since their upper surfaces were pointing only to the lid of the jar. Kreeb (1960) improved the microdesiccator by replacing the liquid with sponge plastic soaked in an appropriate solution. This avoided difficulties resulting from splashing and also permitted the sample to be completely surrounded by the solution. The jar was weighted with a piece of lead resting in the bottom. Kreeb also recommended that the sample, instead of being exposed directly on a piece of gauze, be placed in a small container, resting on the gauze, to eliminate contact with salt solution. However, Jarvis and Jarvis (1963a) found that stacked discs reached equilibrium slowly, so although they used Kreeb's modified microdesiccator, they preferred to spread the discs out directly on the gauze, as Slatyer (1958) originally recommended. Lemée and Gonzalez (1965) also used discs spread directly on the gauze. These workers used a jar in which the lid was held in place by a spring clip. This may be preferable to a screw top. Figure 14 shows a microdesiccator drawn after both Kreeb (1960) and Lemée and Gonzalez (1965), which includes these modifications. Kreeb (1960) also suggested that all samples should be handled in a high-humidity cabinet.

Despite these improvements, Kreeb and Önal (1961) repeatedly found ψ to be zero or to show completely anomalous positive values. This led them to identify dry weight loss due to respiration during the equilibration period as an additional source of error. This error persisted, particularly in tissue with high ψ values, even when exposure time was reduced to 5 hours. Kreeb (1960) had earlier shown that for a 5 bar salt solution at least, ψ was correctly estimated by any exposure period from 5 to 48 hours. Kreeb and Önal therefore routinely cut each sample of leaf discs into two to provide initial and final estimates of dry weight so that they could correct for this unwanted component of weight change. Jarvis and Jarvis (1963a) also found it necessary to apply a similar correction, but they used two parallel samples of whole

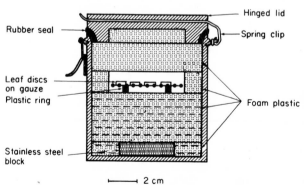

FIG. 14. Equilibration chamber for the gravimetric vapor-phase technique for determining tissue water potential. Modified from Kreeb (1960) and Lemée and Gonzalez (1965).

discs. This seems preferable because errors resulting from failure to exactly bisect the discs are avoided. Kreeb (1965a) has reported the use of only a 2- to 3-hour exposure period to avoid the "very complex and not quite dependable manipulations" necessary for applying this correction. However, as Kreeb pointed out, with such a short equilibration period there is uncertainty that the correct relative vapor pressure has been attained. This error will be more important with high ψ values as the high relative vapor pressures required take longer to attain. This modified gravimetric method again lends itself to graphical interpolation of the isopiestic value.

Ulehla *et al.* (1965) described a simplified version of the technique in which leaf discs are equilibrated between two strips of filter paper protected from evaporation by polythene sheets. Known concentrations of sodium chloride flowed through the strips, which were separated by nylon mesh or perforated polyvinyl chloride separators from the leaf discs. No temperature control or correction for respiration losses was applied.

c. Measurement of Change in Solution Weight. This approach was tried by Thut (1938) when he attempted to measure the relative humidity (or relative vapor pressure) over a solution that would be isopiestic with that within a leaf. Although the technique was crude, it constituted an attempt to measure ψ for an attached leaf. Few workers have attempted this difficult but important problem. Thut's technique was to attach "humidity bottles" containing a graded series of KOH or NaOH solutions to the underside of leaves for 8 hours. The isopiestic solution was then determined by plotting the change in solution weight against relative humidity. Thut does not seem to have realized the importance of temperature control in these experiments, so it is not surprising that his values were almost impossibly low, ranging between 57% RH (*Hibiscus*) and 91% (*Lantana*) or lower than -700 bars to approximately -100 bars. The principle behind this approach has recently been adopted by Whiteman and Koller (1964), see Section IV,B,5.

3. Direct Measurements of Vapor Pressure or of Relative Humidity in the Vapor Phase

As mentioned earlier, this group of methods involves isolation of a sample in a sealed chamber and measurement of vapor pressure (or relative humidity) following attainment of equilibrium between the gas phase and the sample.

a. From the Rate of Evaporation of a Hanging Drop. This method was introduced by Macklon and Weatherley (1965b) and is based on the empirical vapor–pressure micro-osmometer of Weatherley (1960), see Section V. Since the vapor–pressure potentiometer differs only in construction of the equilibration chamber, only the latter will now be considered. The method is illustrated in Fig. 15. Thirty leaf discs, each 0.95 cm in diameter, are placed

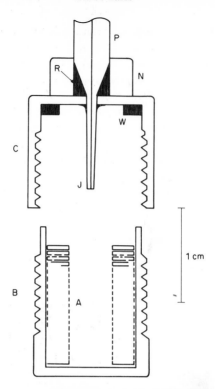

FIG. 15. The leaf water potentiometer capsule. A, leaf annuli in position; B, capsule base; C, cap; J, jet; N, collar; P, pipette; R, epoxy resin cement; W, rubber ring washer. From Macklon and Weatherley (1965b.)

in the lower portion of the chamber and their centers are removed by a 0.5 cm cork borer with its taper on the inside to minimize crushing the discs. The lower portion of the chamber is now sealed to the upper by screwing it on tightly. (Perhaps a worthwhile modification would be to replace the screw thread by two O-ring seals and to eliminate the upper seal W; this would ensure a very quick, easy, and certain seal.) The chamber, together with a consider- able length of the protruding pipette, is placed in a constant-temperature water bath. After 2 hours of equilibration, a drop of water is almost com- pletely extruded so that it hangs from the tip of the pipette. After a 5-minute " settling period " the drop is withdrawn into the pipette until its upper end is aligned with a reference mark, and the position of the lower end is read by a traveling microscope. The drop is then extruded again, this time for 10 minutes timed with a stopwatch. It is withdrawn into the pipette again, up to the reference level, and evaporation is measured by noting how much nearer the lower meniscus is to the upper one. The 10-minute exposure is immediately repeated to give a second measurement of evaporation rate, and the mean of the two is taken. Calibration is effected by exposing the drop to a known ψ range. This is obtained by placing filter paper in the chamber, two discs line the bottom and an oblong piece of filter paper, rolled up to give a cylinder of the same diameter (0.5 cm) as is punched in the pile of leaf discs, is located centrally. The paper is then soaked in a known concentration of NaCl solution and the excess is drained off. Equivalent ψ is calculated from data given by Robinson and Stokes (1959). The calibration curves so obtained are linear. Table II shows equivalent ψ values for a wide range of NaCl concentrations and temperatures.

b. *Measurements Based on Psychrometry.* The relative vapor pressure in a space is also effectively the relative humidity of that space. It is therefore possible to assess corresponding ψ [Eq. (7)] by measuring wet-bulb depression. Two types of sensor have been used, the thermocouple and the thermistor. The former has so far been more extensively employed.

i. *The thermocouple psychrometer.* In the early 1930's biomedical researchers devised techniques for measuring π that essentially involved differential wet-bulb psychrometry using either a thermopile (Hill, 1930) or opposed thermocouples (Baldes, 1934). These devices could be used only with liquids. A drop of control solution was placed on one junction and a drop of unknown solution on the other junction. The simple wet- and dry-bulb thermocouple psychrometer, which can be used to measure either π of solutions or ψ of plant or soil samples, was first successfully employed to this end by Spanner (1951). An alternative version was described by Richards and Ogata (1958). Russell and Richards (1938) had earlier considered its use but encountered technical difficulties. Both types of psychrometer are now widely used to measure ψ in plant tissues.

Before describing the two instruments in detail, the thermoelectric effects on which they are based are briefly outlined. Figure 16a shows a very simple electric circuit of two different metals formed into two junctions. If a temperature difference exists between the two junctions, an electric current will flow between them in such a direction as to tend to equalize the difference. This is the Seebeck effect. If, on the other hand, both junctions are initially at the same temperature, then, by passing an electric current through them, one junction will cool and the other will heat. This is the Peltier effect. The direction of current flow determines which junction is warmed and which is cooled. Figure 16b shows that the output from the thermocouple may be measured by inserting a meter at A without affecting the voltage output, provided A_1 and A_2 are kept at the same temperature. The Spanner (1951) thermocouple is used essentially in this form. A slightly modified version of the Spanner thermocouple is shown in Fig. 17A. Figure 16c shows essentials of the Richards and Ogata (1958) thermocouple, which differs from the

TABLE II

WATER POTENTIALS OF SODIUM CHLORIDE SOLUTIONS (JOULES/KG)[a]

Molality	Temperature (°C)								
	0	5	10	15	20	25	30	35	40
0.05	−214.4	−218.4	−222.3	−226.2	−230.1	−233.9	−237.7	−241.6	−245.4
0.1	−423	−431	−439	−447	−454	−462	−470	−477	−485
0.2	−836	−852	−868	−884	−900	−915	−930	−946	−961
0.3	−1247	−1272	−1297	−1321	−1344	−1368	−1391	−1415	−1437
0.4	−1658	−1693	−1727	−1759	−1791	−1823	−1855	−1886	−1917
0.5	−2070	−2115	−2158	−2200	−2241	−2281	−2322	−2362	−2402
0.6	−2484	−2539	−2593	−2644	−2694	−2744	−2794	−2843	−2891
0.7	−2901	−2967	−3030	−3091	−3151	−3210	−3270	−3328	−3385
0.8	−3320	−3398	−3472	−3543	−3612	−3682	−3751	−3818	−3885
0.9	−3743	−3832	−3917	−3998	−4079	−4158	−4237	−4314	−4390
1.0	−4169	−4270	−4366	−4459	−4550	−4640	−4729	−4815	−4901
1.1	−4599	−4713	−4820	−4924	−5026	−5127	−5226	−5322	−5418
1.2	−5032	−5160	−5278	−5394	−5507	−5620	−5730	−5835	−5941
1.3	−5470	−5611	−5742	−5869	−5994	−6119	−6239	−6354	−6471
1.4	−5912	−6068	−6210	−6350	−6487	−6623	−6754	−6880	−7006
1.5	−6359	−6529	−6684	−6837	−6986	−7134	−7276	−7411	−7548
1.6	−6811	−6996	−7163	−7330	−7491	−7652	−7805	−7950	−8097
1.7	−7260	−7460	−7640	−7820	−8000	−8170	−8330	−8490	−8650
1.8	−7730	−7940	−8130	−8330	−8520	−8700	−8880	−9040	−9210
1.9	−8190	−8430	−8630	−8840	−9040	−9240	−9430	−9600	−9780
2.0	−8670	−8920	−9130	−9360	−9570	−9780	−9980	−10160	−10350

[a] From Lang (1967).

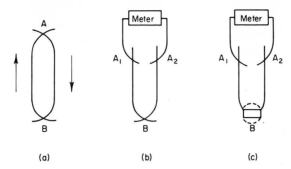

FIG. 16 Thermoelectric effects used in thermocouple psychrometry. *a*, The Seebeck effect; current flows due to a temperature difference between junctions A and B, *b*, Measurement of temperature difference between A and B. B may initially be cooled by the Peltier effect (Spanner psychrometer). *c*, Maintenance of permanently wet junction at B. (Richards and Ogata psychrometer.) After L. A. Richards (1965a), in *Agronomy Monographs*, **9**.

Spanner thermocouple only in the insertion of a silver ring at junction B. A slightly modified version of the Richards and Ogata thermocouple is shown in Fig. 17B.

The Richards and Ogata thermocouple (Fig. 16c) can be used as a psychrometer, provided junctions A_1 and A_2 are maintained at a reference dry-bulb temperature and the silver ring is filled with water so that it can take up the appropriate wet-bulb temperature. The output of the psychrometer, like wet-bulb depression, will be larger at low humidities; the two, in fact, are linearly related. The ring is filled by dipping it into water before inserting it into an equilibration chamber containing the sample being measured. By this means the free junction (in Fig. 16c) is kept continually wet since the drop held in the ring lasts for many hours. The Spanner thermocouple (Fig. 16b) may similarly be used as a psychrometer if junction B is first cooled to the dew-point by passing a Peltier cooling current through the psychrometer in the correct direction. For the psychrometer shown in Fig. 17A, 6 mA for 30 seconds, passing from the constantan wire to the chromel-P wire, is optimal. A second important difference between the Richards and Spanner psychrometers is that the free junction in the latter dries out between readings, as the amount of water condensed is very small and soon evaporates.

Although the Peltier current tends to heat the reference junctions of the Spanner psychrometer while the free junction is cooled, temperature rise is negligible due to the rapid outflow of heat along the massive copper wires (c in Fig. 17A). Spanner (1951) used bismuth and bismuth–5% tin in his original version, for which only 2 mA for 10 seconds were necessary. This combination of metals is preferable since the thermoelectric power (126 μV per °C) is twice as high as in constantan and chromel-P. A further point in its favor is

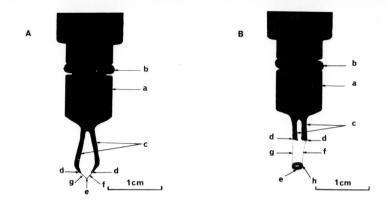

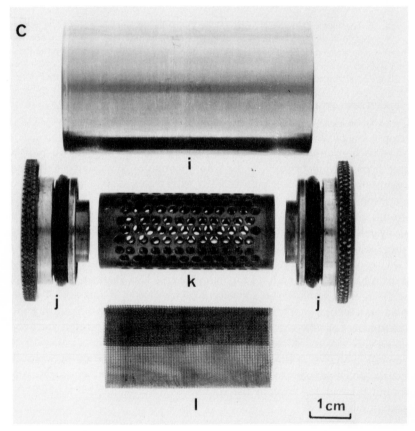

FIG. 17. A, Silhouette of Spanner-type thermocouple psychrometer; B, silhouette of Richards and Ogata-type thermocouple psychrometer; C, equilibration chamber and heat sink. a, brass mount; b, O-ring seal; c, twin core, PVC-covered copper flex (14×0.0076 inch.), bared in this region; d, reference junctions; e, free junction; f, Chromel-P 0.001 inch. diameter; g, Constantan 0.001 inch diameter; h, silver cylinder; i, stainless steel equilibration chamber; j, brass end cap; k, drilled copper tube (heat sink); l, stainless steel wire mesh. From Barrs (1965b).

that the maximum Peltier cooling possible is 4.9°C as against 1.5°C. It is important to note that there is a maximum Peltier cooling, since it follows from this that a Peltier-cooled psychrometer cannot be read below the corresponding wet-bulb temperature, which is about half this (dew-point) temperature depression, as it will not then be possible to condense dew on its free junction. With most biological systems this is not an important limitation, since such low potentials usually are not encountered. However, using chromel-P and constantan, the lower useful limit would be about − 65 bars. This limit would of course be considerably extended using bismuth and bismuth–5% tin. Despite these advantages of increased range and sensitivity, most workers have preferred constantan and chromel-P since these are commercially available as 0.001-inch diameter wires, whereas bismuth and bismuth–5% tin must be drawn down to size by the experimenter.

Various modifications of these two basic thermocouple psychrometers have been proposed. Two of the most useful are the shortening of the fine wires in the Richards psychrometer and the replacement of the silver ring by a loop of the fine wire. Klute and Richards (1962) shortened the wires from the original 8 mm (Richards and Ogata, 1958) to 4 mm, thereby improving the strength of the couple since the wetted junction swings far less; the performance was unaltered. Lang and Trickett (1965) suggested substitution of a wire loop for the silver ring. Rawlins (1966) showed by a theoretical analysis that the fine wires could be reduced to 1 mm in length without significantly changing the performance. He also points out that the silver ring does not approximate well to the ideal wet junction, which should be completely wetted and freely expose a spherical drop. A silver ring may not be wetted on the outside. Also the drop is only exposed at the ends of the ring. These factors would tend to reduce efficiency of the thermocouple. A wire loop should more nearly meet the ideal requirements. However, as Rawlins' data showed, even with the silver ring, the Richards psychrometer is highly efficient, and the substitution of a wire loop therefore cannot be expected to increase efficiency greatly.

The main modification of the Spanner psychrometer has been to increase the diameter of the wires used, so as to facilitate assembly and make the instrument more robust (Box, 1965b; Kramer and Brix, 1965; Lambert and Schilfgaarde, 1965; Monteith and Owen, 1958). The last-named authors reported only a negligible drop in sensitivity in the modified instrument. However, since the psychrometer is larger, more dew must be condensed. This is reflected in the heavier Peltier currents and longer cooling times reported by the various authors above. This means that the system is disturbed considerably more each time a reading is taken, and associated errors that may arise are magnified (such errors are considered later). In practice the fine wire psychrometers are durable, provided they are well made and handled carefully. Hence, they are preferable to the more massive versions.

Thermocouple psychrometers may be constructed by soft soldering, silver soldering (generally only the thick-wire versions of the Spanner psychrometer), welding, or a combination of these techniques. Richards and Ogata (1958) and Monteith and Owen (1958) found soft soldering to be a convenient and effective method of forming the junctions. Barrs (1966b) described a suitable procedure in detail. Thinned polyvinyl acetate enamel (two coats) dried at 300°F after each application may be used to protect the wet junction of the Richards psychrometer in those applications (discussed later) where the water is replaced by a solution (Boyer and Knipling, 1965). Lang and Trickett (1965) described a welding technique that they found satisfactory for production of both Spanner and Richards psychrometers. Waister (1964) and Manohar (1966b) described a combination of both these techniques in the production of Spanner psychrometers, welding the free junction under oil and soldering the reference junctions. Rawlins (1966) reported that commercially available welded constantan–chromel junctions were more stable electrically than hand-soldered ones. Box (1965b) described a massive Spanner psychrometer in which the free junction was silver soldered. This may not be feasible with the preferable fine wires. Useful references on welding of fine wires are Gelb *et al.* (1964), Hart and Elkin (1946), Kiernan (1955), Specht (1959), Stover (1960), and Wecksler (1963).

Macklon and Weatherley (1965b) reported that the presence of glass or epoxy resin in their hanging drop potentiometer gave anomalous results. This has also been the writer's experience in thermocouple psychrometry, and it seems advisable to avoid these materials as far as possible. A convenient form of thermocouple mount and equilibration chamber for either type of psychrometer is shown in Fig. 18. The mount is made from brass (stainless steel is preferable although harder to work), and the equilibration chamber is made from stainless steel. This metal is preferable since it is unaffected by the NaCl solutions used in calibration. The polyvinyl chloride insulation on the thermocouple leads is roughened where it passes through the brass tube in the mount and fixed in the mount using Araldite (the two-tube pack does not form a copper amide with brass). The Araldite should not be allowed to spread over the lower surface of the mount. The O-ring forms an easy and effective seal. The small plug, again sealed by an O-ring, is inserted last and therefore ensures that pressure will not build up in the chamber. Richards and Ogata (1958) pointed out that the psychrometer reading is pressure dependent, although their figures show that the effects of diurnal variations in barometric pressure usually are negligible. In use, the equilibration chamber is immersed in a controlled temperature water bath to maintain the reference junctions at a constant, known temperature. Sufficient length of lead should be immersed in the bath (coiled if necessary) to prevent error arising from heat conduction along it.

FIG. 18. Equilibration chamber and mount for thermocouple psychrometer; the gauze is used with soil and small leaves that will not otherwise line the chamber properly. From Barrs (1966b).

Alternative chambers have been proposed. The only significant variants are those which permit the psychrometer to be transferred from one sample to another (Richards and Ogata, 1958; Ehlig, 1962) or several samples to be transferred to a fixed psychrometer (Campbell et al., 1966). An example of the former, described by L. A. Richards (1965a), is disadvantageous because the thermocouple mount protrudes above the water level in the bath, and this may affect the reference junction temperature by thermal conduction along the tube. Provided the top of the bath is insulated and the bath is operated at room temperature, this effect is unimportant (L. A. Richards, 1965a). However, under these conditions separate cooling for the bath is essential, whereas it may not be necessary for an open bath. The sample changer of Campbell et al. (1966) is preferable since the whole apparatus is immersed. It must be pointed out, however, that transfer of either psychrometer or sample is presently a manual process and prevents the adoption of automatic scanning, with consequent time-saving. In practice, the elimination of between-psychrometer error apparently does not lead to a worthwhile increase in accuracy. Other sources of error presumably are much larger.

Thermocouple psychrometers are calibrated like the hanging drop potentiometer of Macklon and Weatherley (1965b) already described. Care must be taken that the filter paper soaked with the requisite salt solution is exposed in the same way as subsequent samples to minimize effects of changed geometry. NaCl solutions (see Table II) are widely used. However, L. A. Richards and coworkers preferred KCl, and he gives (1965a) a brief table relating KCl concentration with π. A wider table may be constructed from data given by Robinson and Stokes (1959). Box (1965b) and Korven and Taylor (1959) provide some data for sulfuric acid solutions. However, the risk of acid vapors would appear to make use of the salt solution preferable. Some workers (Boyer, 1966) used sucrose solutions. Useful tables for this purpose are given by Molz (1926a) and Walter (1931), but rapid deterioration of these solutions because of fungal action is likely. Ursprung and Blum (1930) suggested that, since vapor pressure is influenced by density, isotonic solutions of different solutes will have different vapor pressures. Thus, they calculated that a NaCl solution of the same vapor pressure as a sucrose solution with $\pi = -45$ bars would have $\pi = -39.9$ bars. Their analysis is not rigorous, however, and it seems to be widely held today that isotonic solutions do have equivalent vapor pressures.

Typical examples of psychrometer calibration curves are given in Fig. 19. The results published by other workers are essentially similar, although the instrumentation used to measure the psychrometer output may affect the result to some extent, at least for the Spanner psychrometer. This is because

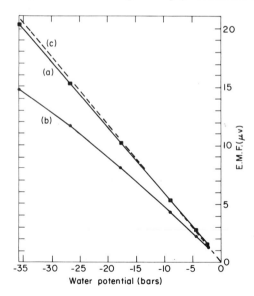

Fig. 19. Calibration curves for thermocouple psychrometers. (a), Richards and Ogata psychrometer; (b), Spanner psychrometer; (c), fully ventilated psychrometer (theoretical). From Barrs (1965a).

the Richards psychrometer has a continual output while the Spanner psychro-meter does not because of the presence of permanently and intermittently wetted free junctions respectively. This difference is illustrated by the full lines in Fig. 24. In constant surroundings the output of the Richards psychro-meter remains constant. The Spanner psychrometer is initially cooled to the dew-point by the Peltier current, subsequently warming rapidly to wet-bulb temperature when the cooling current is stopped. Thereafter, it remains at the wet-bulb temperature for a short time and finally returns to the reference temperature. The lower the surrounding humidity, the quicker the wetted junction dries and consequently the shorter is the dwell-time at the wet-bulb temperature. Curves published by Rawlins (1966) illustrate this effect. If the dwell-time is less than the response time of the measuring instrument, the apparent reading will be less than equivalent to wet-bulb depression. Sufficiently sensitive galvanometers have longer response times than electronic amplifiers; consequently, the former will start to give a reduced output before the latter. This probably explains the linear Spanner psychrometer calibration curve (at least down to −46 bars) found by Lang and Trickett (1965), using an elec-tronic amplifier, although Rawlins (1966) and Zollinger et al. (1966), also using electronic amplifiers, reported a departure from linearity at somewhat lower outputs. Rawlins found the output from the Spanner psychrometer to be slightly higher than that from the Richards instrument at high ψ values, an effect attributed to reduced heat flow along the wires as a result of moisture condensing both on them and on the free junction.

These results show that the observed output of the Spanner psychrometer will have an empirical content and that it will be similar to or less than that of the Richards psychrometer. The latter, as Fig. 19 shows, has an output close to the theoretical output of a fully ventilated psychrometer, and this will approximate the wet-bulb depression, although at very high ψ values the output departs slightly from linearity with potential (L. A. Richards, 1965b). It therefore is not correct to say, as have Bennett-Clark (1959), Korven and Taylor (1959), and Monteith and Owen (1958), that readings of the output of a Spanner psychrometer correspond to the dew-point temperature depression. The dew-point will be vacated as soon as the cooling current is stopped. This is indicated by Box (1965b) and has been noted by the writer (unpublished) using a fast response digital voltmeter.

Measurement of psychrometer output has already been partly discussed under calibration. Two basic approaches are possible: (1) measurement of current directly with a reflecting galvanometer or (2) measurement of potential using some form of potentiometer. Whatever system is adopted, it must be borne in mind that high sensitivity ($\pm 0.01\ \mu V$) and stability are required. A reflecting galvanometer will measure output from either a Spanner or a Richards psychrometer quite satisfactorily simply and cheaply, although it requires considerable time and concentration from the observer. Spanner (1951) pointed out that the galvanometer should include an adjustable magnetic shunt; provision should also be made for a standardizing current and connection to an adjustable voltage source for the Peltier cooling current. His circuit is shown in Fig. 20. The microswitch permits rapid switching between galvanometer and Peltier source, and the portion of the circuit enclosed within the dotted line is immersed in an oil bath to reduce parasitic thermal electromotive forces. A galvanometer has also been used by Barrs and Slatyer (1965), Korven and Taylor (1959), Manohar (1966b), Monteith and Owen (1958), and Waister (1964). These papers should be consulted for further details; Waister illustrates a circuit permitting the reading of psychrometers sequentially. Kramer and Brix (1965) and all the workers just mentioned except Monteith and Owen used a ballistic method, in which the maximum galvanometer deflection was read.

Richards and Ogata (1958) used a microvolt potentiometer (Teele and Schuhmann, 1939) to measure output of the Richards psychrometer. Their arrangement is described in detail by Klute and Richards (1962). Essential features are the use of a wall galvanometer as a null detector and manual counterbalancing of the thermocouple output. This arrangement permitted detection of a balancing error of 0.01 μV. Such a system theoretically is preferable to the direct use of a galvanometer alone, since no power is drawn from the psychrometer. However, outputs obtained by both methods are very similar, so there is no real advantage of this manual potentiometric method in practice. Furthermore, such a method is limited to the Richards psychrometer, since it would not be feasible to balance manually the ballistic output of the Spanner psychrometer.

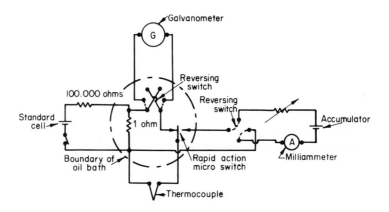

FIG. 20. Circuit for measuring output from a Spanner psychrometer, using a galvanometer. From Spanner (1951).

Automatic potentiometric measurement, using a recording potentiometer coupled to an electronic amplifier, was found convenient and satisfactory by Barrs (1966b), Box (1965b), Lambert and Schilfgaarde (1965), and Zollinger et al. (1966). Lang and Trickett (1965) used a peak voltmeter to store the amplified output of Spanner or Richards psychrometers until it could be recorded by a multipoint recorder. An important advantage of the thermocouple psychrometer over many other techniques (both liquid and vapor phase) is that this electric transducer is comparatively easy to automate (Lang and Trickett, 1965, 1966; Lambert and Schilfgaarde, 1965). Russell (1963) previously described a low-level thermocouple scanner. A successful random-access scanner has been built by Trickett and Barrs (1967).

A galvanometer is considerably cheaper than an electronic amplifier and a recorder but is less convenient. Thus, it provides no permanent output record and does not readily lend itself to automation. This problem is not insurmountable, as Rider and Bradley (1962) have shown, but a galvanometer has yet to be included in an automatic system for thermocouple psychrometers. However, when only a few readings are required, the expense of automatic recording may not be justified. Considerable further effort is necessary to operate and scan psychrometers automatically, so this should only be considered in problems requiring frequent readings over long periods.

Such an application has been the measurement of ψ for plants in situ over periods of 10 hours or more, using intact plants. The principle of these experiments is to enclose an attached leaf and maintain it at a constant temperature, at the same time measuring its equilibrium ψ with a thermocouple psychrometer. Lang and Barrs (1965) did this with a Richards psychrometer. Rawlins (1963) and Lang and Barrs (1965) argued that enclosing the leaf would reduce its transpiration rate to zero, causing gradual abolition of the energy gradient between the leaf and the stem xylem at the point of insertion of the leaf. In this way the leaf would come to have the same ψ as the xylem, and so the psychrometer would estimate this xylem ψ. The enclosed leaf, in effect, could be regarded as a (negative) pressure gauge protruding from the stem. A similar approach has been made by Lambert and Schilfgaarde (1965) using a Spanner psychrometer, which more readily lends itself to this application because of the ease with which the free junction may be rewetted. Lang (1966) also used a Spanner psychrometer in his later measurements. Lambert and Schilfgaarde do not discuss the exact nature of their measurement.

For reasons to be discussed later, Boyer (1965b, 1966) and Boyer and Knipling (1965) suggested an isopiestic technique, using the Richards psychrometer to determine ψ for detached leaves. Successive drops of solution of known π were placed on the wet junction and steady state readings were taken. The readings and drop π values are linearly related, so the isopiestic solution is determined by interpolation of plotted data (see Fig. 8B). Boyer and Knipling consider that a reasonably accurate estimate of the isopiestic point may be made by connecting two plotted points, although accuracy is improved when one of the experimental points is close to the isopiestic value. Figure 21 shows results.

Strict temperature control is essential for successful thermocouple psychrometry. This is because a wet-bulb depression of 1°C approximates to a ψ value of -80 bars. Assuming a required accuracy of ± 0.1 bar, the corresponding wet-bulb depression will have to be read to ± 0.001°C. Some latitude is perhaps permissible; a slow, smooth drift in temperature may be tolerable, provided the reference temperature is known at the time of measurement and an interpolation to this temperature can be made from calibrations carried out over a range of temperatures. Using this approach, in an apparatus designed to make *in situ* measurements of plant ψ, Lang and Barrs (1965) found a sample standard deviation of ± 0.27 μV, as against ± 0.078 μV for psychrometers calibrated in a constant temperature water bath controlled to ± 0.001°C. It is important to avoid sudden fluctuations in temperature occurring within the space of time required for a reading. Barrs (1966b) described a simple water bath permitting calibration of psychrometers to ± 0.1 bar, which is sufficiently accurate for most work with plant tissues. The bath was cooled by evaporation from its open surface to a constant temperature room that was a few degrees cooler. Weatherley (1960) pointed out that an uncontrolled bath will equilibrate at 1–2°C below constant room temperature.

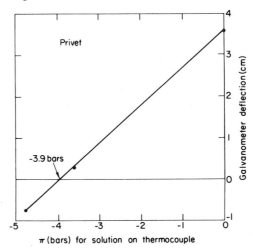

Fig. 21. Isopiestic measurement of leaf water potential, using a Richards and Ogata psychrometer. The isopiestic value, -3.9 bars, is shown by a determination at the *x* intercept. The output at the *y* intercept corresponds to a normal determination of -3.6 bars (galvanometer deflection = (1 cm bar^{-1}). From Boyer and Knipling (1965), courtesy *National Academy of Science*.

Thus, the room could probably be run at bath temperature to aid the approach to equilibrium after immersion of the chambers.

A disadvantage of this type of bath, since it lacks refrigeration, is that it cannot be run below ambient temperature. Progressively more complicated refrigerated baths using odorless kerosene as the bath liquid are described by Richards and Campbell (1948) and Klute and Richards (1962). L. A. Richards (1965b) described a bath in which maximum temperature fluctuations and drift were held to less than $\pm 0.0001°C$ for days at a time. If other factors do not become limiting, this would increase psychrometer accuracy by an order of magnitude. More sophisticated water baths and control equipment are described by Kijne and Taylor (1963), Korven and Taylor (1959), and Spanner (1951). Kreeb (1965a) has described a water bath for use in the field.

Adequacy of temperature control may be checked by reading psychrometer output when the free junction is dry. Provided this fluctuates less than the accuracy with which wet-bulb depression is read, temperature control is adequate. The equilibration chamber itself helps further to buffer temperature changes (Kreeb, 1965b). However, the writer has not found the use of a modulator, that is, a metal block in which the chamber is inserted (Box, 1965b), to significantly improve temperature control.

ii. The Thermistor Psychrometer. A disadvantage of the thermocouple psychrometer is its low overall output, necessitating measurements to $0.01 \mu V$. One way of overcoming this, which has yet to be exploited successfully, would be to replace the individual junctions with miniature thermopiles. This would increase output to more easily measurable levels. An alternative approach is to replace thermocouples by thermistors. Kreeb (1965b) used a system where a wet thermistor tip formed one arm of a bridge circuit. It was kept wet by a copper shoe that completely surrounded the tip and prevented evaporation. The thermistor therefore measured chamber dry-bulb temperature. When the shoe was lowered the thermistor cooled to wet-bulb temperature, and the required humidity was given by the difference between the two corresponding readings. The out-of-balance signal was displayed on a recorder after passing through an amplifier.

B. G. Richards (1965a) described a basically similar approach for measurement of soil ψ. One important difference is the use of two thermistors, one wet and the other dry in two arms of a Wheatstone bridge circuit. In many cases readings showed a constant linear drift with time, attributed to change in wet-bulb size. The linear calibration curve was obtained by extrapolating these readings to zero time. Sensitivity was increased about 100 times by using thermistors instead of thermocouples.

B. G. Richards also reported (1965b,c) successful measurement of soil ψ by a technique relying on the adsorption, by the glass coating of a thermistor, of vapor from the ambient atmosphere in equilibrium with soil. The amount of heat or time required to evaporate the adsorbed moisture from the thermistor is calibrated against salt solutions of known π. A second, control thermistor is kept at the same temperature and pressure but under constant humidity (0 or 100%). Each forms one arm of a Wheatstone bridge circuit; the second thermistor reduces the need for temperature and pressure control or corrections. Such a technique could be applied to plant material.

4. Direct Pressure Measurement

a. The Pressure-Bomb. This technique is in a sense isopiestic. It was extensively used by Scholander *et al.* (1964, 1965, 1966). In their 1965 paper it is referred to as "our new pressure-bomb technique." However, Dixon attempted this simple technique in 1914. It is illustrated in Fig. 22. An excised leafy twig, with the bark and phloem peeled back at the cut end, is put into the pressure-bomb. The cut end is sealed gas-tight through the lid, using a rubber compression gland. The protruding cut end is then observed through a lens or microscope as the gas pressure in the pressure-bomb is raised by admitting nitrogen under pressure. The pressure at which the cut end of the twig is just wetted is taken as equal and opposite to the tension existing in the xylem of the twig (that is, xylem ψ) before the twig was excised. Care should be taken not to shorten the twig after it is cut off as this allows error to develop when leaf ψ has risen (because of release of xylem tension) after the initial cut.

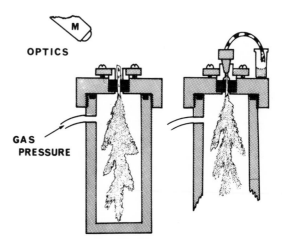

Fig. 22. Pressure-bomb technique. (left: For measuring xylem water potential in an excised twig; right: for collecting xylem sap. Copyright American Association for the Advancement of Science. From Scholander *et al.* (1965).

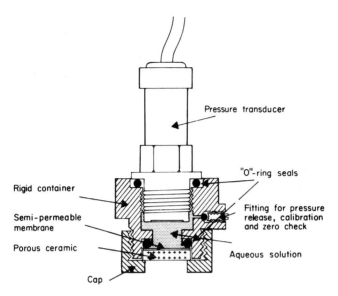

Pressure transducer

"O"-ring seals

Rigid container

Fitting for pressure release, calibration and zero check

Semi-permeable membrane

Porous ceramic

Aqueous solution

Cap

FIG. 23. Equipment for water potential measurement using a pressure transducer. From Peck and Rabbidge (1966b).

b. Change in Pressure of a Reference Cell. This technique was recently developed to measure ψ or ψ_m for soil (Peck and Rabbidge, 1966a), but it probably could be used with plant material. Figure 23 shows the version used to measure soil ψ_m. The apparatus is essentially an osmometer. An important feature is that the aqueous solution (Carbowax 20,000) is always initially at a lower ψ than the sample.

If the hydrostatic pressure (P) in the osmometer is initially zero, P will rise as water flows into the osmometer. Finally, $-\psi$ (actually ψ_m for nonsaline soils) $= -\pi + P$, at equilibrium. This is in fact Eq. (1), discussed earlier, describing the water relations of a plant cell. The apparatus is so constructed that solution concentration remains virtually constant, so the required potential is the difference between the hydrostatic pressure, measured by a pressure transducer, and the known initial π of the enclosed solution. For measurements of ψ for plant or soil samples, it would be necessary to include a vapor gap between the sample and osmometer, although this would increase the time constant of the instrument.

5. Extrapolation of the Relation Between Transpiration Rate and ψ of the Air

This method (Whiteman and Koller, 1964) is similar in principle to that of Thut (1938), see Section IV,B,2,c. It involves estimation of the equilibrium vapor pressure of the external atmosphere at which net flux of water vapor between a plant shoot and the surrounding air is zero. This is achieved by enclosing a shoot in a transparent chamber and measuring the rates at which CO_2 must be added and water vapor removed to maintain chamber atmosphere constant. Such an apparatus, essentially a "null point compensating system," was described by Koller and Samish (1964). Measurements are carried out at different humidity levels, but with constant illumination, and for any one run, constant CO_2 uptake was assumed to indicate constant stomatal aperture. The transpiration values so obtained were corrected for differences between leaf and air temperature and plotted against the corresponding equivalent ψ in the atmosphere (see Fig. 8B), although, of course, only positive transpiration values were available. The technique was used in the field, and it was not possible to raise the humidity sufficiently to stop transpiration, so rather long extrapolations to the isopiestic atmospheric ψ had to be made.

6. Sources of Error in Vapor Phase Methods

Although determination of ψ in the vapor phase automatically eliminates many of the errors associated with liquid phase determinations (injection of intercellular spaces or solute uptake), other sources of error arise. These are effects resulting from unwanted temperature or vapor pressure gradients persisting in systems that ideally should be at equilibrium. Although these sources of error may exist simultaneously, they will be discussed separately.

a. Persistent Temperature Gradients. Ursprung and Blum (1930) pointed out the necessity of preventing temperature gradients within the equilibration chamber, since such gradients would cause unwanted vapor exchange. They therefore recommended temperature control by immersion of the chamber in a water bath. As already discussed, liquid baths providing very precise temperature control have since been devised. Despite the use of such baths, two main sources of persistent temperature gradients have been found: the liberation of heat by respiring tissue and the heat of condensation of vapor at the surface of the sample. The former was described by Barrs (1964, 1965b) and the latter by Zollinger *et al.* (1966).

Barrs (1965b) found leaf ψ values measured by the Richards psychrometer were persistently higher than those from the Spanner psychrometer. This difference was due to the space inside the chamber becoming slightly warmer than the water bath in which the chamber was immersed, as a result of heat released by leaf respiration. Figure 24 shows how this effect would cause the disparity between ψ as measured by the two psychrometers. In each instrument, the construction is such that the reference junctions are tied to the reference water bath temperature. The Richards psychrometer therefore always will read water bath minus chamber wet-bulb temperature because of its persistent wet-bulb. The required difference is, of course, chamber dry-bulb minus chamber wet-bulb, and this will be greater than water bath minus

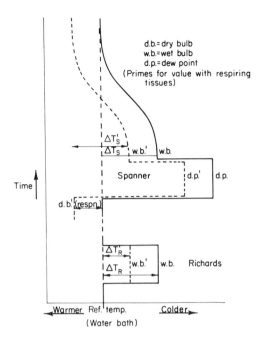

FIG. 24. Effect of heat of respiration on the determination of tissue water potential by the Richards or the Spanner thermocouple psychrometer. From Barrs (1966b).

chamber wet-bulb, if chamber temperature is raised by respiration. Consequently, the Richards psychrometer will give spuriously high ψ readings. Correct readings may be obtained with the Spanner psychrometer, provided the readings before and after passing the cooling currents are combined. The first reading will give the dry-bulb difference between chamber and bath since the free junction is then dry. The second will give bath dry-bulb minus chamber wet-bulb; combining the two gives the required chamber dry-bulb minus chamber wet-bulb. Barrs (1965b) demonstrated that this simple procedure completely corrects for respiratory heat. If the equilibration chamber is lined with a single layer of leaf tissue, the respiration error is of the order of 10 to 20% (Barrs, 1965a), but a double layer may greatly increase error (Barrs, 1964). This source of error may be virtually eliminated by the use of a heat sink (Fig. 17C), but an undesirable consequence is a very considerable extension of the time required to reach equilibrium (Barrs, 1965b).

Error arising from the liberation of heat when water vapor diffusing from a Richards psychrometer condenses on a soil sample has been described by Zollinger *et al.* (1966). They calculated that this could elevate the temperature at the surface of the soil sufficiently to raise ψ. The effect was larger in dry than in wet soils because of reduced thermal conductivity in the former. In very dry soils they found ψ was underestimated by some 15 bars. These workers calculated that the Spanner psychrometer, during the time that it was cooled, condensed water at only one-fortieth of the rate at which water diffused from the Richards psychrometer. They therefore concluded that errors due to vapor transfer effects are probably negligible in most cases, provided a Spanner psychrometer is used. In a comparison of ψ in leaves of five species, as measured by the two psychrometers, no significant differences were found over a wide range of ψ values, provided a correction for respiratory heat was applied to both instruments. Hence, heat of condensation here played a negligible role. This was probably because the leaf samples were thinner and had a greater exposed surface area than did the soil samples.

The effect of temperature gradients due to heat of condensation in other vapor phase systems for measuring plant samples therefore may also be low, provided the sample exposed is thin and lines the chamber walls. Since significant temperature rise as a result of respiratory heat has been found even with thin samples, this may be a significant source of error in other vapor phase techniques. To date, these sources of error have not been adequately evaluated in most other vapor phase techniques. They could conceivably affect all the ones described earlier except the pressure-bomb. Thus, in the vapor phase gravimetric method, if the leaf discs are warmer than the solutions, there will be a tendency for water to distil from the discs to the solution that would otherwise have been isopiestic with them. In the same way, water would tend to distil to the otherwise isopiestic capillary tube in Ursprung and Blum's (1930) method. The only relevant data known to the writer are those of Boyer (1966). He found that, at equilibrium, leaf tissue was 0.007°C warmer than the solution it stood over in a stirred desiccator. Surprisingly enough, he concluded that the leaf ψ would be *higher* (at -5.3 bars) than the solution ψ (-5.6 bars). Weatherley (1960) demonstrated that his vapor–pressure osmometer does not require precise temperature control and that small changes in the level of control or a slow drift in water bath temperature are unimportant. However, this is not the same as demonstrating the lack of any effect of a permanent temperature difference between the wetted filter paper used for calibration and the stack of leaf annuli in the vapor–pressure potentiometer of Macklon and Weatherley (1965b). Such a difference might be higher here than in an equilibration chamber lined with a single layer of leaf, since the distance between the inner and outer diameters of the annuli is about 0.25 cm and the whole exposed surface is cut, which may lead to elevated respiration in the wounded tissue (ap Rees, 1966). Kreeb's (1965c) thermistor psychrometer corrects for temperature differences in much the same way as a Spanner psychrometer, since the thermistor tip, although wet, is first prevented from cooling by evaporation and therefore takes up chamber dry-bulb temperature initially. It is then exposed, measuring chamber wet-bulb temperature. Whiteman and Koller (1964) pointed out that an unavoidable uncertainty in their technique (Section IV,B,5) arises from an inaccuracy of leaf temperature measurement of $\pm 0.3°C$, corresponding to an uncertainty of about ± 25 bars in their ψ measurements. Unfortunately, it is a large error since it completely spans the whole range of plant ψ values normally of interest. Millar (1966) raised the possibility that plant ψ may be more temperature-dependent than solution π (for example, Table II) since temperature change may affect the number of solute molecules present via altered metabolism and may also affect ψ_m and P in plant tissue. Therefore, he advocated determination of tissue ψ at their *in situ* temperatures. However, the magnitude of the error involved by making all determinations at one temperature has yet to be determined.

b. Persistent Vapor Pressure Differences. Monteith and Owen (1958) pointed out that evaporation from a wet-bulb might raise the humidity if it were confined in a small space. Rawlins (1964) calculated that leaf permeability of tobacco, laurel, and philodendron was sufficiently low to allow considerable rise in ψ in the chamber, causing a spuriously high estimate of leaf ψ. The error apparently varied from about 15 to 85%, depending on species and ψ value. He attempted to check the calculation by directly measuring leaf ψ in detached leaves of pepper plants. The plant had first stood in the dark overnight in a -7 bars Carbowax solution. Rawlins argued that under low transpiration conditions the plant should also have ψ approximating to this value: In fact, the ψ values he obtained were about 60% *higher*, which he attributed to low leaf permeability and consequent elevation of chamber ψ by water vapor from the Richards psychrometer.

It is mainly for this reason that Boyer and Knipling (1965) proposed their isopiestic technique already described (Section IV,B,3). They pointed out that there will be no vapor transfer between a leaf sample and a Richards thermocouple when the silver ring contains the isopiestic solution. Hence, errors resulting from effects of leaf permeability are eliminated. After including a correction for respiration they compared the results of this technique with readings obtained by Spanner and Richards psychrometers in the normal way. They concluded that the latter procedure gave spuriously high ψ values (by 2.5 to 7.5% and 4.5 to 12% for the Spanner and Richards psychrometers, respectively).

Barrs (1965a) argued that if low leaf permeability were an important factor then the Spanner psychrometer should give spuriously low ψ values. This is because during the initial cooling period when dew is condensed on the free junction, there will be a greater drop in humidity in the chamber than would occur using the equivalent salt solution. The Richards psychrometer, on the other hand, as Rawlins and as Boyer and Knipling had proposed, should raise measured ψ values. Zollinger *et al.* (1966) reiterated this view of the opposite effects of low sample permeability on estimates of ψ by the two psychrometers and Manohar (1966c) demonstrated in a model system that greatly decreased permeability spuriously depressed ψ as measured by a Spanner psychrometer. Box (1965a) likewise considered that low permeability could affect readings of the Spanner psychrometer in this way, but his calculations showed the effect on estimates of leaf ψ to be negligible.

If this view is correct, then a simple comparison of ψ as estimated by the two psychrometers should be an adequate test. If they both agree, then the error, which is in the opposite direction for each, must be negligible. Barrs (1965a) showed that this was the case for leaves of pepper, sunflower, tobacco, and Pelargonium, each at four different levels of stress. Zollinger *et al.* (1966) confirmed these results, obtaining agreement between values from the two psychrometers for sunflower, corn, apple, peach, and chestnut leaves over a wide range of ψ values. Barrs (1965a) obtained further evidence for this conclusion by comparing leaf ψ estimated by the Spanner psychrometer using either a 10- or 60-second cooling period. In the latter case it was estimated that about 6 times as much water was condensed onto the couple as in the former. Despite this large difference, the pairs of ψ values were in very close agreement, so either a negligible quantity of water was transferred from the leaf or resistance to its movement was negligible. Barrs (1966a) later confirmed the reversed ψ gradient Rawlins (1964) had reported for a pepper plant standing in the dark in a Carbowax solution, but he showed that the effect was due to root pressure rather than to low leaf permeability.

Data of Boyer and Knipling (1965) reveal two apparent anomalies. First, and most important, the errors from the two psychrometers are in the *same* direction. They both give higher ψ values than the isopiestic method. If, as claimed, this is the result of low leaf permeability, then some additional explanation is required in view of the statements and results of Barrs, Box, Zollinger *et al.* and Manohar already discussed. Second, although overall the error is greater for the Richards than for the Spanner psychrometer, it is less for the former instrument in the Geranium data. No explanation is offered of this anomaly. The matter should be investigated further before an effect of low permeability can be established. It is not contended that the isopiestic technique is in error. Indeed, Boyer's (1966) data strongly suggest it is not. It is suggested that any significant influence of low tissue permeability is unproven and that an isopiestic approach therefore may be an unnecessary complication.

Such an error should be small in other vapor phase techniques. The leaf potentiometer of Macklon and Weatherley (1965b) appears to have a geometry and hanging drop size roughly equivalent to that of a Richards psychrometer in its equilibration chamber, so permeability may be unimportant here, too, especially as transfer is across cut edges, although no data are available to test this suggestion. The Peck and Rabbidge (1966a,b) potentiometer should come to a true equilibrium, eliminating permeability effects. The extrapolation procedure of Whiteman and Koller (1964) should not be affected by leaf permeability.

c. *Method of Tissue Exposure.* Three main approaches have been adopted: (1) The equilibration chamber is lined by a single layer of leaf tissue, using pieces as large as possible (Barrs, 1965b); (2) where the tissue is too small for this, it may be supported in the chamber by a gauze cylinder (Ehlig, 1962, using leaflets of *Lotus corniculatus*); (3) a pile of annuli is placed in the chamber (Macklon and Weatherley, 1965b). The last-named investigators reported that a gauze cylinder in their hanging-drop potentiometer interfered with measurement of soil ψ by slowing the approach to equilibrium. Hence, they speculated that such a cylinder would cause spuriously low leaf ψ. Macklon and Weatherley also criticized the use of relatively intact tissue (that is, a single lining layer), suggesting that spuriously low ψ values were obtained because of stomatal closure and a consequent slow rate of approach to equilibrium.

Barrs (unpublished) further investigated these possibilities, using the Spanner psychrometer. In the case of soil (Manbulloo sand), a stainless steel gauze was used to support soil during determination of its water-release curve, and the -15 bar $\%$ moisture content was interpolated. This value, 5.2%, agreed well with the -15 bar value (5.3%) obtained in a pressure membrane apparatus. These results do not confirm Macklon and Weatherley's findings. A possible explanation is that Barrs used a much longer equilibration period (12 hours). Similarly, for a paired sample of a single layer of sunflower leaf, the presence of a gauze did not affect the equilibrium ψ value although time to equilibrium was increased in the chamber containing the gauze. Hence, Macklon and Weatherley's criticism of Ehlig's (1962) leaf data using a gauze would be valid only if his results had not been equilibrium values. However, he followed thermocouple output until a steady state was reached.

Table III supports Macklon and Weatherley's finding that ψ values are appreciably higher in leaves with scored epidermis than in parallel samples with intact epidermis, the scoring being done after positioning the tissue in the equilibration chamber. The table shows that the effect occurs in both sunflower and pepper but less so in the former and is less marked at lower ψ values. It also occurs whether a Spanner or Richards psychrometer is used. Macklon and Weatherley explained this difference as resulting from a slower approach to equilibrium in the intact tissue. However, Table IV suggests that this is not the cause since equilibrium was reached in both treatments. Cutting the tissue should reduce P and therefore *lower* ψ, so this is unlikely

TABLE III

COMPARISON OF WATER POTENTIALS (BARS) IN SLICED AND UNSLICED LEAVES
OF PEPPER AND SUNFLOWER (EACH PAIR FROM ONE LEAF)[a]

Pepper							
Unsliced:	−6.5	−7.0[b]	−7.1	−7.1	−12.5	−15.2	−17.8
Sliced:	−2.9	−3.6[b]	−3.6	−4.2	−11.2	−14.5	−17.4
Sunflower							
Unsliced:	−3.9	−3.9	−4.8	−6.0	−5.4	−8.3	
Sliced:	−1.9	−2.5	−2.9	−3.1	−4.1	−6.4	

[a] From Barrs (unpublished).
[b] Measured with a Richards psychrometer, all other values with a Spanner psychrometer.

to be the explanation. Alternatively, cutting the tissue may release water held in the cell wall (Gaff and Carr, 1964), although other data in the same paper show cutting the tissue is also accompanied by considerable solute release. The writer is unable to offer an explanation of these results but feels that intact samples are preferable to sliced ones. Further work is necessary on this problem.

Shmueli and Cohen (1964) criticized methods of measuring ψ. They pointed out that detaching tissue may alter ψ. There does not seem to be any way around this problem at present, since ψ measurements on attached tissue, as already discussed, may measure stem xylem ψ rather than leaf ψ because of the need to enclose the leaf. Detaching tissue may lead to a rise in ψ as tensions are released, and the final ψ measured will be a mean for the whole tissue. How far this departs from individual component potentials originally present is not known. These investigators also question how truly an equilibrium is established between the tissue and its surroundings. As noted above, Table IV demonstrates the attainment of definite equilibria. Shmueli and Cohen's final criticism is that tissue ψ may change as it approaches equilibrium. The taking up of a uniform mean value, as just discussed, seems likely. A second possible effect is that anaerobic conditions

TABLE IV

COMPARISON OF APPROACH TO EQUILIBRIUM WATER POTENTIAL (BARS) OF SLICED
AND UNSLICED TISSUE FROM THE SAME PEPPER LEAF (SETUP 0930)[a]

Time:	1015	1115	1205	1320	1420	1545	1640	2030
Intact:	−7.4	−7.2	−7.2	−7.1	−7.0	−7.1	−7.1	−7.1
Sliced:	−4.7	−3.9	−3.6	−3.6	−3.6	−3.6	−3.6	−3.6

[a] From Barrs (unpublished).

may arise, because of utilization of most of the oxygen in the chamber. Barrs (1965b) showed that this can lead to a progressive lowering of ψ to the value of π. Anaerobic conditions could conceivably arise in all vapor phase methods, even in the pressure-bomb method that uses nitrogen gas. In methods permitting continuous monitoring of ψ, such an effect may be picked up by departure of ψ from the previous steady state. In methods that do not permit continuous monitoring, this will not be possible, and additional care will be required to avoid error from this source. However, pressure-bomb determinations should be possible before toxic effects become apparent, since a long equilibration period is unnecessary.

d. Surface Contamination Effects. Extraneous sinks for water vapor in the chamber, such as salt contaminating either the tissue or the chamber, could affect the psychrometer reading (Rawlins, 1964, 1966). This may be one of the principal reasons that equilibration takes hours instead of minutes. Rawlins concluded that some contamination of the walls of the chamber is almost unavoidable. Leaf surfaces will likely be similarly contaminated mainly by dust, which can, however, be washed off easily. Salt accumulation on leaf surfaces could cause spurious negative values, but this effect could be eliminated by washing leaves the day before sampling (Ehlig 1962). Similar difficulties were found in the salt-exuding species *Limoniastrum*, *Atriplex*, and *Tamarix*, and Kreeb (1963) could not reliably measure ψ and π in these species. Barrs (unpublished) observed apparent liquid secretion onto the surface of cotton leaf tissue after enclosure for some hours in an equilibration chamber. Further investigation has shown, Table V, that the conductivities of washings from cotton leaf tissue increase with the period of enclosure in the chamber. These conductivities are far higher than from sunflower leaves, which do not increase with time and are only twice as large as the blank. The possibility therefore cannot be ruled out that cotton leaf ψ values may be spuriously low because of salt secretion. Inspection of the data of Ehlig and Gardner (1964) shows that cotton leaf ψ values were considerably

TABLE V

COMPARISON OF CONDUCTIVITIES (λ) OF 5 ML WASHINGS FROM COTTON
AND SUNFLOWER LEAVES AS AFFECTED BY PERIOD OF ENCLOSURE IN AN
EQUILIBRATION CHAMBER[a]

Time in chamber (hours):	0	3	4	5
Cotton:	—	0.151	0.208	0.262
Sunflower:	—	0.044	0.034	0.031
Blank:	0.017	—	—	—

[a] From Barrs (unpublished).

below those of pepper, trefoil, and sunflower at the same RWC. Similarly, data of Lang and Barrs (1965) show that well-watered cotton had $\psi = -11.4$ bars, whereas in well-watered pepper, $\psi = -4.6$ bars. Box (1965a) reported ψ of -6 to -13 bars for cotton leaf tissue previously floated on water.

Manohar (1966c), Monteith and Owen (1958), and Waister (1963) stressed the importance of avoiding contamination of the cap of the chamber by salt solution. Manohar (1966c) showed that such contamination can lead to a slow decline in output of the Spanner psychrometer and that removal of the contamination (by boiling the cap) returns the output to its original value of a month earlier. Waister (1963) also found that the calibration of a Spanner psychrometer was stable for a month or more. Rawlins (1966), however, found calibration to shift by 0.1 μV or more over a week (equivalent to 0.3–0.4 of a bar). He suggested that this reflected a change in the wetting characteristics of the thermocouple surface, presumably by contamination.

The presence of spurious sinks could presumably influence all vapor phase techniques considered, except the pressure-bomb and the extrapolation procedure of Whiteman and Koller (1964). However, this source of error has not as yet been critically studied in these techniques. To reduce water adsorption, Boyer (1966) used petroleum jelly to cover those portions of the wall of his psychrometer equilibration chamber not covered by a sample. Ehlig (1962) earlier showed that all the water held by a Richards and Ogata psychrometer could be adsorbed onto the walls of an empty chamber.

e. Extension Growth Effects. Tinklin and Weatherley (1966) could not obtain ψ values above -1.4 bars for apparently fully turgid leaves of *Ricinus communis.* They suggested that this could be the result of depression of ψ because of continued growth after the excision of the tissue. Such growth was envisaged as analogous to phase II uptake by floating leaf discs (Barrs and Weatherley, 1962). However, the lowering of ψ by growth in the absence of a water supply would simultaneously lower P and thus stop growth once some critical level of P reduction had been reached. Presumably, the ψ value of -1.4 bars corresponded to this level.

7. Final Recommendations and Comments

The selection of an appropriate technique for evaluating tissue ψ will be a compromise between the required accuracy and feasibility of obtaining and setting up the necessary equipment. The simplest techniques would appear to be the modification by Ulehla *et al.* (1965) of the vapor phase gravimetric method and the capillary method (Ursprung and Blum, 1930). The main source of error in these techniques would probably be a lack of adequate temperature control. Unfortunately, no data on the accuracies of these methods (when used for measuring ψ) are available. The pressure-bomb is not a standard piece of laboratory equipment, but once made it should be a convenient, portable apparatus largely unaffected by small temperature variations. It may well be the most useful vapor phase technique for the field laboratory at the present time and probably is quite accurate, with reading usually reproducible to 1% (Scholander *et al.*, 1965).

Many vapor phase techniques (for example, psychrometry, the hanging-drop potentiometer) require accurate temperature control of an equilibration chamber. This is no longer a technical problem in a central laboratory, but it has largely prevented the use of these techniques in field laboratories. However, Kreeb (1965a) described a portable battery-operated water bath that should permit the wider use of these techniques. With this equipment Kreeb found the accuracy of the vapor-phase gravimetric method to be ± 1–2 bars, which is in close agreement with Slatyer's (1958) figure of from $+1$ to -3 bars, using a mains-operated bath.

In all techniques it is essential to minimize drying of the sample during the time between its collection and its installation in the measuring device. Tinklin and Weatherley (1966) reported that such drying could lower ψ for turgid leaves by 2 bars. The writer has found it best to avoid sampling leaves *in situ*. Instead, a whole leaf is removed from a plant and placed immediately in a polyethylene bag that is kept shaded and flat with its top folded over several times. As soon as practicable the bag is transferred to a high-humidity handling cabinet, where the leaf is sampled.

The thermocouple psychrometer gives high precision but at the cost of greater instrumentation if a permanent record is required or if the readings are to be automated. Otherwise, a reflecting galvanometer is adequate, although the need to prevent vibration could be troublesome in a field laboratory. The writer has found a steel cylinder standing in a large drum of sand useful for this purpose. Instrumentation for thermocouple psychrometry has been discussed in detail in the preceding section. As explained there, psychrometers may be automated when necessary. No other technique for ψ presently permits this. A further advantage of this technique is that readings may be continued until equilibrium has definitely been established. Waister (1965) assessed the accuracy of the Spanner psychrometer and found the standard error of measurement of salt solution π was 0.09 bars and the within-chamber error for leaf tissue was 0.06 bar. However, variation between samples from the same leaf was 0.25 bar. He concluded that this represented the maximum accuracy necessary. Ehlig (1962) found the performance of the Richards psychrometer was very similar.

With regard to the relative merits of the Spanner and the Richards psychrometers, the discussion in the previous section suggests that errors resulting from low tissue permeability are negligible and that heat-of-respiration effects are readily corrected by reading the Spanner psychrometer with its free junction first dry and then wet. From this it follows that reliable ψ measurements can be made with the Spanner psychrometer without replacing it by another thermocouple during the course of the determination. In practice, this is very useful, and it is almost essential where automatic scanning is envisaged. Respiration corrections are applied to a Richards psychrometer by taking readings with the junction first wet and then dry. This is plainly inconvenient. An alternative (Barrs, 1965b) is to combine the outputs of a wet and a dry Richards psychrometer, but again this is somewhat unsatisfactory. The Spanner psychrometer is therefore preferred. The isopiestic technique of Boyer and Knipling (1965) seems to be a somewhat unnecessary complication. A possible advantage, when drops of different known π are applied to the same psychrometer, is that calibration is unnecessary. However, when different psychrometers are used (Boyer, 1966), error because of difference between their outputs must be taken into account.

As explained earlier, the thermistor psychrometer has a considerably higher output than the thermocouple psychrometer, and this should eliminate the difficulties of microvolt measurement inherent in the latter technique. However, the final accuracy of the only published equipment for use with plants (Kreeb, 1965b) is a rather disappointing 1–2 bars.

The hanging-drop potentiometer of Macklon and Weatherley (1965b) appears to have an accuracy similar to that of the thermocouple psychrometer, the confidence limits of a single reading of a salt solution being ± 0.26 bars. Error in determination of leaf ψ is apparently no higher than this.

Thut's (1938) technique clearly gives erroneous results and cannot be recommended. The basically similar approach of Whiteman and Koller (1964) suffered from an uncertainty of about ± 25 bars resulting from inaccuracy of leaf temperature measurement of $\pm 0.3°C$. These were field measurements; greater accuracy might be possible under artificial environment conditions.

Many vapor phase techniques have been developed recently, and there is a need for a further assessment of their validity and utility. Comparison of the type carried out by Boyer (1966), in which ψ of preequilibrated tissue is measured by a technique whose validity is being tested, seems a worthwhile approach. Comparisons of different vapor phase techniques, for example, the thermocouple psychrometer and the pressure-bomb, would also be worthwhile.

Perhaps the most pressing need is for a simple technique for measuring the ψ of attached tissues. Present methods of measuring attached tissue (Lambert and Schilfgaarde, 1965; Lang and Barrs, 1965; Manohar, 1966 b,c,d) are not completely satisfactory as the tissue is enclosed and cannot transpire normally.

The merits of ψ as a measure of water stress were considered in Section II,A.

V. MEASUREMENT OF OSMOTIC POTENTIAL (π)

A. OSMOTIC POTENTIAL AS A MEASURE OF WATER STRESS

Osmotic potential π was used as a measure of the harshness of a plant's environment long before total water potential ψ was measured. The lower the π, the higher was water stress within the plant. The realization that water flow is primarily along ψ gradients gave the lie to this simple picture; a plant can have a low π value without suffering from water deficit. Kramer and Brix (1965) have criticized the use of π as it will be affected by cell solute or water content and also because π values differ among plants. They prefer ψ to π as a measure of water deficit and state that ψ should directly affect enzyme activity. However, ψ must also be affected by variations in solute or water content, and it also varies widely among plants.

Walter has maintained (1931, 1963a) that the degree of imbibition of hydration of protoplasm depends on π rather than on ψ. Recently (1966), he clarified this view, in response to criticism by Shmueli and Cohen (1964). Cell hydrature is now equated with "specific" relative vapor pressure, that is, the vapor pressure of a solution or colloid referred to that of free water under the same conditions, particularly under the same pressure. According to Walter, hydrature so defined does not depend on ψ or turgor pressure but on π. Since he also maintains that the functioning of the protoplasm would depend on its hydrature, it follows that π should be an important factor governing functioning of protoplasm.

Slavik (1965) showed that photosynthetic rates of *Conocephalum conicum* were highly correlated with π and that the former declines with the latter as a plant dries. However, he showed that photosynthesis and water content were just as closely correlated. Doubtless the relation between ψ and photosynthetic rate would have been as close. Hence, these experiments do not permit a decision as to whether ψ or π is the more valid indicator of water stress under these conditions.

Boyer (1965a) lowered the π of cotton leaves by adding NaCl to the culture solution. Transpiration and stomatal aperture were unaffected, although ψ leaf and π leaf declined with increasing NaCl concentration. Respiration also remained constant, but the net photosynthetic rate declined. These results could be interpreted as showing a direct effect of π on net photosynthesis, although CO_2 permeability in the cytoplasm may have been reduced by the treatment, or the high NaCl concentrations may have been toxic.

There is no doubt that π decreases more slowly than ψ with decreasing water content of plant tissues. In this sense at least, π is a less sensitive indicator of water deficit than ψ. This applies even in cases (Slavik, 1963b; Weatherley, 1965) in which π decreased more than would be expected from concentration effects due to decline in cell volume, since ψ includes this extra contribution. Figure 1 shows that ψ and π are equal only in a wilted cell, and then only in the absense of negative turgor.

B. Methods Based on Measurements of Expressed Sap

1. Refractive Index (RI)

Measurements of RI are quickly and easily made, even under field conditions. This is probably the main reason that the relation between RI and π has received considerable attention. Despite the ease of measuring RI of expressed sap, the relation between RI and π is variable. Hence, although RI is readily established, the corresponding π is not.

In principle, all that is involved in the measurement of RI is the placing of a small quantity of expressed sap (0.02 ml may be sufficient; Slavik, 1959b) on the prism of the refractometer followed by reading of the instrument. Sufficient accuracy often is obtained with a hand refractometer in the field. The use of suitable American, Soviet, Polish, and German instruments has been described by Davis (1963), Filippov (1961), and Kreeb (1965a). To convert RI to equivalent sucrose concentration, appropriate tables are consulted. These usually are drawn up only for 20°C, so appropriate temperatute corrections generally must be made. Rodionov (1962) sampled at the time of day when the temperature was approximately 20°C, thereby avoiding this correction. Davis (1963) found the diurnal temperature range was considerably reduced by keeping the equipment in trouser pockets between readings. When measurements are made using a laboratory instrument (for example, at high sugar concentrations to get a clear reading; Filippov, 1961), it may be worthwhile to control temperature of the prism at 20°C if numerous measurements are made. Some instruments (Schläfli, 1964) incorporate temperature control. In others in which the prism is water jacketed, connection to a combined pump and thermostat (for example, Braun Thermomix II) operating in a bath at 20°C takes little time. If necessary, the bath may be cooled by a coil connected to a cold water supply.

However, direct conversion of RI to equivalent sucrose concentration and hence equivalent π (Lobov, 1949) generally is not permissible since sucrose may not be the only constituent of cell sap and often is not the major one. Necas (1965) showed that in leaves, stems, and petioles of potato, reducing sugars contributed less than 10% to the total π of expressed sap, whereas electrolytes contributed 60 to 90%.

Slavik (1959b) supported this view, stating that sap π was determined first by inorganic salts, then by sugars, organic acids, and their salts. Kozinka and Niznansky (1963) agreed with this view. As early as 1948, Maximov and Petinov pointed out direct conversion could only give very approximate values of π. From the foregoing, it is apparent that such values would be considerable underestimates.

As Slavik (1959b) pointed out, an accurate relation between RI and π can only be obtained from an empirical calibration curve relating the two. Osmotic potential usually is determined by cryoscopy (discussed later) on parallel subsamples. In this way a rather precise relation between RI and π can be established (Fig. 25). Similar relationships have been found by Scheumann (1965) ($r = 0.95$ for Δt vs. n_D), Slavik (1959a) and Vaclavik (1964).

Unfortunately, the relative contributions of total solutes to π may vary, and this may not be matched by a corresponding change in RI (Önal, 1964a; Slavik, 1959b). Önal found that addition of water to wheat sap caused parallel changes in RI and π, whereas addition of NaCl caused an increase in π but did not affect RI measurably. Gum arabic, on the other hand, caused RI to rise and π to fall. Slavik found that addition of inorganic salts or organic acids to sucrose solutions caused a large change in π but only a small change in RI. Clearly, if the relative proportions of solutes in the sap change ("active change in hydrature," Kreeb, 1965a), then the relation between RI and π will be altered. A change in the proportion of solvent present ("passive change in hydrature") will not disturb the relation. Such active changes in hydrature can be readily induced, for example, by watering bean plants with NaCl soltuions, π may be lowered considerably, but RI may also fall at a low concentration of added salt; even at higher concentrations, RI only returned to its original value (Kreeb, 1965a). Similar effects have been reported for oats (Jaeger, 1966) when mineral fertilization was

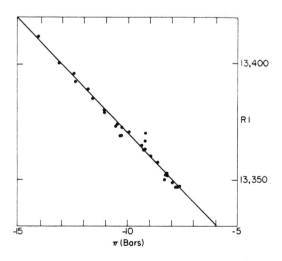

FIG. 25. Relation between refractive index and osmotic potential (determined cryoscopically) of cell sap in *Nicotiana Sanderae* hort. From Slavik (1963b).

increased. For these cases, in order to determine π from RI, it would be necessary to determine the relation between the two at frequent intervals. This procedure is still necessary, even for normal plants, although perhaps at not quite such frequent intervals since seasonal shifts in proportions of solutes seem to be quite widespread and have been reported by many workers (Belik, 1962; Chunosova, 1963; Farkas and Pratt, 1961; Goryunov and Ogryzkova, 1964; Kozinka and Niznansky, 1963; Kreeb, 1963; Lobov, 1949; Necas, 1965; Önal, 1964a; Rodionov, 1962; Slavik, 1959a,b, 1963b). The general pattern seems to be that electrolyte concentration decreases with time, but sugar concentration increases. As Levitt (1964) pointed out, this need for frequent calibration may completely vitiate the advantages of ease and speed of the technique.

The few studies that have been made of validity of the technique in following diurnal variation in π have been somewhat more reassuring; the relation between π and RI appears to remain fixed over such short periods of time (Necas, 1965; Önal, 1964a).

Because of the age effects noted above, it is common practice to adopt a standardized sampling procedure. Sampling typically is restricted to a leaf a certain number of leaves away from an apex (Amanov, 1965; Davis, 1963; Fiedler, 1964; Filippov, 1959; Goryunov and Ogryzkova, 1964; Kreeb, 1963; Kozinka and Niznansky, 1963). Alternatively, age effects may be eliminated by sampling, for example, from leaves progressively lower down the stem (Farkas and Pratt, 1961). Considerable replication is still necessary; even with such a standard procedure, Davis (1963) found coefficients of variation ranging from 12 to 22%. Russian workers frequently replicate tenfold (Chunosova, 1963; Goryunov and Ogryzkova, 1964; Rodionov, 1962).

In general, clearing of expressed sap is not necessary as a sharp line can be detected in the refractometer even with quite turbid material. However, Belik (1960) filtered sap of tomato leaves before determining RI. Chunosova (1963) restricted the sap source to the upper third of the main vein in sugar beet leaf, since this gave a transparent solution. Filippov (1959) found that abundant N could cause cloudiness in cell sap from cotton leaves. Application of heat before sap extraction permitted the subsequent expression of clear sap. Necas (1965) cleared sap from potato leaves and stems by centrifugation.

Boiko and Boiko (1959) suggested a modified use of the refractometer to measure π that avoided direct measurement of RI of sap. Instead, 0.2 ml subsamples of the sap were placed in collodion sacks and then sealed and immersed, one each, in a series of graded sucrose solutions for 1 to 2 hours. The isopiestic solution was determined with a refractometer. Levitt (1964) pointed out that collodion is not perfectly semipermeable and that this could affect the accuracy of the method. However, Boiko and Boiko offer rather meager data (two comparisons) showing good agreement between their techniques and a cryoscopic one (the latter is discussed below). An alternative and less accurate method is to estimate volume change of the sacks visually.

2. Determination of Freezing Point (Cryoscopy)

This is the most widely used method for measuring π. It usually gives values of sufficient accuracy and is physically sound. It is based on the principle that solutes lower the vapor pressure of water and thus disturb the vapor pressure equilibrium between water and ice. This causes ice to melt, with consequent heat absorption and temperature decline, until the vapor pressures of the solid and liquid phases are again equal at the freezing point of the solution.

Vapor pressure lowering is proportional to the mole fraction of solute added (Raoult's law). Further, vapor pressure: temperature curves for dilute solutions are approximately parallel with those of pure water. From these two facts it can be shown (Crafts et al., 1949) that the freezing point depression is linearly related to π, in fact $\pi = 12.06\,\Delta T - 0.021(\Delta T)^2$. Harris and Gortner (1914) and Harris (1915) compiled conversion tables based on this equation. A small correction to bring π from the value at 0°C to some higher temperature, such as that at which parallel measurements of total potential have been made, is effected by assuming the gas laws are obeyed, $\Delta T_{20} = \Delta T_0 \times 293/273$ (Hatakeyama and Kato, 1965; Kreeb, 1963). However, Crafts et al. (1949) doubt the validity of this correction when sap is high in colloids.

The conventional technique employs a Beckman thermometer with its bulb immersed in the sap in a small tube jacketed by a larger one that is immersed in a freezing mixture in a Dewar flask. The inner tube is stirred continuously as the temperature falls, and supercooling usually occurs, so that when ice formation commences, the temperature rises to a brief plateau before declining again. The maximum temperature reached (ΔT_2) is the observed freezing point; if the initial minimum temperature (ΔT_1) is noted, then the true freezing point (ΔT) may be calculated by

$$\Delta T = \Delta T_2 - (\Delta T_2 - \Delta T_1)/80 \times \Delta T_2$$

A correction for heat capacity effects may also be applied if the volume of the sap is small compared with that of the thermometer and the sample tube (Crafts et al., 1949). This conventional technique is described further by Loomis and Shull (1937). It is little used today since it is slow. Each determination takes some 20 minutes and requires a large quantity of sap (15 ml).

Currier (1944) described an essentially similar technique that was improved, however, by reduction of the sap volume to 0.7 ml., and replacement of the Beckman thermometer with a special one having a much smaller bulb and direct calibration. A further advantage is that undercooling and heat capacity corrections may be eliminated by empirical calibration, using known sugar solution concentrations and applying a correction to the observed values for differences between them and correct values (obtained from the International Critical Tables, 1933). The freezing points obtained are accurate to $\pm 0.01°C$. Up to six determinations an hour are possible. Further details are given by Crafts et al. (1949) and Levitt (1964).

Cryoscopic techniques have been improved by the development of truly micro methods and electrical transducers as temperature sensors. Hargitay et al. (1951) reduced sample size to 0.1–1 μl by placing the sample in a capillary and using a polarizing microscope that detected the presence of ice crystals by their birefringence. The small sample size was advantageous since concentration differences resulting from melting were evened out within a few seconds. Furthermore, the sample could be rapidly frozen and allowed to thaw slowly, eliminating difficulties associated with undercooling. Accuracy of the measurement was about $0.002°C$. Ramsay and Brown (1955) modified this technique to permit easier introduction of the sample into the controlled-temperature bath. For samples of $01^{-3}–10^{-4}$ mm^3, sufficient magnification was provided by the ordinary low power of the microscope. The samples were still placed in glass capillaries. This phase of the technique is tedious and time-consuming. Accuracy was $\pm 0.003°C$ for depressions of 1–2°C. Prager and Bowman (1963) developed an ultramicro technique of great convenience and accuracy but of relatively complex instrument design. The technique permits almost simultaneous determination of freezing points for up to eight samples in one run (three standards and five unknowns). The standards give a calibration each time the apparatus is used. The samples (of milli-microliter size), first pipetted into recessed holes in a copper block and then covered with castor oil to prevent evaporation, are subsequently observed microscopically. The Peltier cooling effect is used for rapid freezing; a portion of the cooling is subsequently reduced via a manually controlled electronic proportional servo system, until the first sample almost thaws completely. The dial reading is then noted, and the entire procedure is repeated for the remaining seven samples. Dial readings are calibrated from the standards and are used to determine freezing points of the unknowns. The process is always under the control of the observer; the final ice crystal can be made to grow, shrink, or remain static. This technique represents the optimum in miniaturization and convenience, although considerable labor might be involved in the initial manufacture and assembly of the apparatus. Accuracy was better than 2%.

Some investigators have replaced thermometers with thermistors or thermocouples. Thermistors are more convenient since they do not require a separate reference junction. Furthermore, stray electromotive forces may interfere with precise thermocouple measurements but not with thermistors. The thermistor typically forms one arm of a Wheatstone bridge circuit (Richards and Campbell, 1948; Marr and Vaadia, 1961; Kreeb, 1965b). Richards and Campbell used a sensitive galvanometer with an optical lever as a null point indicator, balancing the bridge with variable decade resistors in the other arm. The system had high sensitivity, 0.1 Ω was equivalent to 0.0003°C, and the standard error was 0.0033°C. Such high sensitivity necessitates a stable voltage supply to the bridge; lead cell batteries were adequate for this purpose. The volume of solution used was 5 ml, but as Marr and Vaadia's work showed, this could be reduced to drop size. Marr and Vaadia also replaced the galvanometer by a recording potentiometer, thus eliminating the need for manual reading. A slight disadvantage of this is that it is necessary to draw lines tangential to the slopes of the curves during and after melting, but the subjective error involved was small. However, it is difficult to draw tangents for curves corresponding to π values below -6 bars, and therefore this is the lowest potential measurable by this technique. The use of a constant voltage is again stressed (1.5 V mercury cells are recommended). Other important points are that the thermistor must be located centrally in the chamber, the gap between thermistor bead and wall must be as small as possible, and the sample should not extend above the bead of the thermistor. The accuracy of the technique is given as better than 0.1 bar. Kreeb (1965b) extended the thermistor approach for use in the field; the out-of-balance output from the Wheatstone bridge was amplified and displayed on a 50 μA meter. Only small amounts of sap (0.15–0.3 ml) were necessary.

Some investigators replaced the Beckman thermometer by copper–constantan thermocouples and measured the output by manual adjustment of a potentiometer using a galvanometer to detect the null point. The reference thermocouple was held at 0°C in a mixture of ice and water (Bodman and Day, 1943). Yoda (1961) used the freezing point of distilled water and the transition point (32.38°C) of sodium sulfate as the standard. He insulated the thermocouple with vinyl resin. Bodman and Day used an empirical relationship between electromotive force and temperature for copper–constantan thermocouples (Bridgman, 1918) to convert readings of known concentrations of sucrose solutions to temperatures. They showed these values were in reasonable agreement with data interpolated from tables of Landolt-Börnstein (1923, 1927) and reported a sensitivity of ± 0.001°C. Yoda showed good agreement between freezing points of mannitol solutions measured by thermocouples and by a Beckman thermometer, giving the accuracy of the measurements as 0.025°C. This technique required only about

0.2 ml of sap. An important point in his technique was the seeding of the solution with a minute ice nucleus of a definite size to minimize undercooling effects. This is worthwhile in all techniques where the sample is not first completely frozen.

Finally, it should be noted that there are commercially available cryoscopes that are simple and rapid in operation, requiring about 1 ml of sap (for example, Aminco-Bowman Catalog No. 5–2050, made by American Instrument Co., Silver Spring, Maryland, and Drucker-Burian-Kreeb, made by W. Schulze, Heppenheim a.d.B., Schunkengasse Nr. 7, West Germany). It should be borne in mind, however, that some techniques (the plasmolytic and especially some vapor phase methods) can be used to measure both ψ and π.

3. Vapor Phase Methods

The principles behind these methods are the same as for vapor phase techniques for the determination of ψ. It is not surprising, therefore, that some of the methods mentioned in the present section also can be used to measure ψ. Consequently, detailed descriptions of a few suitable techniques have already been given; these will be indicated by text cross references.

a. The Barger–Halket Osmometer. In this technique (Fig. 26) the isopiestic solution is that which has no net transfer of water vapor with the sap samples. This is detected by measuring the lengths of the sap drops (except the end ones) with a binocular microscope and micrometer before and after a 24-hour equilibration period. During equilibration temperature fluctuations are minimized by immersing the slide on which the tubes are mounted in a Petri dish of water. Accuracy may be increased by graphical interpolation (Fig. 8B) and is about ± 0.2 bar. The tubes are filled by closing one end with a finger and touching alternately into one of the standard solutions

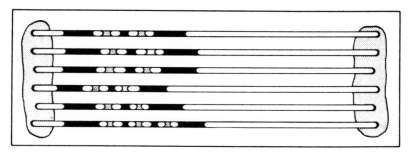

FIG. 26. The Barger–Halket method of determining osmotic potential of plant sap. The capillary tubes contain alternate columns of a stock sucrose solution and sap samples (stippled). Each tube contains one of a suitable range of sucrose concentrations. From Levitt (1964), in " Instrumentation in Experimental Biology ", Macmillan, New York.

and the unknown, releasing the finger momentarily between solutions. Finally, the ends are sealed in a flame and the tubes are mounted on a slide. Bennett-Clark (1959) pointed out that filling was greatly facilitated by first siliconing the tubes; each drop was then rounded off and the risk of mixing was greatly reduced. The technique was modified for use with plant sap by Halket (1913) from Barger's (1904) method for determining molecular weight. The long equilibration period is somewhat inconvenient. A more convenient form of the technique, in which each capillary is filled with one of a range of reference solutions and is left open so that it can distill to or condense from the unknown, was devised by Ursprung and Blum (1930). This technique may also be used to measure ψ (see Section IV,B,2,a).

b. *The Differential Wet-Bulb Psychrometer.* The van Andel (1952) osmometer was the first version of this instrument developed specifically for plant sap. It consists essentially (Fig. 27) of two loop thermocouples A, in a moist chamber K. A drop (about 0.1 ml) of the unknown solution is placed on one thermocouple and a reference solution is placed on the other thermocouple and also used to thoroughly moisten filter paper lining the walls of the chamber. Depending on the direction of the osmotic gradient, water will distill from or condense on the unknown solution with accompanying loss or gain of heat. The consequent temperature difference between the unknown and reference thermocouples (the latter of course remaining at ambient temperature, since no net vapor loss or gain occurs) is linearly related to the difference in π between the two solutions. The instrument is calibrated with solutions of known concentration difference, and linearity is maintained up to at least 0.2 M concentration difference of boric acid. However, it is usual not to exceed a difference of 0.03 M NaCl. If the unknown is not more concentrated than this, water may be substituted for the known solution. The calibration error is equivalent to 0.001–0.002 M boric acid. The output is read with a reflecting galvanometer. Accuracy is improved by reversing the polarity of the galvanometer connections and measuring the two readings and also by reversing the two drops on the thermocouples (after washing and drying) and again measuring the two readings. The thermocouples must always be returned to the same positions in the chamber.

The temperature of the reference junction is maintained constant by immersing the apparatus in a water bath controlled to $\pm 0.02°C$. The thermocouples are lacquered to prevent spurious chemical electromotive forces. A steady output, indicating equilibrium, is reached in about 35 minutes. Ryczkowski (1960a,b) also used the method successfully.

The van Andel instrument is only slightly modified from that of Baldes (1934). One rather unfortunate modification is the relocation of the copper–manganin junctions in the head of the instrument instead of nearer its

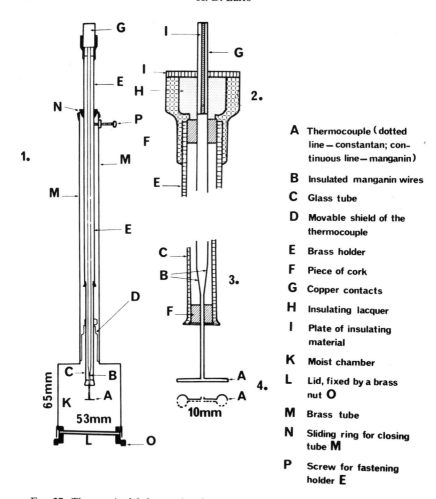

A   Thermocouple (dotted line — constantan; continuous line — manganin)
B   Insulated manganin wires
C   Glass tube
D   Movable shield of the thermocouple
E   Brass holder
F   Piece of cork
G   Copper contacts
H   Insulating lacquer
I   Plate of insulating material
K   Moist chamber
L   Lid, fixed by a brass nut O
M   Brass tube
N   Sliding ring for closing tube M
P   Screw for fastening holder E

FIG. 27. The van Andel thermoelectric osmometer. From van Andel (1952).

base where temperature stability would be better and thermal electromotive forces would be minimal. The technique was modified and thoroughly investigated by several investigators. It was originated by Hill (1930), using a silver–constantan thermopile to the opposite ends of which filter papers wet with 0.2 ml of reference or unknown solution were applied. Baldes (1934) replaced this sensor by the simpler pair of manganin–copper junctions to which liquid drops could be applied, since he found the thermopile was only 6% efficient because of poor thermal contact between the filter papers and the thermopile. He also recommended drop manipulation using a micropipette in a humid atmosphere, although sensitivity is independent of drop size. Later (1939) he calculated efficiency of the thermocouple pair as greater than 95% and showed that the dilution error was less than 0.1%, provided equilibrium was reached in 30 minutes. Details of thermocouple construction using a jig are given by Baldes and Johnson (1939). They pointed out that one large chamber can be used to advantage for several thermocouples with a consequent saving in equilibration time. Roepke and Baldes (1938) concluded that errors due to surface films, difference in coefficients of diffusion of water in the sample and reference solutions, greater nonsolvent volume in the sample, differences in drop shape and amount of junction wetted because of differences in surface tension, and volatile solutes were all negligible. Interestingly enough, they found that heat production within blood cells was a small source of error but was an appreciable one in tissue cells with a high metabolic rate. They were not able to suggest a practical way of eliminating this error.

Kinsey (1950) replaced the somewhat inconvenient reflecting galvanometer by a dc amplifier feeding into a milliameter. He also reported that a very vigorously stirred uncontrolled bath gave temperature control as good as a closely controlled bath with normal stirring. These two modifications could make the apparatus readily usable in a field laboratory.

A commercial osmometer is now available in which the approach (Lifson and Lorber, 1945) of syringe drop injection and rapid reading (after 2 minutes) is fully exploited (Mechrolab Osmometer Model 301A; Mechrolab, Inc., 1062 Linda Vista Avenue, Mountain View 3, California). The thermocouples have been replaced by thermistors in a Wheatstone bridge circuit, thereby increasing sensitivity. The bridge is balanced manually. Sample size is normally 50 μl but optionally can be reduced to $10 - 20$ μl. Using this equipment, Ruf et al. (1963) reported π values measured to 0.01 bar. The replacement of thermocouples by thermistors has also been described by Lockhart (1959).

c. Simple Wet-Bulb Psychrometers. These may also be used to measure ψ. Osmotic potentials have mainly been measured with the thermocouple psychrometers of Spanner (1951) or Richards and Ogata (1958), although the thermistor psychrometer (Kreeb, 1965b, B. G. Richards, 1965a,b,c) can also be used. See Section IV,B,3,b.

Osmotic potential measurements with a thermocouple psychrometer were first described by Ehlig (1962), who used the Richards and Ogata instrument. The procedure used for measuring π was similar to that for ψ except that the sample chamber was first wrapped in aluminum foil and frozen in dry ice. The method differs from the others using killed tissue so far discussed, since subsequent expression of the sap is not necessary. The same technique may be used with the Spanner psychrometer, and Waister (1965) has shown that standard errors of such measurements are ±0.06 bar (within the chamber) and ±0.17 bar (between samples). Some workers preferred to freeze the chamber and sample while it was in a freezing mixture of dry ice and alcohol (Rawlins, 1963) or dry ice and acetone (Klepper, 1963). This may be more convenient than dry ice alone but does not lower the freezing temperature (about $-40°C$) further to $-80°C$, as Klepper reported.

An alternative approach, if π is not to be determined immediately after freezing, is to withdraw samples from the chamber, wrap them in aluminum foil, and freeze them in dry ice for 15 minutes. The samples are then carefully wrapped in plastic and stored in a deep freeze until required. When taken from the deep freeze the samples should be allowed to thaw completely while still in the foil. Any condensed moisture may then be wiped off before undoing the samples and will not dilute them. Such samples are fragile and brittle when frozen. Therefore, they should be handled carefully to keep them in one piece to facilitate lining the walls of the chamber.

Boyer (1965a) used a microtechnique with the Richards and Ogata psychrometer. After freezing and thawing plant tissue, a drop of sap (expressed in a press at 60,000 psi) is placed on the ring junction of the psychrometer, which is then placed in a chamber whose walls are lined with filter paper wet with distilled water. The sap is warmed by condensation, and the temperature of this junction rises above that of the reference junctions, the temperature difference being linearly related to the π of sap. The technique consists essentially in running the psychrometer in reverse. Advantages claimed for it are that only 1 to 8 μl of sap are needed and equilibrium is reached in 20–60 minutes. If a plunger psychrometer of the type that can be inserted into a pre-equilibrated chamber (Boyer and Knipling, 1965) is available, inspection of the curves of approach to equilibrium suggests that 15–20 minutes of equilibration is adequate. The technique is basically that of van Andel (1952) except that the reference junction is dry rather than wet. Presumably, the same precautions already noted for the van Andel device should be observed. In particular, the drop dilution should be minimized by using a reference solution (instead of water) of similar concentration to the sample, if this is highly concentrated. Little published information is available on the accuracy of the technique; sensitivity would be expected to be about that of the normal psychrometer (approximately ±0.1 bar). Boyer's (1965) data show the microtechnique gave consistently lower π's than Ehlig's (1962) technique by up to 4 bars, although Boyer does not comment further on this rather large discrepancy. The accuracy of Ehlig's technique may be checked, somewhat indirectly, by comparing measurements of ψ and π in wilted leaf tissue. Provided effects attributable to ψ_m or negative turgor are negligible, ψ and π should be equal. Figure 28 shows that this is so, suggesting the validity of Ehlig's technique. The heat of respiration is a negligible error in frozen and thawed tissue

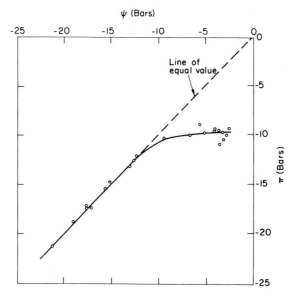

FIG. 28. The relation between total (ψ) and osmotic (π) potentials in pepper (*Capsicum frutescens*) leaves. From Barrs (unpublished).

when it lines the wall of an equilibration chamber (Barrs, 1965b). However, the effect of any residual respiration would be much greater in Boyer's technique where the drop is largely prevented from losing heat by conduction. The temperature of the drop could be erroneously elevated, corresponding to a spurious lowering of potential. The nature of this discrepancy should be investigated further, since Ehlig's π technique is now quite widely used.

d. The Weatherley (1960) *Micro-Osmometer.* Use of this device (Fig. 29) to measure ψ was described earlier. The principle of operation is to measure the rate of distillation between the plant sap and a solution of known π. Normally, the sap (0.06 ml) is placed in the capsule C and the standard solution in the pipette P. The standard solution is extruded, so that it hangs as a drop, by turning the screw plunger S. It is left in this preliminary "settling" position for 10 minutes before the mean evaporation over two consecutive 20-minute periods is measured as described previously, using the traveling microscope M. Sap sample size can be reduced to 0.001 ml by putting the sample into the pipette and the standard into the capsule. However, this approach is limited to solutions whose surface tension is not much lower than that of water; otherwise they will not hang properly. Xylem and phloem saps may be used in this way. Unlike the measurement of ψ with this instrument, the chamber walls are not lined with filter paper. A further difference is that a separate calibration curve is required for every standard, with each standard having a

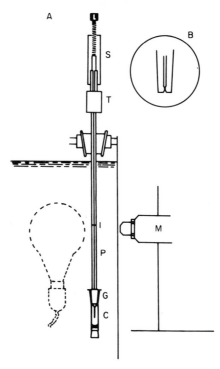

Fɪɢ. 29. A, The Weatherley micro-osmometer in position in the water bath. C, capsule; G, ground glass cone; I, reference line; M, traveling microscope; P, pipette; S, screw plunger device; T, pressure tubing. B, magnified view of jet. From Weatherley (1960).

range of about 9 bars. The standard deviation of single determinations is a uniform ± 0.06 bar over the range investigated (0–28 bars). Calibration curves are obtained in which both evaporation from and condensation to the hanging drop occur. Apart from these differences, the calibration procedure is as described for ψ measurements. As before, it is necessary to immerse most of the instrument in a constant temperature water bath, controlled to better than 0.1°C Weatherley (1960) gave details of construction, pipette filling, etc. See Section IV,B,3,a also.

e. The van den Honert Osmometer. This instrument is similar in principle to the Weatherley osmometer; change in length of a capillary of fluid ($CaCl_2$) is measured. However, the solution is permanently exposed via a sintered glass plate and the complications of drop extrusion and retraction are not necessary. Despite its simplicity and tolerance of a temperature fluctuation of ± 0.12–0.3°C, the instrument has not been widely used. It was originally described by van den Honert (1935) and recently reviewed by Levitt (1964).

C. Methods Based on Living Tissue

1. Limiting Plasmolysis

This very old method was first used with plant tissue by De Vries and Pfeffer about 1877 (Crafts *et al.*, 1949). Since then the technique has been very widely used. Its popularity is now declining, but provided it is used properly, it remains a valuable reference technique.

Plasmolysis of a cell immersed in a hypertonic solution is characterized by separation of the protoplast from the cell wall. This is brought about by the outward flow of water from the cell and the subsequent contraction of the protoplast. The space between the protoplast and cell wall so formed is filled with the plasmolyzing solution. Various forms of plasmolysis are recognized; the most common is convex plasmolysis, in which the protoplast becomes convex where it is separated from the cell wall (Crafts *et al.*, 1949; Bennett-Clark, 1959).

The principle behind the limiting plasmolysis technique is to determine microscopically the point at which the protoplast just begins to separate from the cell wall. This state of incipient plasmolysis may be approximated to the condition of limiting plasmolysis, which is the point at which the turgor pressure P of a cell first declines to zero (Fig. 1). Incipient plasmolysis is a useful condition since it provides a visible reference point in the Höfler diagram (Fig. 1). If a cell in volume equilibrium with a bathing solution is at incipient plasmolysis, π cell and π solution must also be in equilibrium and equal.

In practice, observations normally are not restricted to a single cell. Instead, hand sections of the tissue, not more than four cells thick, are cut and quickly distributed among a range of concentrations of osmotic solutions. A range is needed such that no plasmolysis occurs in the most dilute solution, but all cells plasmolyze in the most concentrated one. Equilibrium is achieved in 30 minutes or so and may be speeded by infiltration using a vacuum pump. Infiltration also facilitates observation of the cells. Counts are then made of the percentage of cells plasmolyzed in each solution. These values are plotted against the corresponding solution π. Interpolation at the point where half the cells are plasmolyzed gives the π of the tissue at incipient plasmolysis. Under favorable conditions, precision can be of the order of ± 0.1 bar.

Levitt (1964) modified the method by replacing the traditional plasmolyticum, sucrose, with $CaCl_2$. Only two or three tissue sections were used. They were initially plasmolyzed before being transferred to progressively more dilute solutions, until only 50% of the cells showed incipient plasmolysis, with the other 50% being nonplasmolyzed. The π of this solution was taken as that of the tissue. As a final check, transfer to a slightly weaker solution should show the complete deplasmolysis of all cells.

The value of π obtained by these methods may be adjusted to the original value of the tissue by applying a correction for volume change V of the cells:

$$\pi_{orig} = \pi_{ip} \times V_{ip}/V_{orig}$$

where orig and ip refer to the original values and to incipient plasmolysis, respectively.

2. The Plasmometric Method

As Höfler (1917) described the method, it should be limited to individual, regular cylindrical cells. The volume of the protoplast is measured after it has been plasmolyzed to occupy only about three fourths of the cell volume. At the same time the total volume enclosed by the cell walls is measured and, as in the plasmolytic method, π is multiplied by the ratio of these two volumes. For a cylindrical cell this is given by

$$[(l_1 - d/3)/(l_2 - d/3)] \times \pi_e$$

where l_1 is the length of the protoplast, l_2 is the length of the cell, d is the diameter which is common to both, and e refers to the plasmolyzing solution. This calculated π will be the value at incipient plasmolysis; for the original π it would be necessary to use the dimensions of the cell *before* plasmolysis.

Error increases as cells depart from the cylindrical model, particularly if they tend to become isodiametric. Härtel (1963) modified the technique to permit measurements on cells that are plasmolyzed on one side or plasmolyzed concavely or even to lamelliform cells. Volume estimation is replaced by area estimation using a point-count technique with a Zeiss integration eyepiece.

3. Methods in Which the Point of Zero Turgor Is Estimated

These are based on measurement of mechanical properties of the tissue that are related to its P. As before, P is varied by immersing the sample in a range of solutions, but measurements usually are made on the one specimen. This comparatively recent approach was apparently initiated by Stow (1936), who used a *Nitella* cell. He was able to deduce π from measurements of the modulus of elasticity in solutions of varying π.

Tazawa (1957) adapted this principle to measurement of π with considerable precision, using a turgor balance (Fig. 30). This instrument permits measurement by the pointer "a" of the change in cell deformation that accompanies and is proportional to the change in cell turgor. The weight applied to the cell can be adjusted with the chainomatic device. Estimation of π is by changing the bathing solution and noting the new deflection of the lever or by a compensation method in which cell deformation is kept constant in different solutions by altering the applied weight. The former method requires calculation of a stress constant that is linearly related to solution π.

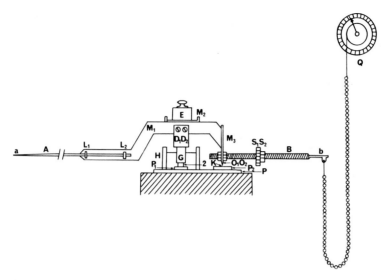

Fɪɢ. 30. The turgor balance for the determination of osmotic potential. From Tazawa (1957).

A zero stress constant value occurs when the cell is turgorless; consequently, extrapolation of the stress constant–solution relation to the zero stress constant value gives that solution in equilibrium with the turgorless cell and hence of equal π. In the second and preferred approach, weight reduction is plotted against the solution π. Extrapolation to zero applied weight gives the required π as before. In neither method is it necessary for the cell to attain incipient plasmolysis, although one experimental point should be close to this to minimize the extrapolation.

Lockhart (1959) described an apparatus based upon this general principle for use with higher plant tissue. He found that deformability of stem sections of pea seedlings was practically zero until P declined to zero, when it suddenly began to increase. Subsequent deformation increased linearly; consequently, extrapolation of this line to zero gives the π value at which turgor is just lost. The technique should be applicable to thin strips of other tissues in which the mechanical strength is derived mainly from P, such as tuber tissue or leaf mesophyll. Virgin (1955) pointed out that the resonance frequency of a small piece of tissue varies with turgor but is expected to become constant at the point of incipient plasmolysis and to remain so as the tissue plasmolyses further. Figure 31 shows that this occurred in tissues from wheat roots; similar results were obtained with potato tuber and ivy leaves. Virgin equated resonance frequency with " relative turgor "; the latter should be distinguished from the " relative turgidity " of Weatherley (1950), see Section II,B,4,c.

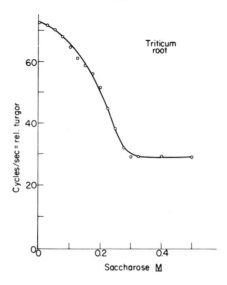

FIG. 31. Determination of osmotic potential of intact tissue by the resonance frequency technique. From Virgin (1955).

4. Estimation of Minimum Volume

Minimum volume (Ursprung, 1923) is rarely measured directly; instead, minimum weight or minimum length is substituted for it. The principle of these methods is that sample weight or length should decline only until limiting plasmolysis is reached and thereafter there should be no change. However, in practice, the decline in weight or length often does not cease abruptly. Consequently, it often is difficult to establish the corresponding solution π precisely. This is shown by the data of Reinhold and Glinka (1966) with sunflower hypocotyl. Ordin *et al.* (1956) produced an essentially similar curve for *Avena* coleoptile sections. The required potential lay between 0.4 and 0.6 *M* mannitol but could not be determined more precisely. However, they cite Ketellaper (1953) as having had success with the same technique and material. Brouwer (1963; Fig. 9) was also successful with this technique. Crafts *et al.* (1949) consider the minimum volume concept as only an approximation. They consider it useful since, from data like those of Fig. 9, it was possible to make rapid estimates of normal P, normal ψ, and both normal π and that at incipient plasmolysis. See Section IV,A,2,b.

5. Estimation of Change in Apparent Free Space (AFS)

AFS is the portion of a tissue that is freely accessible to a bathing solution. If it is assumed that a solute cannot pass the cell membranes, then AFS in a turgid cell will be restricted largely to cell walls and will remain relatively constant until turgor is lost. As the cell plasmolyses, AFS will suddenly increase because of the penetration of osmoticum into the cell between the cell wall and the retreating protoplast.

Bernstein and Nieman (1960) demonstrated the feasibility of this approach using mannitol or NaCl solutions to determine AFS of bean roots by an exodiffusion technique. Although the absolute percentage of AFS differed between mannitol and NaCl, the π values at which AFS began to increase rapidly were in close agreement. Additional data were given by Bernstein (1961).

Similarly, Ingelsten (1966) obtained π at incipient plasmolysis for wheat roots. The mannitol or chloride solutions were labeled with radioactive sulfate and this, rather than the plasmolyzing agents themselves, was determined by an exodiffusion technique. As before, AFS increased sharply at the same π value of mannitol or NaCl solutions.

Briggs and Robertson (1957) and Falk et al. (1966) also reported high AFS values after plasmolysis. Briggs and Robertson pointed out that the apparent osmotic volume (that is, volume not penetrated rapidly by solute) will decrease suddenly at the point of incipient plasmolysis, so this, too, may be used to estimate π. They briefly outline a suitable weighing method. Falk (1965) showed that AFS increased linearly as π of the plasmolyzing solution decreased.

6. Pressure Bomb

This apparatus was described previously for determination of ψ. Scholander et al. have shown (1964, 1965) that for a cell with zero P the molal concentration of solutes in the cell should be proportional to the sap pressure, $S/(I - V) = KP$, or $I - V = K_1 P^{-1}$, where S is the solute, I is the cell volume, V is the water run out, and P is the equilibrium pressure. A plot of $1/P$ against V therefore will be linear for a cell with zero P but will deviate when P is positive. Hence, a curve of this type permits interpolation of the applied pressure just causing zero turgor. This pressure will correspond to π at incipient plasmolysis. See Section IV,B,4,a.

7. Technique for Leaf Hairs (Woolley, 1964)

A leaf hair is punctured near its base; when some sap escapes, the remainder retreats into the tip of the hair, with the formation of a clearly marked meniscus at the air–sap interface. The portion of the hair above the puncture is inserted into a special irrigator made from two concentric glass tubes. The hair is then irrigated with solutions of sucrose or mannitol of known π, and the movement of the meniscus indicates whether the solution π is higher or lower than that of the hair. The isopiestic solution is that which causes no movement of the meniscus. Osmotic potentials ranging between -6 to -13 bars were measured for hairs of young, greenhouse-grown soybean leaves.

D. Sources of Error in π Measurements

1. In Methods Based on Expressed Sap

Once sap has been expressed, most methods used for subsequent π determination give results of reasonable accuracy. The only exception is the measurement of RI, which is open to considerable error if the relative proportions of solutes alter between determinations. Errors associated with these techniques then, are almost entirely due to uncertainty regarding the constitution and origin of expressed sap.

It is generally accepted that sap pressed from living tissues is largely filtered by the semipermeable membranes (Broyer, 1939; Crafts *et al.*, 1949). Scholander *et al.* (1964, 1965) found that the application of pressure to leaves in the pressure-bomb squeezed out almost pure water. This apparatus permits application of pressure without the damaging effects of shear associated with most hydraulic presses.

However, sap sometimes is still obtained from living tissue. Where cell size is sufficiently large to permit the use of a puncture technique, followed by withdrawal of the sap in a pipette (e.g., *Valonia*, *Nitella*), there is little objection to this procedure. The range of suitable material is increased by the use of micropuncture techniques. Schmidt-Nielsen and Schrauger (1963) described the use of hand-drawn quartz pipettes with a tip diameter of 2–4 μ to withdraw a sample $1 \times 10^{-4} \mu l$ of vacuolar sap from the contractile vacuole of Amoeba. Phloem sap may be obtained by the aphid-stylet technique of Kennedy and Mittler (1953).

Stem xylem sap can be obtained in the laboratory by centrifugation (Levitt, 1964) or in the field by suction applied by an automobile tire pump with a reversed piston valve (Scholander *et al.*, 1966). In the latter technique slight contamination from cut cells occurs. Leaf xylem sap may be collected using the pressure-bomb. However, only the very first fraction will be representative, the rest will be almost pure water filtered out of the cells.

Maceration techniques in which living tissue is squeezed inside polyvinyl chloride tubing have been described by McComb and Rendig (1960), Ruf *et al.* (1963), and Gifford *et al.* (1964). Many users of the RI technique have expressed sap by squeezing leaves in pliers, a garlic press, or a similar hand vice (Farkas and Pratt, 1961; Filippov, 1961; Lobov, 1949; Maximov and Petinov, 1948). Error resulting from dilution by filtration is at least a possibility in such techniques, though specific tests do not seem to have been made.

In view of these difficulties, it is usual today to kill the tissue before trying to extract sap. The semipermeability of the membranes is thereby destroyed and possible filtration effects are eliminated. Sap may then be expressed readily; only slight pressure (a few bars) is necessary since the composition of the expressed sap in killed tissue, unlike living tissue, is not a function of applied pressure (Wiebe, 1966). High pressures for example, 10,000 psi (Bernstein, 1961) or 15,000 psi (Slatyer, 1957) are quite unnecessary.

Tissue may be killed by exposure to heat, cold, or toxic vapors. Solid CO_2 is very convenient to use. Squeezing tissue in polyvinyl chloride tubing after freezing it with dry ice is satisfactory (Scholander et al., 1966). Klepper (1963) reported π to be spuriously depressed by the aggregation of colloids when moss samples were frozen with dry ice, thereby giving rise to anomalous "negative turgor." This effect is not universal, it does not occur in Capsicum (Fig. 28), in sunflower, nor trefoil (Gardner and Ehlig, 1965).

Tissues may be killed by applying heat (Walter, 1963b), usually by immersing the sample in a closed test tube in a water bath at 100°C for 20 minutes (Kozinka and Niznansky, 1963; Slavik, 1959b). Walter has shown that either heat or cold usually yield sap of the same π value, although heat may hydrolyze glycosides in some species. Toxic vapors that have been used include chloroform, ether, or toluene; they may be unsatisfactory for bulky tissue (Broyer, 1939). However, Necas (1960) found that the π values for sap expressed from the same tissue after boiling, freezing, or exposure to chloroform were the same. All three methods are probably usually effective. If doubt exists, the technique that gives the lowest π value should be used. Kreeb (1963) described a technique for determining π on previously dried samples, which gave the same π values as tissues immediately killed by heating.

The dilution of vacuolar sap by water held by matric forces (for example, in the cell wall) after killing is usually considered a negligible effect. Gaff and Carr (1964), however, suggested appreciable error could arise from this source. Kreeb (1965d) found a high proportion of the water held by matric forces was lost at applied pressures of 1–2.5 bars, and he concluded that this source of error would usually be negligible in mesophytes. The ψ_m data of Wiebe (1966) support this conclusion. Kreeb and Walter (1963b) consider that even in turgid cells the cell walls will not be fully imbibed due to pressure from the protoplast.

Walter (1963b) considered the effects arising from the mixing of vacuolar with cytoplasmic sap (Currier, 1944; Kramer and Currier, 1950), or with xylem sap, to be negligible.

2. In Methods Based on Living Tissue

Plasmolysis does not occur naturally, at least in cells of terrestrial plants. Therefore, it is pertinent to inquire whether π values obtained from cells in an atypical condition can be valid. This question is all the more important if plasmolysis is damaging to cells. Bennett-Clark (1959) considered that plasmolysis is at least not completely disruptive, since active ion uptake occurs even in plasmolyzed cells. Levitt (1964) considered plasmolysis is not injurious, provided it is allowed to persist only for a few minutes. He pointed out that plasmolysis eliminated errors arising from adhesion of the cytoplasm to the cell wall (Buhmann, 1935; Currier, 1944). He also considered that sufficiently rapid plasmolysis to avoid damage resulted from plasmolysis with $CaCl_2$ rather than from sucrose solution. However, Ordin et al. (1956) found that subsequent elongation of deplasmolyzed cells is slower than that of cells that have never been plasmolyzed. They concluded that plasmolysis itself apparently causes some irreversible damage. Henkel and Pronina (1963) and Henkel and Bakanova (1965) have reported that in nondormant cells of onion scale epidermis, plasmolysis is concave, and some plasmodesmata at least are ruptured, with a consequent increase in cell permeability. These reports suggest the possibility of damage at least in certain tissues, even when plasmolysis is of short duration.

Liquid phase techniques for π determination implicitly assume the plasmolyticum is excluded from the vacuole and has no side effects. Eaton (1943) queried whether exclusion of sucrose or mannitol was complete. Cznosnowski (1962) found sucrose was not effectively excluded, but Gregory and Cocking (1966) found isolated protoplasts were stable in 10–20% sucrose. Cznosnowski found mannitol was excluded, and Ruesink and Thimann (1965) found isolated protoplasts were stable in 0.5 M mannitol for at least 2 days. However, mannitol occurred in the guttate from barley, pea, and sunflower plants (Groenewegen and Mills, 1960; Kozinka and Klenovska, 1965), although actual penetration of the cells was not demonstrated. Manohar and Heydecker (1965) found that mannitol penetrated germinating seeds. It stimulated root growth in Agrostis (Jackson, 1965) but was toxic to radish (Taylor, 1965).

Carbowax has been found satisfactory by Manohar and Heydecker (1965), Cheesman et al. (1965), and Janes (1966). Lagerwerff et al. (1961) found Carbowax 6000 toxic, but Carbowax 20,000 satisfactory after dialysis. Walter (1963b) found Lutrol (probably equivalent to Carbowax 400) a satisfactory plasmolyticum. Each batch of Carbowax should be checked for equivalent π values and also passed through ion exchanges or dialyzed if necessary. Carbowax is probably the safest plasmolyticum available. Pilot tests for penetration or side effects should be made before routine use of any new plasmolyticum.

Bennett-Clark (1959) and Briggs and Robertson (1957) recommended that the relation $P(V - b) = $ a constant should be used, rather than $PV = $ a constant, in making volume corrections to plasmolyzed protoplasts, owing to the nonideal behavior of the relatively concentrated vacuolar sap. Bennett-Clark also considered the cytoplasm itself to exert a wall pressure on the vacuole of about 2.5 bars, causing spuriously high π values in liquid phase techniques.

The walls of some cells may undergo plastic (irreversible) stretching or shrinking during severe plasmolysis or deplasmolysis (Crafts *et al.*, 1949). Such material is not suitable for determining π by plasmolysis. These investigators discussed other error sources. Effects of cutting sections or small pieces of tissue on π is similar to the effects on ψ discussed earlier, Section IV,A,4,c.

E. FINAL COMMENTS AND RECOMMENDATIONS

A discussion of the concept of active water relations is beyond the scope of this chapter. However, it should be pointed out that this concept is largely based on reports (Bennett-Clark *et al.*, 1936) that lower π values are obtained by plasmolytic than by cryoscopic methods. These are often termed plasmolytic–cryoscopic discrepancies, or PCD's. If there is an active component of water transfer in plant tissues, then it seems likely that this will be included in (plasmolytic) measurements on living tissues and excluded in measurements on killed tissue. More recent work in general has not confirmed the existence of such large PCD's (Currier, 1944) and in some cases has cast doubt on their actual existence (Levitt, 1947).

If there were an active component of π, then a comparison of other techniques using living tissue with cryoscopic techniques should show discrepancies similar to PCD's. Such comparisons offer little evidence for PCD's (Lockhart, 1959; Bernstein, 1961; Scholander *et al.*, 1965). Reinhold and Glinka (1966) reported a PCD but used the unsatisfactory and insensitive minimum weight method. The possible existence of an active component of π does not seem to be a factor to be taken into account when deciding whether to work with living tissue or expressed sap.

Tazawa (1957) found excellent agreement between π as estimated on unplasmolyzed tissue using his turgor balance and an incipient plasmolysis technique. It therefore seems likely that possible errors due to damage by plasmolysis are unimportant.

The reasonable general agreement found between this wide range of techniques suggests that they are all free from gross error. Some workers prefer plasmolytic or similar techniques (Levitt, 1964; Weatherley, 1965); others are as strongly in favor of cryoscopy (Slatyer, 1961). Overall, the actual measurement accuracy of techniques based on expressed sap may be higher. But as Waister (1965) and Levitt (1964) have pointed out, it is probably pointless to pursue accuracy beyond the ± 0.1 bar level since this seems to represent the order of natural variation between subsamples. Therefore, the actual technique used in a particular investigation will depend largely on the facilities available, the preference of the investigator, and the nature of the experimental object. For instance, measurements of π for particular cells, for example, guard cells (Ursprung, 1929; Mouravieff, 1965; Nishida, 1963; Pallas *et al.*, 1965) can usually only be made using plasmolytic techniques.

However, the plasmolytic technique may be difficult to apply where cell contents are colorless or heterogeneous, for example, the leaf mesophyll (Weatherley, 1965). The plasmolytic and associated techniques give π at a known state of the tissue, but this has to be corrected to give the original value. The latter is obtained directly when expressed sap is used, but in this case no reference point is available. This difficulty can be overcome by making the tissue fully turgid first by floating on water if comparisons of π at full turgor will be meaningful. Alternatively, the RWC of the tissue may be determined and used as a guide to its relative volume (Slavik, 1963b; Weatherley, 1965).

VI. MEASUREMENT OF TURGOR PRESSURE (P)

A. Evaluation of Turgor Pressure as a Measure of Water Stress

In many plant tissues turgor pressure P will be a sensitive measure of water deficit (WD). Thus, P changes from zero to its maximum value while π and volume show only small changes (Fig. 1). Illustrative data from Ursprung (1929) for the pith of *Impatiens* show that P ranged from 0 to 9.3 bars (full turgor) while cell volume changed from 132 to 148 arbitrary units and π, from -10.5 to -9.3 bars. Similarly, Kamiya *et al.* (1963) found for *Nitella* that P changed from 0 to 6.45 bars; π, from -6.69 to -6.45 bars; and cell volume, by not quite 4%. However, the greatest changes, as Fig. 1 predicts, are in ψ (from -10.5 and -6.69 to 0 bars, respectively). P is then a moderately sensitive criterion of WD, if not the most sensitive one. But its disadvantage is that it normally declines to zero while π and ψ may continue to decrease to considerably more negative values (Fig. 1).

The relation between growth and P, although beyond the scope of this chapter, is by no means firmly established. P is also difficult to measure. These factors together with its limited range considerably reduce its utility as a measure of WD.

B. Methods for Measuring Turgor Pressure

1. Direct Methods

Turgor pressure P is an actual hydrostatic pressure and so only can be measured directly with a pressure-sensitive sensor. Such a measurement is simple in principle, involving nothing more than the insertion of a suitable transducer into a cell. However, the practical difficulties are enormous, owing to the small size of most plant cells. The problems have only rarely been overcome, and then only with particularly favorable material that is not necessarily representative of most cells of higher plants.

Green (1966) used a technique in which a capillary, closed at one end and opening at the other into a syringe-needle tip, was inserted into a cell of *Nitella*. The higher the P, the more the air in the capillary is compressed—

for example, if the gas is compressed one-seventh of its initial volume, then the gas is at 7 atm pressure and the turgor is this pressure minus atmospheric pressure. Unfortunately, the bubble slowly dissolves under these high pressures. This is counteracted by reducing the pressure by $\frac{2}{3}$ atm every $\frac{1}{2}$ hour. To do this the entire setup is placed in a pressure chamber and connected to a vacuum pump. The volume of the bubble changes from V_1 to V_2. The pressure of the bubble is $(\frac{2}{3}$ atm $\times V_2)(V_1 - V_2)$. The smaller the change in volume, the greater the pressure.

Bourdeau and Schopmeyer (1958) and Buttery and Boatman (1964, 1966) have used an essentially similar technique to measure P in the oleoresin ducts of *Pinus elliotti* and the latex vessel system of *Hevea brasiliensis*, respectively. Results obtained by both groups of workers were strikingly similar. Such techniques have yet to be adapted to the microscale necessary for working with individual cells of higher plants.

Buttery and Boatman (1964) pointed out that direct measurement of sieve tube turgor might be possible, although very difficult, by using micromanometers together with the aphid-stylet technique of Kennedy and Mittler (1953). Kollman (1965) showed that the aphid stylet finally enters a phloem cell. This technique therefore would avoid the difficulty of not knowing exactly what tissues had been sampled, which is inherent in the procedures of Bordeau and Schopmeyer (1958) and Buttery and Boatman (1964, 1966).

2. Indirect Methods

Most investigators have estimated P from the difference between ψ and π with effects due to ψ_m assumed to be negligible. However, Kamiya *et al.* (1963) attempted a semidirect determination in *Nitella* of the relation between P and cell volume. This was done using the cell wall tube obtained after cutting a cell at one end and squeezing the contents out gently in water. The tube was filled with mercury and then pressure was applied to it in a special apparatus; the change in volume of the cell with applied pressure was measured by the movement of the mercury meniscus in a capillary. Pressure was applied stepwise until the normal full turgor of the cell was attained, as calculated from measurements of π in living cells. Their results clearly showed a closed hysteresis loop when P was plotted against V. Assuming that this relation holds in a living cell, it follows that both P and ψ may have at least an upper and a lower value corresponding to a particular cell volume and presumably may take up intermediate values between these extremes. If this is so, then clearly a unique relation between ψ or P and cell volume will not exist. Their curves indicate that the maximum width of the hysteresis loops is about 1 bar. This effect could explain some of the scatter in published curves of ψ or π against volume or RWC.

Kamiya *et al.* (1963) compared the P vs. V relation so obtained with that for a living cell, equating P with the difference (at equilibrium) in π between the living cell and the bathing solution. They found good agreement; hence, it seems likely in this case at least that valid estimates of P can be obtained from $\psi - \pi$.

A relation between P and resonance frequency has been demonstrated by Virgin (1955). Falk *et al.* (1958) calibrated resonance frequency in terms of P, but this calibration was essentially based on estimating P and corresponding volume from differences in π between tissue and a range of bathing solutions, so P was not determined directly. Their results showed P and resonance frequency were not linearly related; hence, it would not be easy to interpret Virgin's resonance frequencies directly as P values, even though maximum P values developed can be estimated from his data.

Many other workers have estimated P from $\psi - \pi$ (Ehlig, 1962; Gardner and Ehlig, 1965; Rawlins, 1963; Slatyer, 1961). From this difference Gardner and Ehlig calculated that the relation between P and tissue volume (expressed as RWC) could be represented adequately by two straight-line segments. Weatherley (1965) pointed out that P estimates based on $\psi - \pi$ are likely to be more erroneous than determinations of either ψ or π alone, since such estimates will include errors of both.

Some investigators found that this procedure can give negative P values; in xerophytes, very large values have been obtained. Grieve (1961) obtained values down to -50 bars in West Australia sclerophylls; Khadzhikubanova (1961), down to -100 bars in *Carex*; Kharanyan (1965), -100 to -150 bars in xerophytes; Kreeb, down to -30 bars in Mediterranean xerophytes (1961) and -65 bars in *Buxus* (1960); Slatyer (1960), down to -60 bars in *Acacia*; and Tyurina (1957), -100 to -150 bars in *Eurotia* and *Artemisia*. Whether these observations are explicable in terms of negative turgor is still an open question. Negative turgor (dotted line Fig. 1) is a condition arising in wilted tissue in which, because of forces of adhesion between the cell walls and protoplast, the protoplast instead of pressing on the wall pulls on it as the volume of the protoplast becomes reduced. If the cell wall is sufficiently thick and strong it is able to resist this pull. Consequently, the protoplast comes under tension, and this depresses ψ below π. It seems to be generally accepted that in mesophytes the cell walls are not strong enough to withstand high tensions, and therefore large negative turgors do not develop; Kreeb and Önal (1961) found values of only -2 bars.

Several investigators have not accepted negative P values. Some consider the phenomenon impossible, others ascribe the results to measurement error; yet others offer alternative explanations. Negative turgor has been considered impossible on the grounds that cells are not airtight (Klepper, 1963). Consequently, air would enter and release tensions before they could develop. Slatyer (1962) considered that dissolved gases would come out of solution and prevent effective negative pressures from developing. He also thought it unlikely that adhesion between the protoplast and wall can rise to the necessary high values, that is, as high as the negative turgor, and stated that no adhesion values of this order are reported in the literature. However, these arguments are not decisive. There seems little doubt that considerable tensions develop in the xylem, for instance, without air entering the vessels. Furthermore, according to Scholander *et al.* (1965), gas bubbles are given off from the xylem sap as it freezes. The gas was present originally in solution but did not come out under the influence of tension alone. Walter (1963a) supports this view. High adhesion values of the order of 300 bars were reported long ago (Renner, 1915; Ursprung, 1915). Briggs (1950) showed the tensile strength of water was 260 bars, which is clearly of the same order of magnitude.

Explanations of negative turgor values as due to error in determination of either ψ or π have been put forward by Gaff and Carr (1964), Klepper (1963), Rehder (1961), Rehder and Kreeb (1961), and Shmueli and Cohen (1964). In general, they do not appear adequate to account entirely for the very large negative turgors mentioned above. Thus, Rehder (1961) found readings for ψ taken after only 30 minutes equilibration were too low by perhaps 15 bars at most. It seems likely that Tyurina (1957), who also used this technique, with an equilibration period of 30 to 60 minutes, therefore would have obtained spuriously low ψ values. The negative turgors she observed were almost an order of magnitude lower; hence, the correction seems relatively unimportant.

Slatyer (1960) considered his negative values (down to -60 bars) to result from the development of imbibitional forces by colloids in cell walls and vacuoles of *Acacia*. It seems that negative turgor pressure values calculated from ψ and π are not unequivocally established. Indeed, some workers obviously believe that such values are spurious. Hence, estimation of P from $\psi - \pi$ should only be carried out with caution, especially when negative P values are obtained. As noted earlier, there is some evidence that positive P values obtained by this procedure are reasonably valid, although they are generally smaller than the negative values.

VII. ESTIMATION OF WATER DEFICIT FROM MEASUREMENT OF STOMATAL APERTURE

A. EVALUATION OF THE RELATION BETWEEN WATER DEFICIT AND STOMATAL APERTURE

It seems to be generally agreed that control over water loss from the plant must be exercised mainly via variation in stomatal aperture (Brouwer, 1961; Ophir *et al.*, 1967; Slatyer and Lake, 1966). Such a dependence of transpiration on stomatal aperture has been shown by many workers, including Allerup (1960), Moss (1963), Mulkey (1966), Oppenheimer (1951), Shimshi (1963), Stålfelt (1932), and Waggoner and Zelitch (1965). If plant water loss is controlled in this way, it must be related to plant water balance. Consequently, stomatal aperture should reflect plant water status, especially in leaves.

However, stomata do not respond solely to water stress, so the correlation between stomatal aperture and water balance is not always perfect. Furthermore, there may be no stomatal response until a definite level of stress has been reached. Thus, Dale (1961a) found that stomatal aperture was not correlated with leaf water content in cotton until the latter had declined to 85% RWC. This corresponds to a considerable degree of stress ($\psi \sim -12$ bars, assuming Slatyer's 1957 data can be applied). Dale's results indicated that other factors such as hour of day, solar radiation, or temperature were more important at higher RWC values. An additional complication is that stomatal aperture actually may be reduced in completely turgid or almost turgid tissue due to the tissue component of P exerted by surrounding cells (Slavik, 1966; Solarova, 1965; Stålfelt, 1961). Consequently, when leaf RWC declines, stomatal aperture increases initially to a maximum at about 95 to 97% RWC before declining as RWC falls further (Solarova, 1965).

Severe water stress may impair the stomatal mechanism (Iljin, 1957), so that later, even though the stress is relieved, the stomata do not open. Glover (1959) found that maize stomata were affected in this way by severe drought, although leaves later regained turgidity and appeared normal. In grain sorghum, on the other hand, the stomatal mechanism was not affected by severe stress. Stålfelt (1963) reported that water stress on one day may delay the completion of the tension phase that night so that the motor phase of stomatal opening is delayed the following morning. Hence, the relation of stomatal aperture to plant water status is not simple and can be changed by severe water stress.

Furthermore, stomatal aperture is affected by many other factors in the plant environment. Consideration of these is beyond the scope of this chapter. However, as a first approximation it is generally true that water status becomes increasingly the dominant factor controlling stomatal aperture as stress increases. It may often be the decisive factor in moderately or severely wilted plants. In the field, this has permitted the use of stomatal aperture as an irrigation criterion (Alvim, 1960; Shimshi, 1964; Shmueli, 1964). Under greenhouse or laboratory conditions, where greater precision is required, it is felt that stomatal aperture should be replaced by more accurate measure of plant water status. As Kramer and Brix (1965) have pointed out, stomatal aperture does not provide a quantitative basis for comparing WD in different kinds of plants. The following discussion of methods therefore is restricted to simple field methods giving approximate estimates of WD.

B. FIELD METHODS FOR ESTIMATING STOMATAL APERTURE

1. Lloyd's Method

First proposed by Lloyd (1908), this method's chief advantage is its simplicity. Pieces of epidermis are peeled from leaves and immediately put into absolute ethyl alcohol. This fixes the stomatal apertures, which may later be examined under the high power of the microscope. The technique is little used today since it is relatively slow and tedious. Stomatal apertures vary considerably, and consequently a considerable number of stomata must be examined if a valid mean estimate is to be obtained. Even so, infiltration or porometric techniques (described below) sample far larger leaf areas, and readings with these techniques represent averages for several thousands of stomata. However, as recently as 1965, Gale and Poljakoff-Mayber used Lloyd's method on cotton, sugar beet, vines, beans, and lettuce. Rees (1961) and MacDowall (1963) calibrated infiltration techniques against stomatal apertures observed with Lloyd's method.

Possible sources of error in Lloyd's technique are twofold. First, completely closed stomata may be difficult to distinguish visually from stomata that are only slightly open (Ashby, 1931; Pallas, 1965; Solarova, 1965). Since some workers (Ting and Loomis, 1963) contend that only the last 5% reduction in stomatal aperture may control transpiration, errors in this region may be important. Second, stomatal apertures may not always be properly fixed (Magness and Furr, 1930; Oppenheimer, 1947). Oppenheimer (1935) suggested that the final aperture was determined by the swelling equilibrium between the liquid and the cell walls. However, in 1949, Oppenheimer found Lloyd's technique satisfactory for tomato provided alcohol was replaced as a fixative by Dioxane. Nadel (1938) found that when the epidermis could be stripped cleanly from the underlying mesophyll, for example, in *Solanum nigrum*, reliable results were obtained. However, when the underlying mesophyll adhered to the strip, considerable reduction in stomatal aperture could occur.

In summary, Lloyd's technique is rather slow and laborious. It is capable of giving good results, but only with a limited number of species, and the ability to obtain a clean epidermal strip is often important. Choice of fixative may also be important. The technique should be checked for gross error by comparison with some other method if it is not definitely known to be suitable for a particular species. Shmueli (1964) reported the technique satisfactory for beet, cowpeas, and alfalfa but not (1953) for banana or maize.

2. Surface Impression Technique

The difficulties associated with stripping the epidermis and possible change of aperture in Lloyd's technique are avoided by taking surface impressions of leaves. These "negatives" are examined directly under the microscope or after first making "positives." Impression techniques are therefore essentially similar to Lloyd's method, likewise involving rather laborious microscopic measurement. However, these direct physical measurements are often helpful in calibrating and interpreting the less direct porometric and infiltration techniques. Impression techniques were initiated by Buscallioni and Pollacci (1902) who used a collodion film painted on to the leaf. One of the main disadvantages of this technique is the ease with which the film becomes opaque due to hardening in high humidity. Later workers have offered alternative formulations for the film (Long and Clements, 1934; North, 1956), but these do not seem to offer any real advantage. Shmueli (1953) reported collodion films suitable for bananas and maize. Later (1964) he found them suitable for nonhairy leaves with nonsunken stomata. Oppenheimer (1949) found collodion films unsuitable for the hairy leaves of tomato.

Sampson (1961) and Zelitch (1961) described the use of fluid silicone rubber to obtain primary, "negative" replicas of leaf surfaces from which transparent, secondary "positive" impressions may be obtained. An important advantage of this procedure over direct collodion films is that the transparent film can be obtained under low humidity and does not become opaque. A further advantage is that the same area of a leaf may be sampled several times in one day with no apparent damage (Zelitch, 1961). The originals are easily stored, may be kept indefinitely, and replicas can be obtained from them as often as required. These advantages have given the technique considerable popularity.

Shimshi (1964) used the silicone rubber technique to calibrate porometer readings in terms of stomatal aperture and established a highly significant linear relation. Macklon and Weatherley (1965a), found the technique correlated well with an infiltration method. They expressed apertures (based on the mean of 50 observations) as width divided by length, so adjusting measured width to a standard pore length.

Some workers found the technique not entirely satisfactory. Johnson and Brun (1966) found difficulty in determining stomatal aperture in banana with it. Similarly, El-Sharkawy and Hesketh (1964) found it insensitive at apertures of less than 1 μ. Solarova (1965) considers the impression only measures the upper borders of the pores. At low RWC these upper borders may separate, although the actual pore remains closed, giving a false impression that the stomates are open. Long and Clements (1934) earlier reported that the collodion film technique may not be satisfactory for small ranges of change in stomatal aperture. Despite these possible disadvantages, the silicone rubber impression technique probably is one of the most versatile methods for measuring stomatal aperture and may be used for practically all leaf types (Shmueli, 1964).

3. Infiltration Techniques

These are ideally suited to the field, being simple, rapid, and requiring a minimum of equipment. Furthermore, no microscopic examination is involved, although the technique can be calibrated in terms of stomatal aperture. The technique consists essentially in observing whether a drop of lipophile liquid when applied gently to a leaf (usually the lower side) will penetrate the stomata and inject the underlying intercellular spaces. Such penetration is visible to the naked eye as a darkened area. According to Heath (1959), both (1) the surface tension between the liquid and the cuticle and (2) the viscosity are involved.

Early workers used a series of different liquids (Dietrich, 1925; Molisch, 1912; Stahl, 1894). Such series have been used more recently by Oppenheimer (1947) for plums and by Oppenheimer and Mendel (1939) for citrus. However, the technique is rendered insensitive by the use of only three or four solutions. Schorn (1929) originated the use of a mixture of two liquids in proportions that could be varied as closely as required. His series consisted of isobutyl alcohol and ethylene glycol in 11 mixtures varying from pure isobutyl alcohol to pure ethylene glycol in steps of 10% by volume. It has been found useful for cotton by Dale (1958), for the West Australian sclerophylls by Grieve (1956), for maize by Oppenheimer (1951), and for citrus by Oppenheimer and Mendel (1939), although isobutanol did not penetrate closed stomata of citrus and maize.

Various mixtures are suitable for different materials. Some workers found mixtures of isopropyl alcohol and water preferable for the oil palm (Ochs, 1963; Rees, 1961). Wormer and Ochs (1959) also found this mixture suitable for peanuts, although the stomata on the upper side of the leaf could not be seen because it was too dark to show infiltration. Alvim and Havis (1954) and Alvim (1960) pointed out that all these agents are toxic, leaving necrotic spots on leaves. They advocated a series based on Nujol mixed with n-dodecane, n-tetradecane, or Bayol-D, which was safe for a wide range of material, permitting the sampling of the same leaf periodically. Grieve (1956) found the series of Alvim and Havis (1954) more sensitive and better for smaller stomates than the Schorn (1929) series, although the infiltrated area was not so easily seen.

Mixtures of medicinal paraffin and commercial kerosene were useful for potatoes, maize, sugar beet, kenaf, sesame, castor bean, sunflower, neuk, tobacco, jute, sorghum, and soybean (Fuehring et al., 1966). The response of each species was different, indicating calibration was necessary for each one if quantitative comparisons were to be attempted. Halevy (1960a,b) and Shillo and Halevy (1964) found these mixtures were suitable for Gladiolus.

A somewhat simpler approach is to use a single liquid and develop a scoring system based on the time taken for infiltration to occur. This may also be weighted by the final amount of infiltration. Kerosene has been found useful for this purpose by Shmueli (1953) working with banana and by Oppenheimer and Elze (1941) with orange trees. MacDowall (1963) used xylene or ethyl alcohol painted onto a certain area of a tobacco leaf and estimated visually the percentage area infiltrated every $\frac{1}{4}$ minute up to 3 minutes.

In general, the technique may be used in one form or another with a fairly wide range of material, although Oppenheimer (1949) reported the tomato leaf as unsatisfactory due to its hairiness and the ease with which it is infiltrated. Parker (1963b) states that an infiltration technique in which Gentian Violet-ethoxyethanol-chloroform-ethyl ether mixture, applied with a dropper and then washed off with water, is the only practicable method for plants with sunken stomata and plugs in the stomatal cavities. Despite its empirical nature, calibrations of the technique have shown it to be closely related to stomatal aperture (MacDowall, 1963; Macklon and Weatherley, 1965a; Rees, 1961; Shmueli, 1953) or stomatal resistance (Dale, 1961b). These techniques have been used in the field to indicate when water deficit is large enough to warrant irrigation. Definite infiltration values have been proposed by Alvim (1960) and Shillo and Halevy (1964). Water deficit is assessed empirically in terms of available soil moisture. Thus, Ophir et al. (1967) found their infiltration index remained at practically 100% until two thirds of the available soil moisture had been used. It seems certain that their cotton plants would have registered a definite deficit before this point was reached, and their observations on the upper stomates (not included normally in their index) confirm this. Such findings point up the empirical nature of these techniques. Their utility seems to lie mainly in determining some arbitrary degree of deficit when irrigation should be applied. Clearly, this is important, but it seems unlikely that such measurements can be related quantitatively to a wide range of water deficit. Shmueli (1964) reported that even for irrigation purposes infiltration techniques are somewhat limited since they may not yield satisfactory results unless carried out by a skilled worker. Possible effects of temperature variation on solution viscosity have received little attention.

4. Field Porometric Techniques

Only in recent years have sufficiently rugged and portable porometers been developed for field use. Like infiltration techniques, one of the principal aims behind their development has been to provide estimates of water deficit for irrigation scheduling. However, porometers appear inherently more accurate and objective than infiltration techniques. Rate of measurement is directly comparable with infiltration techniques (Shmueli, 1964), but the leaf is not damaged. Two main groups of field porometer are recognized: the pressure-drop viscous flow instrument pioneered by Alvim (1965) and the diffusional porometer of Wallihan (1964). Although the pressure-drop porometer may be calibrated in precise physical units ($cm^3 cm^{-2} min^{-1}$), readings with this instrument only indicate resistance of the leaf to viscous flow and so should give little information about diffusive capacity of the stomates. However, Shimshi (1964) reported a linear relation between stomatal width for the stomates on the upper leaf surface of cotton and leaf permeability as indicated by this type of porometer. As Wallihan (1964) points out, results with the diffusional porometer afford direct estimates of the relevant stomatal resistance. However, for assessing WD in terms of stomatal aperture, this advantage is of little significance. A greater advantage is that the diffusional porometer can be used to measure stomatal aperture on either side of the leaf and is equally effective with leaves having stomata on one or both sides, whereas the pressure-drop porometer can only be used in amphistomatous leaves where the ratio of the number of the stomata on the two surfaces is not above 4:1. This applies to most agricultural crops, but citrus, grape, and peach are exceptions.

Alvim's original (1965) pressure-drop porometer was very simple. The porometer cup was mounted on one arm of a tongue forceps with a rubber washer on the other arm. The cup was connected via a three-way valve to a rubber bulb, a rubber air reservoir, and an aneroid sphygmomanometer. It is commercially available (Alvim, 1966). Bierhuizen et al. (1965) described a version in which the porometer itself was improved by furnishing it with a spring to provide a constant but adjustable sealing pressure against the leaf. More recently Shimshi (1967) improved the circuitry and portability as shown in Fig. 32. A combination of this circuitry with the porometer of Bierhuizen et al. would be a further improvement. With stopcock E in position I and stopcock D open air pressure is built up to about 250 mm Hg (read on the aneroid sphygmomanometer I), and the cups are clamped on the leaf. Stopcock E is turned to position II, and the stopwatch J is started at 200 mm pressure. Ten seconds later, stopcock E is turned to position III, isolating the gauge for the convenient reading of the final pressure. The principal advantage of this version, apart from the ability to isolate the gauge, lies in the use of larger and smaller rigid air reservoirs C_1 and C_2. If the initial decline in pressure is very slow, stopcock D is closed (before the 200 mm mark is reached), thereby reducing the effective volume of compressed air in the system and so hastening the pressure drop.

The use of a 10-second reading period enables faster readings, which is important both because of the natural variability of stomatal aperture and because longer clamping times may cause changes of stomatal aperture resulting from shading and/or partial dehydration of the enclosed tissue by

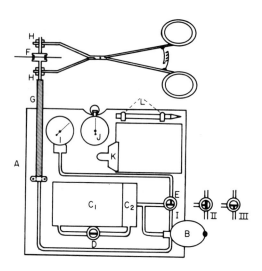

Fig. 32. A double-range pressure-drop porometer for measuring stomatal resistance. From Shimshi (1967).

pressure on the supplying vascular tissue by the porometer cup (Shimshi, 1967).

As mentioned earlier, Wallihan's (1964) diffusion porometer is more versatile than the pressure-drop porometer since it gives readings for the upper and lower epidermis separately and thus can be used for hypostomatous leaves. Since the upper stomates, in cotton at least, apparently respond before the lower ones to stress (Shimshi, 1964), greater sensitivity perhaps might be obtained with the diffusion porometer than with the pressure drop type. The diffusion porometer consists essentially of a cup containing an Aminco–Dunmore humidity sensor, whose resistance varies inversely with humidity, and a portable resistance meter. The cup is clamped to a leaf, and the required time for impedance to change from 1 MΩ to 300,000 Ω is measured with a stopwatch. The wider the stomatal openings, the more rapid the change. Bavel et al. (1965) described an improved version. A difficulty with the apparatus in its present form is that with only slightly open stomata a reading may take several minutes. Furthermore, since the sensor and leaf must be at the same temperature, the leaf must be shaded for 60 seconds to bring it to the known shade temperature before readings are commenced. Shimshi (1964) reported that whether a leaf is in light or shade may greatly affect stomatal aperture in some species. His comments on the effects of long clamping times for the pressure-drop porometer, noted above, may well apply, although perhaps to a lesser extent to the diffusion porometer. Stiles (1966) has modified the diffusion porometer for use with grass leaves.

Other porometers for field use have been proposed by Moreshet (1964), Raschke (1965), and Weatherley (1966). Moreshet's porometer is a portable version of the Wheatstone bridge porometer of Heath and Russell (1951). In its present form it needs two operators and thus is at a disadvantage. Raschke's instrument is a very sensitive, low pressure-drop porometer incorporating a soap-bubble flow meter. Measurements are possible within some seconds and no high pressures need to be applied, minimizing associated errors. Weatherley's porometer is in effect a portable rotameter in which a falling mercury plug draws air through a leaf cup with a standard capillary resistance bridged by a mercury manometer. The time to equilibrium is rather long when leaf conductance is low, and a rather large pressure difference is then necessary.

5. General Sampling Precautions

Sampling should be restricted to fully exposed leaves on sunny days. The leaves should be of similar age and condition. A standard position on the leaf should be used; the tip may often be the most sensitive area and hence be the most useful (Alvim, 1966). Sampling in the early afternoon may increase sensitivity still further, since stress is maximal then. The reading procedure should be carried out as quickly as possible with minimum handling of the leaf to minimize induced changes in stomatal aperture. A large number of samples are necessary to provide a valid mean estimate of stomatal aperture.

Acknowledgment

My very sincere thanks are due to Miss M. Russell, CSIRO Irrigation Research Division librarian, and her staff, without whose considerable assistance this work would not have been possible.

REFERENCES

Ackley, W. B. (1954). Seasonal and diurnal changes in the water contents and water deficits of Bartlett pear leaves. *Plant Physiol.* **29**, 445.

Alcock, M. B. (1964). An improved electronic instrument for estimation of pasture yield. *Nature* **203**, 1309.

Allerup, S. (1960). Transpiration changes and stomata movements in young barley plants. *Physiol. Plantarum* **13**, 112.

Alvim, P. de T. (1960). Stomatal opening as a practical indicator of moisture deficiency in *Cacao. Phyton (Buenos Aires)* **15**, 79.

Alvim, P. de T. (1965). A new type of porometer for measuring stomatal opening and its use in irrigation studies. *UNESCO Arid Zone Res.* **25**, 325.

Alvim, P. de T. (1966). Stomatal opening as a practical indicator of moisture stress in cotton. *Physiol. Plantarum* **19**, 308.

Alvim, P. de T., and Havis, J. (1954). An improved infiltration series for studying stomatal opening as illustrated with coffee. *Plant Physiol.* **29**, 97.

Amanov, M. A. (1965). Water conditions of certain varieties of wheat of Uzbekistan under conditions of dry farming. *Plant Physiol.* (*USSR*) (*Engl. Transl.*) **12**, 291.

Anderson, D. B., and Kerr, T. (1943). A note on the growth behaviour of cotton bolls. *Plant Physiol.* **18**, 261.

ap Rees, T. (1966). Evidence for the widespread occurrence of induced respiration in slices of plant tissue. *Australian J. Biol. Sci.* **19**, 981.

Arcichovskij, V. (1931). Untersuchungen über die Saugkraft der Pflanzen. I. Über die Methoden der Saugkraftmessungen. *Planta* **14**, 517.

Arcichovskij, V., and Arcichovskaja, N. (1931). Untersuchungen über die Saugkraft der Pflanzen. II. Die gravimetrische Methode der Saugkraftmessungen an den Blättern. *Planta* **14**, 528.

Ashby, E. (1931). Comparison of two methods of measuring stomatal aperture. *Plant Physiol.* **6**, 715.

Ashby, E., and Wolf, R. (1947). A critical examination of the gravimetric method of determining suction force. *Ann. Botany* (*London*) [N.S.] **11**, 261.

Bachmann, F. (1922). Studien über die Dickenänderungen von Laubblättern. *Jahrb. Wiss. Botan.* **61**, 372.

Baldes, E. J. (1934). A micromethod of measuring osmotic pressure. *J. Sci. Instr.* **11**, 223.

Baldes, E. J. (1939). Theory of the thermoelectric measurement of osmotic pressure. *Biodynamica* **46**, 1.

Baldes, E. J., and Johnson, A. F. (1939). The thermoelectric osmometer; its construction and use. *Biodynamica* **47**, 1.

Barger, G. (1904). A microscopical method of determining molecular weights. *J. Chem. Soc.* **85**, 286.

Barrs, H. D. (1964). Heat of respiration as a possible source of error in the estimation by psychrometric methods of water potential in plant tissue. *Nature* **203**, 1136.

Barrs, H. D. (1965a). Psychrometric measurement of leaf water potential: lack of error attributable to leaf permeability. *Science* **149**, 63.

Barrs, H. D. (1965b). Comparison of water potentials in leaves as measured by two types of thermocouple psychrometer. *Australian J. Biol. Sci.* **18**, 36.

Barrs, H. D. (1966a). Root pressure and leaf water potential. *Science* **152**, 1266.

Barrs, H. D. (1966b). *Australia, CSIRO, Conf. Instrumentation Plant Environment Measurements, Aspendale, 1966*, p. 21. Society of Instrument Technology, Melbourne.

Barrs, H. D., and Slatyer, R. O. (1965). Experience with three vapour methods for measuring water potential in plants. *UNESCO Arid Zone Res.* **25**, 369.

Barrs, H. D., and Weatherley, P. E. (1962). A re-examination of the relative turgidity technique for estimating water deficits in leaves. *Australian J. Biol. Sci.* **15**, 413.

Bartholomew, E. T. (1926). Internal decline of lemons. III. Water deficit in lemon fruit caused by excessive leaf evaporation. *Am. J. Botany* **8**, 102.

Bartos, J., Kubin, S., and Setlik, I. (1960). Dry weight increase of leaf disks as a measure of photosynthesis. *Biol. Plantarum* **2**, 201.

Basler, E., Todd, G. W., and Meyer, R. E. (1961). Effects of moisture stress on absorption, translocation and distribution of 2,4-dichlorophenoxyacetic acid in bean plants. *Plant Physiol.* **36**, 573.

Bavel, C. H. M. van, Nakayama, F. S., and Ehrler, W. L. (1965). Measuring transpiration resistance of leaves. *Plant Physiol.* **40**, 535.

Begg, J. E., Bierhuizen, J. F., Lemon, E. R., Misra, D. K., Slatyer, R. O., and Stern, W. R. (1964). Diurnal energy and water exchanges in bulrush millet in an area of high solar radiation. *Agr. Metereol.* **1**, 294.

Belik, V. F. (1960). Diagnostics of the demand by tomato plants for water based on the transpiration and the concentration of the cell sap of the leaves. *Plant Physiol. (USSR) (Engl. Transl.)* **7**, 73.

Belik, V. F. (1962). Growth and development of cucumbers and the concentration of cell sap in their leaves at different soil moistures. *Plant Physiol. (USSR) (Engl. Transl.)* **8**, 393.

Bennett-Clark, T. A. (1959). *In* "Plant Physiology" (F. C. Steward, ed.), Vol. II, p. 105. Academic Press, New York.

Bennett-Clark, T. A., Greenwood, A. D., and Barker, J. W. (1936). Water relations and osmotic pressures of plant cells. *New Phytologist* **35**, 277.

Bernstein, L. (1961). Osmotic adjustment of plants to saline media. I. Steady state. *Am. J. Botany* **48**, 909.

Bernstein, L., and Nieman, R. H. (1960). Apparent free space of plant roots. *Plant Physiol.* **35**, 589.

Bierhuizen, J. F., Slatyer, R. O., and Rose, C. W. (1965). A porometer for laboratory and field operation. *J. Exptl. Botany* **16**, 182.

Bliss, L. C., Kramer, P. J., and Wolf, F. A. (1957). Drought resistance in tobacco. *Tobacco* **145**, 20.

Bobkova, L. P. (1965). Causes of wilting of musk melon during excessive irrigation. *Plant Physiol. (USSR) (Engl. Transl.)* **12**, 53.

Bodman, G. B., and Day, P. R. (1943). Freezing points of a group of California soils and their extracted clays. *Soil Sci.* **55**, 225.

Boiko, L. A., and Boiko, L. A. (1959). A method for determining the osmotic pressure of cell sap using collodion sacks. *Plant Physiol. (USSR) (Engl. Transl.)* **6**, 639.

Bormann, F. H., and Kozlowski, T. T. (1962). Measurements of tree growth with dial gage dendrometers and vernier tree ring bands. *Ecology* **43**, 289.

Bourdeau, P. F., and Schopmeyer, C. S. (1958). *In* "The Physiology of Forest Trees" (K. V. Thimann ed.), p. 313. Ronald Press, New York.

Box, J. E., Jr. (1965a). Measurement of water stress in cotton plant leaf discs with a thermo-couple psychrometer. *Agron. J.* **57**, 367.

Box, J. E., Jr. (1965b). *Humidity Moisture, Papers Intern. Symp., Washington, D.C., 1963,* **1**, 110. Reinhold, New York.

Box, J. E., Jr., and Lemon, E. R. (1958). Preliminary field investigations of electrical resistance—moisture stress relations in cotton and grain sorghum plants. *Soil Sci. Soc. Am. Proc.* **22**, 193.

Boyer, J. S. (1965a). Effects of osmotic water stress on metabolic rates of cotton plants with open stomates. *Plant Physiol.* **40**, 229.

Boyer, J. S. (1965b). Isopiestic technique for determination of water potential of plant tissue with a thermocouple psychrometer. *Plant Physiol.* **40** (Suppl.), xxxiv.

Boyer, J. S. (1966). Isopiestic technique: measurement of accurate leaf water potentials. *Science* **154**, 1459.

Boyer, J. S., and Knipling, E. B. (1965). Isopiestic technique for measuring leaf water potentials with a thermocouple psychrometer. *Proc. Natl. Acad. Sci. U.S.* **54**, 1044.

Bridgman, P. W. (1918). Thermo-electromotive force, Peltier heat, and Thompson heat under pressure. *Proc. Am. Acad. Arts Sci.* **53**, 269.

Briggs, L. J. (1950). Limiting negative pressure of water. *J. Appl. Phys.* **21**, 721.

Briggs, R. E., and Robertson, R. N. (1957). Apparent free space. *Ann. Rev. Plant Physiol.* **8**, 11.

Brouwer, R. (1953). Water absorption by the roots of *Vicia faba* at various transpiration strengths. I. Analysis of the uptake and the factors determining it. *Koninkl. Ned. Akad. Wetenschap., Proc. Ser. C* **56**, 106.

Brouwer, R. (1961). Water transport through the plant. *Jaarb. Instituut voor Biologisch en Scheikundig Onderzoek van Landbouwgewassen, Wageningen.* **1961**, 11.

Brouwer, R. (1963). The influence of the suction tension of the nutrient solutions on growth, transpiration and diffusion pressure deficit of bean leaves (*Phaseolus vulgaris*). *Acta Botan. Neerl.* **12**, 248.

Broyer, T. C. (1939). Methods of tissue preparation for analysis in physiological studies with plants. *Botan. Rev.* **5**, 531.

Brun, W. A. (1965). Rapid changes in transpiration in banana leaves. *Plant. Physiol.* **40**, 797.

Buhmann, A. (1935). Kritische Untersuchungen über vergleichende plasmolytische und kryoscopische Bestimmungen des osmotischen Wertes bei Pflanzen. *Protoplasma* **23**, 579.

Burström, H. (1953). Growth and water absorption of *Helianthus* tuber tissue. *Physiol. Plantarum* **6**, 685.

Buscalioni, L., and Pollacci, G. (1902). L'applicazione delle pellicole di collodio allo studi di alcuni processi fisiologici nell piante ad in particular moda alla transpirazione. *Atti. Ist. Botan. Univ. Pavia* **2**, 83, 127.

Buttery, B. R., and Boatman, S. G. (1964). Turgor pressures in phloem: measurements on *Hevea* latex. *Science* **145**, 285.

Buttery, B. R., and Boatman, S. G. (1966). Manometric measurement of turgor pressures in laticiferous phloem tissues. *J. Exptl. Botan.* **17**, 283.

Campbell, A. G., Phillips, D. S. M., and O'Reilly, E. D. (1962). An electronic instrument for pasture yield estimation. *J. Brit. Grassland Soc.* **17**, 89.

Campbell, G. S., Zollinger, W. D., and Taylor, S. A. (1966). Sample changer for thermo-couple psychrometers; construction and some applications. *Agron. J.* **58**, 315.

Carr, D. J., and Gaff, D. F. (1962). The role of the cell-wall water in the water relations of leaves. *UNESCO Arid Zone Res.* **16**, 117.

Čatsky, J. (1959). The role played by growth in the determination of water deficit in plants. *Biol. Plantarum* **1**, 277.

Čatsky, J. (1960). Determination of water deficit in disks cut out from leaf blades. *Biol. Plantarum* **2**, 76.

Čatsky, J. (1963). *In* " The Water Relations of Plants " (A. J. Rutter, ed.), Brit. Ecol. Soc. Symp., **3**, p.101. Blackwell, Oxford.

Čatsky, J. (1965). Leaf-disc method for determining water saturation deficit. *UNESCO Arid Zone Res.* **25**, 353.

Cheesman, J. H., Roberts, E. C., and Tiffany, L. H. (1965). Effects of nitrogen level and osmotic pressure of the nutrient solution on incidence of *Puccinia graminis* and *Helminthosporium sativum* infection in Merion Kentucky Bluegrass. *Agron. J.* 57, 599.

Chunosova, V. N. (1963). Determination of irrigation regime for sugar beet on the basis of cell sap concentration. *Plant Physiol. (USSR)(Engl. Transl.)* **10**, 189.

Clausen, J. J., and Kozlowski, T. T. (1965). Use of the relative turgidity technique for measurement of water stress in gymnosperm leaves. *Can. J. Botany* **43**, 305.

Cockroft, B. (1963). Timing of irrigations in Goulburn Valley orchards. *J. Agr. (Melbourne)* **61**, 492.

Compton, C. (1936). Water deficit in *Citrus. Proc. Am. Soc. Hort. Sci.* **34**, 91.

Cornejo, A., and Vaadia, Y. (1960). Preliminary study of two methods for determining the condition of water in plant leaves and its relation with the condition of water in the soil. *Agronomia (Peru)* **27**, 211.

Crafts, A. S., Currier, H. B., and Stocking, C. R. (1949). "Water in the Physiology of Plants." Chronica Botanica, Waltham, Massachusetts.

Currier, H. B. (1943). Water relations of root cells of *Beta vulgaris*. Ph.D. Thesis, Univ. of Calif., Berkeley, California.

Currier, H. B. (1944). Cryoscopy of small amounts of expressed tissue sap. *Plant Physiol.* **19**, 544.

Cznosnowski, J. (1962). Metabolism of excised embryos of *Lupinus luteus* L. II. The water uptake as influenced by external concentration. *Acta Soc. Botan. Polon.* **31**, 683.

Dale, J. E. (1958). The use of the infiltration method in the study of the stomata of upland cotton. *Empire Cotton Growing Rev.* **35**, 254.

Dale, J. E. (1961a). Investigations into the stomatal physiology of upland cotton. 1. The effects of hour of day, solar radiation, temperature and leaf water-content on stomatal behaviour. *Ann. Botany (London)* [N.S.] **25**, 39.

Dale, J. E. (1961b). Investigations into the stomatal physiology of upland cotton. 2. Calibration of the infiltration method against leaf and stomatal resistances. *Ann. Botany (London)* **25**, 94.

Dancer, J. (1964). The measurement of water deficits in tree crops with special reference to *Robusta* coffee. *Intern. Hort. Congr. 16th Brussels* **4**, 483.

Danilin, A. I. (1955). The measurement of soil moisture by means of gamma rays. *Pochvovedenie* **7**, 74.

Davis, R. M. (1963). The refractometer reading of muskmelon leaf sap in relation to growing conditions. *Proc. Am. Soc. Hort. Sci.* **83**, 599.

Denny, F. E. (1930). The twin-leaf method of studying changes in leaves. *Am. J. Botany* **17**, 818.

De Vries (1884). Eine Methode zur Analyse der Turgorkraft. *Jahrb. Wiss. Botan.* **14**, 267.

Dietrich, M. (1925). Die Transpiration der Schatten und Sonnenpflanzen in ihren Beziehungen zum Standort. *Jahrb. Wiss. Botan.* **65**, 98.

Dixon, H. H. (1914). "Transpiration and the Ascent of Sap in Plants." Macmillan, London.

Dowling, E. J., Spencer, K., and Bouma, D. (1965). The performance of a capacitance measuring instrument in estimating yield of subterranean clover pasture. *Australia, CSIRO, Div. Plant Ind. Field Sta. Record* **4**, 103.

Eaton, F. M. (1943). The osmotic and vitalistic interpretations of exudation. *Am. J. Botany* **30**, 663.

Ehlig, C. F. (1962). Measurement of energy status of water in plants with a thermocouple psychrometer. *Plant Physiol.* **37**, 288.

Ehlig, C. F., and Gardner, W. R. (1964). Relationship between transpiration and the internal water relations of plants. *Agron. J.* **56**, 127.

Ehrler, W. L. (1963). Water absorption of alfalfa as affected by low root temperature and other factors of a controlled environment. *Agron. J.* **55**, 363.

Ehrler, W. L., Nakayama, F. S., and Bavel, van. C. H. M. (1965). Cyclic changes in water balance and transpiration of cotton leaves in a steady environment. *Physiol. Plantarum* **18**, 766.

Ehrler, W. L., Bavel, van. C. H. M., and Nakayama, F. S. (1966). Transpiration, water absorption and internal water balance of cotton plants as affected by light and changes in saturation deficit. *Plant Physiol.* **41**, 71.

El-Sharkawy, M. A., and Hesketh, J. D. (1964). Effects of temperature and water deficit on leaf photosynthetic rates of different species. *Crop Sci.* **4**, 514.

Ernest, E. C. M. (1931). Suction-pressure gradients and the measurement of suction pressure. *Ann. Botany (London)* **45**, 717.

Ernest, E. C. M. (1934a). Studies in the suction pressure of plant cells. II. *Ann. Botany (London)* **48**, 293.

Ernest, E. C. M. (1934b). The effect of intercellular pressure on the suction pressure of cells. *Ann. Botany (London)* **48**, 915.

Ernest, E. C. M. (1934c). The water relations of the plant cell. *J. Linnean. Soc. (London) Botany* **49**, 495.

Falk, H. (1965). Physiology of plasmolyzed cells. I. Labelling the plasmolysis free-space with isotopes. *Z. Pflanzenphysiol.* **53**, 19.

Falk, H., Luttge, U., and Weigl, J. (1966). Investigations on the physiology of plasmolyzed cells. II. Ion uptake, oxygen exchange, and transport. *Z. Pflanzenphysiol.* **54**, 446.

Falk, S., Herz, C. H., and Virgin, H. I. (1958). On the relation between turgor pressures and tissue rigidity. I. Experiments on resonance frequency and tissue rigidity. *Physiol. Plantarum* **11**, 802.

Farbrother, H. G. (1957). Of an electrical resistance technique for the study of soil moisture problems in the field. *Empire Cotton Growing Rev.* **34**, 71.

Farkas, L., and Pratt, A. J. (1961). Irrigation by refractometer. *Farm Res. (N.Y.)* **27**, 14.

Ferguson, H., and Gardner, W. H. (1962). Water content measurement in soil columns by gamma ray absorption. *Soil Sci. Soc. Am. Proc.* **26**, 11.

Fiedler, W. (1964). Research on the suitability of refractometry for the determination of the hydrous condition of fruit trees. *Deut. Akad. Landwirtschaftswiss. Tagunsber.* **65**, 211.

Filippov, L. A. (1959). The concentration of the cell sap of the leaves as a physiological index of the moisture regime of cotton. *Plant Physiol. (USSR) (Engl. Transl.)* **6**, 82.

Filippov, L. A. (1961). Refractometric method of estimating water content of leaves of apple trees. *Plant Physiol. (USSR) (Engl. Transl.)* **8**, 103.

Fischer, R. A., and Kohn, G. D. (1966). Soil water relations and relative turgidity of leaves in the wheat crop. *Australian J. Agr. Res.* **17**, 269.

Fletcher, J. E., and Robinson, M. E. (1956). A capacitance meter for estimating forage weight. *J. Range Management* **9**, 96.

Fraser, D. A., and Dirks, H. T. (1959). Internal water relations of yellow birch at Chalk River. *Can. J. Botany* **37**, 789.

Fuehring, H. D., Mazaheri, A., Bybordi, M., and Khan, A. K. S. (1966). Effect of soil moisture depletion on crop yield and stomatal infiltration. *Agron. J.* **58**, 195.

Furr, J. R., and Taylor, C. A. (1939). Growth of lemon fruits in relation to moisture content of the soil. *U.S. Dept. Agr. Tech. Bull.* **640**.

Gaff, D. F., and Carr, D. J. (1961). The quantity of water in the cell wall and its significance. *Australian J. Biol. Sci.* **14**, 299.

Gaff, D. F., and Carr, D. J. (1964). An examination of the refractometric method for determining the water potential of plant tissue. *Ann. Botany (London)* [N.S.] **28**, 351.

Gale, J., and Poljakoff-Mayber, A. (1965). Antitranspirants as a research tool for the study of the effects of water stress on plant behaviour. *UNESCO Arid Zone Res.* **25**, 269.

Gardner, W. R., and Ehlig, C. F. (1965). Physical aspects of the internal water relations of plant leaves. *Plant Physiol.* **40**, 705.

Gardner, W. R., and Nieman, R. H. (1964). Lower limit of water availability to plants. *Science* **143**, 1460.

Gej, B. (1962). Dynamics of water content and the rate of respiration of spring wheat leaves. *Acta Soc. Botan. Polon.* **31**, 603.

Gelb, G. H., Marcus, B. D., and Dropkin, D. (1964). Manufacture of fine wire thermocouple probes. *Rev. Sci. Instr.* **35**, 80.

Gifford, R. O., Ruf, R. H., Jr., and Eckert, R. E., Jr. (1964). Apparatus for extracting plant sap. *Agron. J.* **56**, 447.

Glover, J. (1959). The apparent behaviour of maize and sorghum stomata during and after drought. *J. Agr. Sci.* **53**, 412.

Goode, J. E., and Hegarty, T. W. (1965). Measurement of water potential of leaves by methods involving immersion in sucrose solutions. *Nature* **206**, 109.

Goryunov, N. S., and Ogryzkova, N. M. (1964). A physiological evaluation of the irrigation conditions for soya. *Plant Physiol.* (*USSR*) (*Engl. Transl.*) **11**, 934.

Green, P. B. (1966). Simultaneous measurement of growth rate and turgor pressure in growing *Nitella* cells. *Am. Soc. Plant Physiol. Ann. Meeting, College Park, Maryland*, p. v.

Greenidge, K. N. H. (1962). Dendrograph patterns in decapitated trees: preliminary observations. *Can. J. Botany* **40**, 1063.

Gregory, D. W., and Cocking, E. C. (1966). Studies on isolated protoplasts and vacuoles. I. General properties. *J. Exptl. Botany* **17**, 57.

Grieve, B. J. (1956). Studies in the water relations of plants. 1—Transpiration of Western Australian (Swan Plain) sclerophylls. *J. Roy. Soc. W. Australia* **40**, 15.

Grieve, B. J. (1961). Negative turgor pressure in sclerophyll plants. *Australian J. Sci.* **23**, 375.

Groenewegen, H., and Mills, J. A. (1960). Uptake of mannitol into the shoots of intact barley plants. *Australian J. Biol. Sci.* **13**, 1.

Gurr, C. G. (1962). Use of gamma rays in measuring water content and permeability in unsaturated columns of soil. *Soil Sci.* **94**, 224.

Gurr, C. G. (1964). Calculation of soil water contents from γ-ray readings. *Australian J. Soil Res.* **2**, 29.

Halevy, A. H. (1960a). Diurnal fluctuations in water balance factors of gladiolus leaves. *Bull. Res. Council Israel Sect. D* **8**, 239.

Halevy, A. H. (1960b). The influence of progressive increase in soil moisture tension on growth and water balance of *Gladiolus* leaves, and the development of physiological indicators for irrigation. *Proc. Am. Soc. Hort. Sci.* **76**, 620.

Halevy, A. H., and Monselise, S. P. (1963). Meaning of apparent midnight decrease in water content of leaves. *Botan. Gaz.* **124**, 343.

Halket, A. C. (1913). On various methods for determining osmotic pressures. *New Phytologist* **12**, 164.

Halma, E. F. (1933). Some phases in the water relations of *Citrus. Proc. Am. Soc. Hort. Sci.* **31**, 108.

Hargitay, B., Kuhn, W., and Wirz, H. (1951). Eine mikrokryoscopische Methode für sehr kleine Lösungsmengen (0.1–1γ). *Experientia* **7**, 276.

Harms, W. R., and McGregor, W. H. (1962). A method for measuring the water balance of pine needles. *Ecology* **43**, 531.

Harris, J. A. (1915). An extension to 5.99° of tables to determine the osmotic pressure of expressed vegetable saps from the depression of the freezing point. *Am. J. Botany* **2**, 418.

Harris, J. A., and Gortner, R. A. (1914). Notes on the calculation of the osmotic pressure of expressed vegetable saps from the depression of the freezing point, with a table for the values of P for $\Delta = 0.001°$ to $\Delta = 2.999°$. *Am. J. Botany* **1**, 75.

Hart, E. D., and Elkin, W. H. (1946). Welding fine thermocouple wires. *J. Sci. Instr.* **23**, 17.

Hart, J. R., Norris, K. H., and Columbic, C. (1962). Determination of the moisture content of seeds by near infrared spectrophotometry of their methanol extracts. *Cereal Chem.* **39**, 94.

Härtel, O. (1963). Über die Möglichkeit der Anwendung der plasmometrischen Methode Höflers auf nichtzylindrische Zellen. *Protoplasma*, **57**, 354.

Hatakeyama, I., and Kato, J. (1965). Studies on the water relation of *Buxus* leaves. *Planta* **65**, 259.

Heath, O. V. S. (1949). Studies in stomatal behaviour. II. The role of starch in the light response of stomata. Pt. 1. Review of literature, and experiments on the relation between aperture and starch content in the stomata of *Pelargonium zonale*. *New Phytologist* **48**, 186.

Heath, O. V. S. (1959). *In* " Plant Physiology " (F. C. Steward, ed.), Vol. II, p. 193. Academic Press, New York.

Heath, O. V. S., and Russell, J. (1951). The Wheatstone bridge porometer. *J. Exptl. Botany* **2**, 111.

Hendrickson, A. H., and Veihmeyer, F. J. (1941). Some factors affecting the growth of pears. *Proc. Am. Soc. Hort. Sci.* **39**, 1.

Henkel, P. A., and Bakanova, L. A. (1965). Some features of the surface of protoplasts of plant cells in the dormant state. *Plant Physiol.* (*USSR*) (*Engl. Transl.*) **12**, 572.

Henkel, P. A., and Pronina, N. D. (1963). Extraction of protoplasts from dormant cells of onion epidermis. *Plant Physiol.* (*USSR*) (*Engl. Transl.*) **10**, 98.

Hewlett, J. D., and Kramer, P. J. (1963). The measurement of water deficits in broadleaf plants. *Protoplasma* **57**, 381.

Hill, A. V. (1930). A thermal method of measuring the vapour pressure of an aqueous solution. *Proc. Roy. Soc.* **A127**, 9.

Hinsch, H., and Niemann, E. G. (1964). A combined device for measuring density and water content in living tree trunks. *Atompraxis* **10**, 372.

Höfler, K. (1917). Die plasmolytisch-volumetrische Methode und ihre Anwendbarkeit zur Messung des osmotischen Wertes lebender Pflanzensellen. *Ber. Deut. Botan. Ges.* **35**, 706.

Hyde, F. J., and Lawrence, J. J. (1964). Electronic assessment of pasture growth. *Electron. Eng.* **36**, 666.

Iljin, W. S. (1975). Drought resistance in plants and physiological processes. *Ann. Rev. Plant Physiol.* **8**, 257.

Impens, I. I., and Schalck, J. M. (1965). A very sensitive electric dendrograph for recording radial changes of a tree. *Ecology* **46**, 183.

Ingelsten, B. (1966). Absorption and transport of sulfate by wheat at varying mannitol concentration of the medium. *Physiol. Plantarum* **19**, 563.

International Critical Tables (1933). McGraw-Hill, New York.

Iyama, J., and Murata, Y. (1961). Studies on the photosynthesis in upland field crops. *Nippon Sakumotsu Gakkai Kiji* (*Proc. Crop. Sci. Soc. Japan.*) **29**, 350.

Jackson, W. T. (1965). Mannitol-induced stimulation of elongation of root hairs of *Agrostis alba* L. *Physiol. Plantarum* **18**, 24.

Jaeger, S. (1966). The hydration of *Avena sativa* with increasing mineral fertilization. II. Hydration and expressed sap analysis. *Plant Soil* **24**, 201.

Janes, B. E. (1964). Adjustment of plants to increase in osmotic pressure of root medium. *Plant Physiol.* **39** (Suppl.), lvii.

Janes, B. E. (1966). Adjustment mechanisms of plants subject to varied osmotic pressures of nutrient solution. *Soil. Sci.* **101**, 180.

Jarvis, P. G., and Jarvis, M. S. (1963a). Effects of various osmotic substrates on the growth of *Lupinus albus* seedlings. *Physiol. Plantarum.* **16**, 485.

Jarvis, P. G., and Jarvis, M. S. (1963b). The water relations of tree seedlings. IV. Some aspects of the tissue water relations and drought resistance. *Physiol. Plantarum.* **16**, 501.

Jarvis, P. G., and Jarvis, M. S. (1965). *In* "Water Stress in Plants" (B. Slavik, ed.), Proc. Symp. Prague 1963, p. 167. Czech. Acad. Sci., Prague.

Jarvis, P. G., and Slatyer, R. O. (1966a). A controlled-environment chamber for studies of gas exchange by each surface of a leaf. *Australia, CSIRO, Div. Land Res. Tech. Paper* **29**, 1.

Jarvis, P. G., and Slatyer, R. O. (1966b). Calibration of β gauges for determining leaf water status. *Science* **153**, 78.

Joffe, A. (1964). The determination of moisture in seeds with special reference to the Marconi electrical conductance method. II. Sorghums. *S. African J. Agr. Sci.* **7**, 563.

Joffe, A., Clarke, B., and Small, J. G. C. (1964). The determination of moisture in seeds with special reference to the Marconi electrical conductance method. I. Maize. *S. African J. Agr. Sci.* **7**, 219.

Johns, G. G., and Watkin, B. R. (1965). A modified capacitance probe technique for estimating pasture yield. II. The effect of different pastures, soil types and dew on the calibration. *J. Brit. Grassland Soc.* **20**, 217.

Johns, G. G., Nicol, G. R., and Watkin, B. R. (1965). A modified capacitance probe technique for estimating pasture yield. I. Construction and procedure for use in the field. *J. Brit. Grassland Soc.* **20**, 212.

Johnson, B. E., and Brun, W. A. (1966). Stomatal density and responsiveness of banana fruit stomates. *Plant Physiol.* **41**, 99.

Jones, R. J. (1963). Electronic pasture sampler. *Australia, CSIRO, Div. Trop. Pastures Ann. Rept.* p. 20.

Jones, R. J. (1964). Electronic pasture sampler. *Australia, CSIRO, Div. Trop. Pastures, Ann. Rept.* p. 26.

Jones, R. J. (1965). Electronic pasture sampler. *Australia, CSIRO, Div. Trop. Pastures, Ann. Rept.* p. 39.

Jones, R. J. (1966). Electronic pasture sampler. *Australia, CSIRO, Div. Trop. Pastures, Ann. Rept.* p. 44.

Kamiya, N., Tazawa, M., and Takata, T. (1963). The relation of turgor pressure to cell volume in *Nitella flexilis* with special reference to mechanical properties of the cell wall. *Protoplasma* **57**, 501.

Kennedy, J. S., and Mittler, T. E. (1953). A method of obtaining phloem sap via the mouthparts of aphids. *Nature* **171**, 528.

Ketellapper, H. J. (1953). The mechanism of the action of indole-3-acetic acid on the water absorption by *Avena* coleoptile sections. *Acta Botan. Neerl.* **2**, 388.

Khadzhikubanova, G. (1961). Seasonal and diurnal fluctuations in the suction and osmotic pressure of the cell sap of the leaves of ephemeral and ephemeroid plants of the southwestern Kyzylkum mountains. *Dokl. Akad. Nauk, Uz. SSR* **11**, 54.

Kharanyan, N. H. (1965). The water retaining capacity of leaves of wilting plants differing with respect to drought resistance. *Plant Physiol. (USSR) (Engl. Transl.)* **12**, 141.

Kiernan, E. F. (1955). Preparation of copper-constantan thermocouples. *J. Sci. Instr.* **32**, 321.

Kijne, J. W., and Taylor, S. A. (1963). A constant temperature bath controlled with a precision of $0.001°$ centigrade. *Soil. Sci. Soc. Am. Proc.* **27**, 110.

Killian, M. C. (1947). Le deficit de saturation hydrique chez les plantes Sahariennes. *Rev. Gen. Botan.* **54**, 81.

Kinsey, V. E. (1950). Modification of the apparatus used for the Baldes thermoelectric method for measuring osmotic pressure. *Rev. Sci. Instr.* **21**, 767.

Klemm, W. (1959). Eine neue Methode zur Bestimmung des Holzfeuchteverlaufes in wachsenden Bäumen mit Hilfe von Gammastrahlen. *Flora (Jena)* **147**, 465.

Klepper, B. (1963). Water relations of *Dicranum scoparium. Bryologist* **66**, 41.

Klute, A., and Richards, L. A. (1962). Effect of temperature on relative vapor pressure of water in soil: Apparatus and preliminary measurements. *Soil Sci.* **93**, 391.

Knipling, E. B. (1965). Comparison of the dye method with the thermocouple psychrometer method for measuring leaf water potentials. *Plant Physiol.* **40** (Suppl.), xxxv.

Koller, R. D., and Samish, Y. (1964). A null-point compensating system for simultaneous and continuous measurement of net photosynthesis and transpiration by gas-stream analysis. *Botan. Gaz.* **125**, 81.

Kollman, R. (1965). Zur Lokalisierung der funktionstüchtigen Siebzellen im sekundären Phloem von *Metasequoia glyptostroboides*. *Planta* **65**, 173.

Korven, H. C., and Taylor, S. A. (1959). The Peltier effect and its use for determining relative activity of soil water. *Can. J. Soil. Sci.* **39**, 76.

Kozinka, V., and Klenovska, S. (1965). The uptake of mannitol by higher plants. *Biol. Plantarum* **7**, 285.

Kozinka, V., and Niznansky, A. (1963). Biometric analysis of the relationship between the osmotic pressure of the cell sap and its refractive index. *Biol. Plantarum.* **5**(1), 77.

Kozlowski, T. T. (1964). "Water Metabolism in Plants," Biological Monographs. Harper, New York.

Kozlowski, T. T., and Clausen, J. J. (1965). Changes in moisture contents and dry weights of buds and leaves of forest trees. *Botan. Gaz.* **126**, 20.

Kozlowski, T. T., and Winget, C. H. (1964). Diurnal and seasonal variation in radii of tree stems. *Ecology* **45**, 149.

Kramer, P. J. (1937). Relation between rate of transpiration and rate of absorption of water in plants. *Am. J. Botany* **24**, 10.

Kramer, P. J., and Brix, H. (1965). Measurement of water deficit in plants. *UNESCO Arid Zone Res.* **25**, 343.

Kramer, P. J., and Currier, H. B. (1950). Water relations of plant cells and tissues. *Ann. Rev. Plant Physiol.* **1**, 265.

Kramer, P. J., and Kozlowski, T. T. (1960). "Physiology of Trees." McGraw-Hill, New York.

Krayevoi, S. Y. (1962). Some possible causes of transpiration resistance. *Plant Physiol. (USSR)* (*Engl. Transl.*) **9**, 375.

Kreeb, K. (1960). Über die gravimetrische Methode zur Bestimmung der Saugspannung und das Problem des negativen Turgors. I. Mitteilung. *Planta* **55**, 274.

Kreeb, K. (1961). Zur Frage des negativen Turgors bei mediterranen Hartlaubpflanzen unter natürlichen Bedingungen. *Planta* **56**, 479.

Kreeb, K. (1963). Untersuchungen zum Wasserhaushalt unter extrem ariden Bedingungen. *Planta* **59**, 442.

Kreeb, K. (1965a). Determination of the internal water balance (hydrature) in the field by measuring suction force and refractive index. *UNESCO Arid Zone Res.* **25**, 385.

Kreeb, K. (1965b). Untersuchungen zu den osmotischen Zustandsgrössen. I. Mitteilung: Ein tragbares electronisches Mikrokryoskop für ökophysiologische Arbeiten. *Planta* **65**, 269.

Kreeb, K. (1965c). Untersuchungen zu den osmotischen Zustandsgrössen. II. Mitteilung: Eine electronische Methode zur Messung der Saugspannung (NTC-Methode). *Planta* **66**, 156.

Kreeb, K. (1965d). Die Bedeutung des Quellungswassers der Zelle bei der kryoskopischen Bestimmung des osmotischen wertes. *Ber. Deut. Botan. Ges.* **78**, 159.

Kreeb, K. (1966). Die Registrierung des Wasserzustandes über die elektrische Leitfähigkeit der Blätter. *Ber. Deut. Botan. Ges.* **79**, 150.

Kreeb, K., and Önal, M. (1961). Über die gravimetrische Methode zur Bestimmung der Saugspannung und das Problem des negativen Turgors. II. Mitteilung: Die Beruckschtigung von Atmungsverlusten während der Messungen. *Planta* **56**, 409.

Kuroiwa, K., Yoshino, R., and Takahashi, G. (1958). Daily growth curve of *Paulownia*. (II) Variation in the growing season. *J. Japan. Forestry. Soc.* **40**, 139.

Lagerwerff, J. V., Ogata, G., and Eagle, H. E. (1961). Control of osmotic pressure of culture solutions with polyethylene glycol. *Science* **133**, 1486.

Lambert, J. R., and Schilfgaarde, J. van (1965). A method of determining the water potential of intact plants. *Soil Sci.* **100**, 1.

Landolt-Börnstein (1923). "Physisch-Chemie Tabellen," Vol. II, p. 1459. Springer, Berlin.

Landolt-Börnstein (1927). "Physisch Chemie Tabellen," Supplement Vol. I, p. 798. Springer, Berlin.

Lang, A. R. G. (1966). *Australia, CSIRO, Conf. Instrumentation Plant Environment Measurements, Aspendale,* 1966 p. 23. Society of Instrument Technology, Melbourne.

Lang, A. R. G. (1967). Osmotic coefficients and water potentials of sodium chloride solutions from 0 to 40°C. *Australian J. Chem.* **20**, 2017.

Lang, A. R. G., and Barrs, H. D. (1965). An apparatus for measuring water potentials in the xylem of intact plants. *Australian J. Biol. Sci.* **18**, 487.

Lang, A. R. G., and Trickett, E. S. (1965). Automatic scanning of Spanner and droplet psychrometers having outputs up to 30 μV. *J. Sci. Instr.* **42**, 777.

Lang, A. R. G., and Trickett, E. S. (1966). *Australia, CSIRO, Irrigation Res. Lab. Ann. Rept.,* **1965–1966**, 29.

Larcher, W. (1965). *In* "Water Stress in Plants" (B. Slavik. ed), Proc. Symp. Prague, 1963 p. 184. Czech. Acad. Sci., Prague.

Lebedev, G. V. (1963). New irrigation conditions for agricultural crops. *Plant Physiol. (USSR) (Engl. Transl.)* **9**, 400.

Lee, T. T. (1965). Sugar content and stomatal width as related to ozone injury in tobacco leaves. *Can. J. Botany* **43**, 677.

Lemée, G., and Gonzalez, G. (1965). Comparison de méthodes de mesure du potentiel hydrique (tension de succion, DPD) dans les feuilles par équilibre osmotique et par équilibre de pression de vapeur. *UNESCO Arid Zone Res.* **25**, 361.

Lemée, G., and Laisné, G. (1951). La méthode réfractométrique de mesure de la succion. *Rev. Gen. Botan.* **58**, 336.

Letey, J., Richardson, W. F., and Valoras, N. (1965). Barley growth, water use, and mineral composition as influenced by oxygen exclusion from specific regions of the root system. *Agron. J.* **57**, 629.

Levitt, J. (1947). The thermodynamics of active (non-osmotic) water absorption. *Plant Physiol.* **22**, 514.

Levitt, J. (1964). *In* "Instrumentation in Experimental Biology" (D. W. Newman, ed), p. 405. Macmillan, New York.

Lifson, N., and Lorber, V. (1945). The time required for the establishment of the thermal steady state in the Hill-Baldes apparatus, with application to the more rapid determination of osmotic activity. *J. Biol. Chem.* **158**, 209.

Linacre, E. T. (1964). Determinations of the heat transfer co-efficient of a leaf. *Plant Physiol.* **39**, 687.

Livingston, B. E., and Brown, G. E. (1912). Relation of daily march of transpiration to variations in water content of foliage leaves. *Botan. Gaz.* **53**, 309.

Lloyd, F. E. (1908). The physiology of stomata. *Carnegie Inst. Wash. Publ.* **82**.

Lobov, M. F. (1949). The problems involved in methods of determining the water requirements of plants under irrigation. *Dokl. Akad. Nauk SSSR* **66**, 277.

Lockhart, J. A. (1959). A new method for the determination of osmotic pressure. *Am. J. Botany* **46**, 704.

Long, F. J., and Clements, F. E. (1934). The method of collodion films for stomata. *Am. J. Botany* **21**, 7.

Loomis, W. E., and Shull, C. A. (1937). "Methods in Plant Physiology." McGraw-Hill, New York.

Louie, D. S. (1963). Studies on abscission. II. Water relations and defoliability of cotton. *Dissertation Abstr.* **24**, 1822.

Lyon, C. J. (1936). Analysis of osmotic relations by extending the simplified method. *Plant Physiol.* **11**, 167.

Lyon, C. J. (1940). Improvements in the simplified method for osmotic measurements. *Plant Physiol.* **15**, 561.

McComb, E. A., and Rendig, V. V. (1960). Technique for extracting juice from plant tissue. *Chemist-Analyst* **49**, 55.

MacDougal, D. T. (1921). Growth in trees. *Carnegie Inst. Wash. Publ.* **307**.

MacDougal, D. T. (1925). Reversible variations in volume, pressure and movement of sap in trees. *Carnegie Inst. Wash. Publ.* **365**.

MacDougal, D. T. (1936). Studies in tree growth by the dendrographic method. *Carnegie Inst. Wash. Publ.* **462**.

MacDougal, D. T. (1938). "Tree Growth." Chronica Botanica, Waltham, Massachusetts.

MacDowall, F. D. H. (1963). Midday closure of stomata in aging tobacco leaves. *Can. J. Botany* **41**, 1289.

Macklon, A. E. S., and Weatherley, P. E. (1965a). Controlled environment studies of the nature and origins of water deficits in plants. *New Phytologist* **64**, 414.

Macklon, A. E. S., and Weatherley, P. E. (1965b). A vapour pressure instrument for the measurement of leaf and soil water potential. *J. Exptl. Botany* **16**, 261.

Magness, J. R., and Furr, J. R. (1930). Stomatal activity in apple leaves. *Proc. Am. Soc. Hort. Sci.* **27**, 207.

Manohar, M. S. (1965). A comparison of two water potential techniques. *Ann. Arid Zone* **4**, 96.

Manohar, M. S. (1966a). Effect of "osmotic" systems on germination of peas (*Pisum sativum*, L.). *Planta* **71**, 81.

Manohar, M. S. (1966b). Measurement of the water potential of intact plant tissues. I. Design of a microthermocouple psychrometer. *J. Exptl. Botany* **17**, 44.

Manohar, M. S. (1966c). Measurement of the water potential of intact plant tissues. II. Factors affecting the precision of the thermocouple psychrometer technique. *J. Exptl. Botany* **17**, 51.

Manohar, M. S. (1966d). Measurement of the water potential of intact plant tissues. III. The water potentials of germinating peas (*Pisum sativum* L.) *J. Exptl. Botany* **17**, 231.

Manohar, M. S., and Heydecker, W. (1965). Water requirements for seed germination. *Ann. Rept. Nottingham Univ. School Agr.* **1964**, 55.

Marinchink, A. F., Buzanov, I. F., and Novitskaya, Y. E. (1964). Effect of concentration of nutrient solution on moisture regime, composition of pigments and productivity of sugar beet depending on climatic conditions. *Plant Physiol.* (*USSR*) (*Engl. Transl.*) **10**, 529.

Marr, A. G., and Vaadia, Y. (1961). Rapid cryoscopic technique for measuring osmotic properties of drop size samples. *Plant Physiol.* **36**, 677.

Mason, T. G., and Maskell, E. J. (1928). A study of diurnal variations in the carbohydrates of leaf, bark and wood, and of the effects of ringing. *Ann. Botany* (*London*). **42**, 188.

Mattas, R. E., and Pauli, A. W. (1965). Trends in nitrate reduction and nitrogen fractions in young corn (*Zea mays*) plants during heat and moisture stress. *Crop Sci.* **5**, 181.

Maximov, N. A., and Petinov, N. S. (1948). Determination of the suction force of leaves by the compensation method with the aid of a refractometer. *Dokl. Akad. Nauk SSSR* **62**, 537.

Mederski, H. J. (1961). Determination of internal water status of plants by beta ray gauging. *Soil Sci.* **92**, 143.

Mederski, H. J. (1963). Beta ray gauge senses plants' water stress. *Ohio Farm Home Res.* **48**, 4.

Mederski, H. J. (1964). Plant water balance determination by beta gauging technique. *Agron. Abstr.* **56**, 126.

Meidner, H. (1952). An instrument for the continuous determination of leaf thickness changes in the field. *J. Exptl. Botany* **3**, 319.

Meyer, B. S., and Wallace, A. M. (1941). A comparison of two methods of determining the diffusion pressure deficit of potato tuber tissues. *Am. J. Botany* **28**, 838.

Meyer, R. E., and Gingrich, J. R. (1966). Osmotic stress effects on wheat using a split root solution culture system. *Agron. J.* **58**, 377.

Millar, B. D. (1964). Effect of local advection on evaporation rate and plant water status. *Australian J. Agr. Res.* **15**, 85.

Millar, B. D. (1966). Relative turgidity of leaves: temperature effects in measurement. *Science* **154**, 512.

Miller, E. C. (1917). Daily variation of water and dry matter in the leaves of corn and the sorghums. *J. Agr. Res.* **10**, 11.

Miller, E. C. (1924). Daily variation of the carbohydrates in the leaves of corn and the sorghums. *J. Agr. Res.* **27**, 785.

Milthorpe, F. L., and Spencer, E. J. (1957). Experimental studies of the factors controlling transpiration. III. Inter-relations between transpiration rate, stomatal movement and leaf water content. *J. Exptl. Botany* **8**, 413.

Moiseev, N. N. (1963). Seasonal peculiarities in the water content of the leaves of stone fruits. *Plant Physiol.* (*USSR*) (*Engl. Transl.*) **10**, 81.

Molisch, H. (1912). Das Offen- und Geschlossensein der Spaltöffnungen, veranschaulicht durch eine neue Methode (Infiltrations Methode). *Z. Botan.* **4**, 106.

Molz, F. J. (1926a) A study of suction force by the simplified method. I. Effect of external factors. *Am. J. Botany.* **13**, 433.

Molz, F. J. (1926b). A study of suction force by the simplified method. II. Periodic variations and the influence of habitat. *Am. J. Botany.* **13**, 465.

Monteith, J. L., and Owen, P. C. (1958). A thermocouple method for measuring relative humidity in the range 95–100%. *J. Sci. Instr.* **35**, 443.

Moreshet, S. (1964). A portable Wheatstone bridge porometer for field measurements of stomatal resistance. *Israel J. Agr. Res.* **14**, 27.

Moss, D. N. (1963). The effect of environment on gas exchange of leaves. *Conn. Agr. Expt. Sta. New Haven, Bull.* **664**, 86.

Mott, G. O., Barnes, R. F., Rhykerd, C. L. (1965). Estimating pasture yield *in situ* by beta ray attenuation techniques. *Agron. J.* **57**, 512.

Mouravieff, I. (1959). Tension de succion et déficit de saturation hydrique du tapis végétal des pelouses sèches de la règion de Grasse (Alpes Maritimes). *Bull. Soc. Botan. France* **106**, 306.

Mouravieff, I. (1964). Sur les proprietes optiques des feuilles. Influence de l'état d'hydration de la feuille sur la transmission de la lumière. *Bull. Mens. Soc. Linneenne Lyon* **33**, 365.

Mouravieff, I. (1965). Effect of irradiation by near ultraviolet rays on stomatic cells in the presence or absence of carbon dioxide. *Compt. Rend. Acad. Sci.* **260**, (*Groupe* 13), 5392.

Mukhin, L. M., and Chistotinov, L. V. (1961). Gamma ray method of determining moisture in coarse fragmentary soils. *Soviet Soil Sci.* (*Engl. Transl.*) **7**, 807.

Mulkey, J. R. Jr. (1966). The role of light quality, air temperature and relative humidity on transpirational water losses of cotton plants. *Dissertation Abstr.* **26**, 3570.

Nadel, M. (1938). Sur la mesure de l'ouverture des stomates. Ph. D. Thesis, Univ. Paris, Paris, France.

Nakayama, F. S., and Ehrler, W. L. (1964). Beta ray gauging technique for measuring leaf water content changes and moisture status of plants. *Plant Physiol.* **39**, 95.

Namken, L. N. (1964). The influence of crop environment on the internal water balance of cotton. *Soil Sci. Soc. Am. Proc.* **28**, 12.

Namken, L. N., and Lemon, E. R. (1960). Field studies of internal moisture relations of the corn plant. *Agron. J.* **52**, 643.

Natr, L. (1965). *In* "Water Stress in Plants" (B. Slavik. ed.), Proc. Symp. Prague, 1963, p. 219 Czech. Acad. Sci., Prague.

Natr, L., and Kousalova, I. (1965). *In* "Water Stress in Plants" (B. Slavik, ed.), Proc. Symp. Prague, 1963, p. 128. Czech. Acad. Sci., Prague.

Necas, J. (1960). Studium des Wasserhaushaltes der Kartoffeln. *Zaverecana sprava VUB Havlickuv Brod.*

Necas, J. (1965). *In* "Water Stress in Plants" (B. Slavik, ed.), Proc. Symp. Prague, 1963, p. 50. Czech. Acad. Sci., Prague.

Nezgovorov, L. A., and Solovev, A. K. (1965). Effect of low temperatures and pathogenic soil microflora on water uptake by thermophilic plants. *Plant. Physiol. (USSR) (Engl. Transl.)* **12**, 433.

Nieman, R. H., and Poulsen, L. L. (1964). Plant-water relationships under saline, drought or high exchangeable sodium conditions. The suppression of cell division in plants by salinity and water stress. *Rep. Collaborators, U.S. Salinity Lab.*, pp. 59-62.

Nishida, K. (1963). Studies on stomatal movement of Crassulacean plants in relation to the acid metabolism. *Physiol. Plantarum* **16**, 281.

Norris, K. H. (1964). Design and development of a new moisture meter. *Agr. Eng.* **45**, 370.

North, C. S. (1956). A technique for measuring structural features of plant epidermis using cellulose acetate films. *Nature* **178**, 1186.

Ochs, R. (1963). Recherches de pédologie de physiologie pour l'étude du problème de l'eau dans la culture du palmier a huile. *Oleagineux* **18**, 231.

Önal, M. (1964a). Untersuchungen zum Wasserhaushalt einiger Kulturpflanzen unter besonderer Berucksichtigung der Refraktometermethode. *Ber. Deut. Botan. Ges.* **77**, 243.

Önal, M. (1964b). Zusammensetzung des Zellsaftes einiger Salzmarschen- und Dünenpflanzen in der Umgebung Neapels. *Landwirtsch. Hochsch. Hohenheim* **30**, 89.

Ophir, M., Shmueli, E., and Moreshet, S. (1967). Stomatal infiltration measurements as an indicator of the water requirements and timing of irrigation for cotton. *Agron. J.* (in press).

Oppenheimer, H. R. (1935). Critical remarks on the value of Lloyd's alcohol fixation method for measuring stomatal aperture. *Palestine. J. Botany. Hort. Sci.* **1**, 43.

Oppenheimer, H. R. (1936). Remarks on two recent critical contributions concerning methods used in plant physiology. *Palestine J. Botany Hort Sci.* **1**, 84.

Oppenheimer, H. R. (1947). Studies on the water balance of unirrigated woody plants. *Palestine J. Botany Rehovot Ser.* **6**, 63.

Oppenheimer, H. R. (1949). Determination of stomatal opening in tomato. *Palestine J. Botany Rehovot Ser.* **7**, 63.

Oppenheimer, H. R. (1951). Physiological behaviour of maize under irrigation. *Palestine J. Botany Rehovot Ser.* **8**, 32.

Oppenheimer, H. R. (1954). Critique expérimentale de deux méthodes employées en vue d'établir le déficit de saturation hydrique (DSH) des feuilles. *Congr. Intern. Botan., 8th, Paris, 1954 Reps. Commun.*, Sect. **III** vol. prélim., p. 218.

Oppenheimer, H. R., and Elze, D. L. (1941). Irrigation of citrus trees according to physiological indicators. *Palestine J. Botany Rehovot Ser.* **4**, 20.

Oppenheimer, H. R., and Mendel, K. (1939). Orange leaf transpiration under orchard conditions. Pt. 1. Soil moisture high. *Palestine J. Botany Rehovot Ser.* **2**, 171.

Ordin, L., Applewhite, T. H., and Bonner, J. (1956). Auxin-induced water uptake by *Avena* coleoptile sections. *Plant Physiol.* **31**, 44.

Pallas, J. E., Jr. (1965). Transpiration and stomatal opening with changes in carbon dioxide content of the air. *Science* **147**, 171.

Pallas, J. E., Jr., Bertrand, A. R., Harris, D. G., Elkins, C. B., Jr., and Parks, C. L. (1965). Research in plant transpiration: 1962. *U.S. Dept. Agr. Prod. Res. Rept.* **87**.

Palmer, J. H., Trickett, E. S., and Linacre, E. T. (1964). Transpiration response of *Atriplex nummularia Lindl.* and upland cotton vegetation to soil–moisture stress. *Agr. Met.* **1**, 282.

Parker, J. (1963a). Causes of the winter decline in transpiration and photosynthesis in some evergreens. *Forest Sci.* **9**, 158.

Parker, J. (1963b). Comparison of some methods of determining stomatal opening. *Plant Physiol.* **38** (Suppl.), xlviii.

Peck, A. J., and Rabbidge, R. M. (1966a). Soil-water potential: direct measurement by a new technique. *Science* **151**, 1385.

Peck, A. J., and Rabbidge, R. M. (1966b). *Australia, CSIRO, Conf. Instrumentation Plant Evironment Measurements, Aspendale* 1966 p. 20. Society of Instrument Technology, Melbourne.

Petinov, N. S., and Shaidurov, V. S. (1964). Determination of irrigation interval from physiological indices. *Plant Physiol.* (*USSR*) (*Engl. Transl.*) **10**, 605.

Petrov, A. P. (1962). The gravimetric method of studying the kinetics of the exosmosis of water from living plant tissues. *Botan. Zh.* **47**, 368.

Phillis, E., and Mason, T. G. (1945). Studies on the foliar hydration in the cotton plant. VI. A gel theory of cell-water relations. *Ann, Botany* (*London*) [N. S.] **9**, 36.

Plaut, Z., and Ordin, L. (1961). Effect of soil moisture content on the cell wall metabolism of sunflower and almond leaves. *Physiol. Plantarum* **14**, 646.

Pollard, E., and Davidson, W. L. (1951). "Applied Nuclear Physics." Wiley, New York.

Polster, H. (1965). *In* "Water Stress in Plants" (B. Slavik, ed.) Proc. Symp. Prague, 1963, p. 228. Czech. Acad. Sci, Prague.

Popova, E. A., and Matveeva, U. S. (1964). Water relations of wilt-afflicted cotton. *Plant Physiol.* (*USSR*) Engl. Transl.) **10**, 571.

Post, B. W. (1962). Effects of light, soil moisture, and mineral nutrient treatments on the growth of seedlings of certain deciduous tree species. *Dissertation Abstr.* **24**, 13

Prager, D. J., and Bowman, R. L. (1963). Freezing point depression: new method for measuring ultramicro quantities of fluids. *Science* **142**, 237.

Pringsheim, E. G. (1931). Untersuchungen über Turgordehnung und Membranbeschaffenheit. *Jahrb. Wiss. Botan.* **74**, 749.

Rahman, A, A. A., Kuiper, P. J. C., and Bierhuizen, J. F. (1959). Preliminary observations on the effect of light intensity and photoperiod on transpiration and growth of young tomato plants under controlled conditions. *Mededel. Landbouwhogeschool. Wageningen* **59**, 1.

Ramsay, J. A., and Brown, R. H. J. (1955). Simplified apparatus and procedure for freezing-point determinations upon small volumes of liquid. *J. Sci. Instr.* **32**, 372.

Raschke, K. (1965). The soap-bubble porometer (measuring stomatal aperture in amphistomatic leaves). *Planta* **66**, 113.

Rastorgueva, L. I. (1964). After-effect of cooling of the root systems on synthesis of protein in leaves. *Plant Physiol.* (*USSR*) (*Engl. Transl.*) **11**, 607.

Rawlins, S. L. (1963). Resistance to water flow in the transpiration stream. *Conn. Agr. Expt. Sta. New Haven, Bull.* **664**, 69.

Rawlins, S. L. (1964). Systematic error in leaf water potential measurements with a thermocouple psychrometer. *Science* **146**, 644.

Rawlins, S. L. (1966). Theory for thermocouple psychrometers used to measure water potential in soil and plant samples. *Agr. Meteorol.* **3**, 293.

Rees, A. R. (1961). Midday closure of stomata in the oil palm *Elaeis guineensis* Jacq. *J. Exptl. Botany* **12**, 129.

Rehder, H. (1961). Saugkraftmessungen an mediterranen Immergrünen mit der Schardakow-Methode. *Ber. Deut. Botan. Ges.* **74**, 84.

Rehder, H., and Kreeb, K. (1961). Verleichende Untersuchungen zur Bestimmung der Blattsaugspannung mit der gravimetrischen Methode und der Schardakow-Methode. *Ber. Deut. Botan. Ges.* **74**, 95.

Reinhold, L., and Glinka, Z. (1966). Reduction in turgor pressure as a result of extremely brief exposure to CO_2. *Plant Physiol.* **41**, 39.

Renner, O. (1911). Experimentelle Beiträge zur Kenntnis der Wasserbewegung. *Flora (Jena)* **103**, 171.

Renner, O. (1915). Theoretisches und Experimentelles zur Kohäsionstheorie der Wasserbewegung. *Jahrb. Wiss. Botan.* **56**, 647.

Richards, B. G. (1965a). *In* "Moisture Equilibria and Moisture Changes in Soils Beneath Covered Areas: a Symposium in Print," p. 47. Butterworth, Sydney.

Richards, B. G. (1965b). Thermistor hygrometer for determining the free energy of moisture in unsaturated soils. *Nature* **208**, 608.

Richards, B. G. (1965c). A thermistor hygrometer for the direct measurement of the free energy of soil moisture. *Australia, CSIRO, Soil Mechanics Sect. Tech. Rept.* **5**.

Richards, L. A. (1965a). Physical condition of water in soils *Agronomy Monographs* **9**, Part 1, 128.

Richards, L. A. (1965b). Metallic conduction for cooling a thermocouple psychrometer bath. *Soil Sci.* **100**, 20.

Richards, L. A., and Campbell, R. B. (1948). Use of thermistors for measuring the freezing point of solutions and soils. *Soil Sci.* **65**, 429.

Richards, L. A., and Ogata, G. (1958). Thermocouple for vapor pressure measurements in biological and soil systems at high humidity. *Science* **128**, 1089.

Rider, N. E., and Bradley, E. F. (1962). Digitization and integration of reflecting galvanometer deflections. *Rev. Sci. Instr.* **33**, 25.

Robinson, R. A., and Stokes, R. H. (1959). "Electrolyte Solutions," 2nd ed. Butterworth, London and Washington, D.C.

Rodionov, V. S. (1962). Possibility of determination of the rate and time of irrigation on the basis of the cell sap concentration in maize. *Plant Physiol. (USSR) Engl. Transl.*) **9**, 66.

Roepke, R. R., and Baldes, E. J. (1938). A critical study of the thermoelectric method of measuring vapor pressure. *J. Biol. Chem.* **126**, 349.

Routley, D. G. (1966). Proline accumulation in wilted Ladino clover leaves. *Crop Sci.* **6**, 358.

Ruesink, A. W., and Thimann, K. V. (1965). The preparation of *Avena* coleoptile protoplasts and some aspects of their physiology. *Plant Physiol.* **40** (Suppl.), lx.

Ruf, R. H., Jr., Eckert, R. E., Jr., and Gifford, R. O. (1963). Osmotic adjustment of cell sap to increases in root medium osmotic stress. *Soil Sci.* **96**, 326.

Russell, A. (1963). An inexpensive thermocouple-scanner using gold-plated relays. *Control* **6** (Sept.) p. 132.

Russell, M. B., and Richards, L. A. (1938). Heat of wetting of soils. *Proc. Iowa Acad. Sci.* **45**, 175.

Rutter, A. J., and Sands, K. (1958). The relation of leaf water deficit to soil moisture tension in *Pinus sylvestris* L. I. The effect of soil moisture on diurnal changes in water balance. *New Phytologist* **57**, 50.

Rychnovska, M., and Bartos, J. (1962). Measurement of photosynthesis by the dry weight increment of samples composed of leaf segments. *Biol. Plantarum* **4**, 91.

Rychnovska-Soudkova, M. (1963). Study of the reversibility of the water saturation deficit as one of the methods of causal phytogeography. *Biol Plantarum* **5**, 175.

Ryczkowski, M. (1960a). Observations on the osmotic value of the sap of the central vacuole of ovules. *Protoplasma* **11**, 657.

Ryczkowski, M. (1960b). Changes of osmotic value during development of the ovule. *Planta* **55**, 343.

Sabinin, D. A. (1925). On the root system as an osmotic apparatus. *Bull. Inst. Rech. Biol. Sta. Biol. Univ. Perm.* **4** (Suppl. 2), 1.

Sampson, J. (1961). A method of replicating dry or moist surfaces for examination by light microscopy. *Nature* **191**, 932.

Samuilov, F. D. (1965). A study of the interrelationship between respiration and absorption of water in corn plants with the aid of heavy water (D_2O). *Plant Physiol. (USSR) (Engl. Transl.)* **12**, 192.

Sands, K., and Rutter, A. J. (1958). The relation of leaf water deficit to soil moisture tension in *Pinus sylvestris* L. II. Variation in the relation caused by developmental and environmental factors. *New Phytologist* **57**, 387.

Satoo, T. (1962). *In* " Tree Growth " (Kozlowski, T. T. ed.), p. 299. Ronald Press, New York

Scheumann, W. (1965). *In* "Water Stress in Plants " (B. Slavik, ed.), Proc. Symp. Prague, 1963, p. 99. Czech. Acad. Sci., Prague.

Schläfli, A. (1964). Über die Eignung der Refraktometer—und der Schardakowmethode zur Messung osmotischer Zustandsgrossen. *Protoplasma* **58**, 75.

Schmidt-Nielsen, B., and Schrauger, C. R. (1963). *Amoeba proteus*: studying the contractile vacuole. *Science* **139**, 606.

Scholander, P. F., Hammel, H. T., Hemmingsen, E., and Garey, W. (1962). Salt balance in mangroves. *Plant Physiol.* **37**, 722.

Scholander, P. F., Hammel, H. T., Hemmingsen, E. A., and Bradstreet, E. D. (1964). Hydrostatic pressure and osmotic potential in leaves of mangroves and some other plants. *Proc. Natl. Acad. Sci. U.S.* **52**, 119.

Scholander, P. F., Hammel, H. T., Bradstreet, E. D., and Hemmingsen, E. A. (1965). Sap pressure in vascular plants. *Science* **148**, 339.

Scholander, P. F., Bradstreet, E. D., Hammel, H. T., and Hemmingsen, E. A. (1966). Sap concentrations in halophytes and some other plants. *Plant Physiol* **41**, 529.

Schorn, M. (1929). Untersuchungen über die Verwendbarkeit der Alkohol fixierungs und Infiltrations methode zur Messung von Spaltöffnungs-weiten. *Jahrb. Wiss. Botan.* **71**, 783.

Shardakov, V. S. (1938). Determination of sucking force of vegetal tissues by the method of streamlets (small jets). *Izv. Akad. Nauk SSSR Ser. Biol.* (5-6), 1297.

Shaw, L. (1933). A method for determining the relative humidity in the intercellular spaces of living plant tissues. *Am. J. Botany* **10**, 675.

Shepherd, W. (1964). Diffusion pressure deficit and turgidity relationships of detached leaves of *Trifolium repens* L. *Australian J. Agr. Res.* **15**, 746.

Shillo, R., and Halevy, A. H. (1964). Experiments in the irrigation of gladioli according to absorption of viscous fluid through stomata. *Israel. J. Agr. Res.* **14**, 89.

Shimshi, D. (1963). Effect of chemical closure of stomata on transpiration in varied soil and atmospheric environments. *Plant Physiol.* **38**, 709.

Shimshi, D. (1964). The use of a field porometer for the study of water stress in plants. *Israel. J. Agr. Res.* **14**, 137.

Shimshi, D. (1967). Some aspects of stomatal behaviour, as observed by means of an improved pressure-drop porometer. *Israel J. Botany* **16** (in press).

Shmueli, E. (1953). Irrigation studies in the Jordan Valley. I. Physiological activity of the banana in relation to soil moisture. *Bull. Res. Council. Israel, Sect. D* **3**, 228.

Shmueli, E. (1964). The use of physiological indicators for the timing of irrigation. *Contrib. Natl. Univ. Inst. Agr. Rehovot, Israel*, 1964, Ser. 677-E.

Shmueli, E., and Cohen, O. P. (1964). A critique of Walter's hydrature concept and of his evaluation of water status measurements. *Israel J. Botany* **13**, 199.

Shou-Ju, O. (1963). A physiological characteristic of drought resistance of certain grape varieties. *Plant Physiol.* (*USSR*) (*Engl. Transl.*) **9**, 564.

Singh, R., and Alderfer, R. B. (1966). Effects of soil-moisture stress at different periods of growth of some vegetable crops. *Soil Sci.* **101**, 69.

Siri, W. E. (1949). "Isotopic Tracers and Nuclear Radiations," p. 58. McGraw-Hill, New York.

Skidmore, E. L., and Stone, J. F. (1964). Physiological role in regulating transpiration rate of the cotton plant. *Agron. J.* **56**, 405.

Slatyer, R. O. (1955). Studies of the water relations of crop plants grown under natural rainfall in northern Australia. *Australian J. Agr. Res.* **6**, 365.

Slatyer, R. O. (1957). Plant response to soil moisture stress. *Australian J. Biol. Sci.* **10**, 320.

Slatyer, R. O. (1958). The measurement of diffusion pressure deficit in plants by a method of vapour equilibration. *Australian J. Biol. Sci.* **11**, 349.

Slatyer, R. O. (1960). Aspects of the tissue relationships of an important arid zone species (*Acacia aneura, F. Muell.*) in comparison with two mesophytes. *Bull. Res. Council Israel, Sect. D* **8**, 159.

Slatyer, R. O. (1961). Internal water balance of *Acacia aneura F. Muell.* in relation to environmental conditions. *UNESCO Arid. Zone. Res.* **16**, 137.

Slatyer, R. O. (1962). Internal water relations of higher plants. *Ann. Rev. Plant Physiol.* **13**, 351.

Slatyer, R. O. (1965). Commentary on an abstract of the physiology of irrigated agricultural plants by N. S. Petinov. *Field. Crop. Abstr.* **18**, 1.

Slatyer, R. O. (1966). An underlying cause of measurement discrepancies in determination of osmotic characteristics in plant cells and tissues. *Protoplasma* **62**, 34.

Slatyer, R. O., and Lake, J. V. (1966). Resistance to water transport in plants—whose misconception? *Nature* **212**, 1585.

Slatyer, R. O., and McIlroy, I. C. (1961). "Practical Microclimatology," *CSIRO*. Australia for UNESCO.

Slatyer, R. O., and Taylor, S. A. (1961). Terminology in plant- and soil-water relations. *Nature* **187**, 922.

Slavik, B. (1959a). Gradients of osmotic pressure of cell sap in the area of one leaf blade. *Biol. Plantarum* **1**, 39.

Slavik, B. (1959b). The relation of the refractive index of plant cell sap to its osmotic pressure. *Biol. Plantarum* **1**, 48.

Slavik, B. (1963a). The distribution pattern of transpiration rate, water saturation deficit, stomata number and size, photosynthetic and respiration rate in the area of the tobacco leaf blade. *Biol. Plantarum* **5**, 143.

Slavik, B. (1963b). Relationship between the osmotic potential of cell sap and the water saturation deficit during the wilting of leaf tissue. *Biol. Plantarum* **5**, 258.

Slavik, B. (1965). *In* "Water Stress in Plants" (B. Slavik, ed.), Proc. Symp. Prague, 1963, p. 195. Czech. Acad. Sci., Prague.

Slavik, B. (1966). *In* "The Growth of Cereals and Grasses" (F. L. Milthorpe and J. D. Ivins, eds.), p. 227. Butterworth, London and Washington, D.C.

Solarova, J. (1965). *In* "Water Stress in Plants" (B. Slavik, ed.), Proc. Symp. Prague, 1963, p. 147. Czech. Acad. Sci. Prague.

Spanner, D. C. (1951). The Peltier effect and its use in the measurement of suction pressure. *J. Exptl. Botany* **2**, 145.

Specht, H. (1959). Welding device for thin thermo-couples. *Z. Metallk.* **50**, 36.

Spomer, G. G. (1964). Preliminary studies of a method for monitoring moisture tensions in woody stems. *Plant Physiol.* **39** (Suppl.), xlii.

Stahl, E. (1894). Einige Versuche über Transpiration und Assimilation. *Botan. Ztg.* **52**, 117.

Stålfelt, M. G. (1932). Der stomätare Regulator in der pflanzlichen Transpiration. *Planta* **17**, 22.

Stålfelt, M. G. (1955). The stomata as a hydrophotic regulator of the water deficit of the plant. *Physiol. Plantarum* **8**, 572.

Stålfelt, M. G. (1961). The effect of the water deficit on the stomatal movements in a carbon dioxide-free atmosphere. *Physiol. Plantarum* **14**, 826.

Stålfelt, M. G. (1963). Diurnal dark reactions in the stomatal movements. *Physiol. Plantarum* **16**, 756.

Startseva, A. V. (1964). Relation of water regime to nitrogen metabolism in leaves of spring wheat as associated with drought resistance. *Uch. Zap. Kazansk. Gos. Univ.* **124**, 200.

Stefanoff, B. (1931). Studien über den Zustand und die Schwankungen des Wassergehaltes in den Blättern und Zweigen einiger Holzpflanzen. *Fortswiss. Centr.* **75**, 784.

Stiles, W. (1966). Stomatal resistance. *Ann. Rept. Rothamsted Expt. Sta.* **1965**, 30.

Stocker, O. (1928). Das Wasserhaushalt ägyptischer Wüsten- und Salzpflanzen. *Botan. Abhandl.* **13**.

Stocker, O. (1929a). Vizsgálatok különbozo termöhelyon nött növények rizhianyának nagyságáról. Über die Höhe des Wasserdefizites bei Pflanzen verschiedener Standorte. *Erdészeti. Kisérl.* **31**, 63, 104.

Stocker, O. (1929b). Das Wasserdefizit von Gefasspflanzen in verschledenen Klimazonen. *Planta* **7**, 382.

Stover, C. M. (1960). Method of butt welding small thermocouples 0.001 to 0.010 inch in diameter. *Rev. Sci. Instr.* **31**, 605.

Stow, I. (1936). On the osmotic work of a plant cell and its elasticity. *Botan. Zool.* **4**, 1336.

Sveshnikova, V. M. (1965). *In* "Water Stress in Plants" (B. Slavik, ed.), Proc. Symp. Prague, 1963, p. 268. Czech. Akad. Sci., Prague.

Sykes, S. M., and Coote, G. G. (1962). The rapid estimation of moisture in dried apples. *Australia, CSIRO, Div. Food Preserv. Tech. Paper.* **29**.

Tanner, C. B. (1963). Plant Temperatures. *Agron. J.* **55**, 210.

Taylor, R. M. (1965). Germination of seeds and growth of plants as affected by differing moisture tensions. *Dissertation Abstr.* **25**, 6144.

Taylor, S. A. (1964). Water condition and flow in the soil-plant-atmosphere system. *Am. Soc. Agron. Spec. Publ.* **5**, 81.

Tazawa, M. (1957). A new method of measuring the osmotic value of a cell. *Protoplasma* **48**, 342.

Teele, R. P., and Schuhmann, S. (1939). A potentiometer for measuring voltages of 10 microvolts to an accuracy of 0.01 microvolt. *J. Res. Natl. Bur. Std. A* **22**, 431.

Thimann, K. V., Loos, G. M., and Samuel, E. W. (1960). Penetration of mannitol into potato discs. *Plant Physiol.* **35**, 848.

Thoday, D. (1909). Experimental researches on vegetable assimilation and respiration V. A critical examination of Sach's method for using increase of dry weight as a measure of CO_2 assimilation in leaves. *Proc. Roy. Soc.* **B82**, 1.

Thomas, A. M. (1966). *In situ* measurement of moisture in soil and similar substances by 'fringe' capacitance. *J. Sci. Instr.* **43**, 21.

Thut, H. F. (1938). Relative humidity variations affecting transpiration. *Am. J. Botany* **25**, 589.

Till, M. R. (1965). Methods of timing irrigations with particular reference to horticultural crops. *J. Australian. Inst. Agr. Sci.* **31**, 196.

Till, M. R. (1966). Diffusion pressure deficit measurements as a means of timing irrigation for tomatoes. *Australian J. Exptl. Agr. Animal. Husbandry* **6**, 66.

Ting, I. P., and Loomis, W. E. (1963). Diffusion through stomata. *Am. J. Botany* **50**, 866.

Tinklin, R., and Weatherley, P. E. (1966). On the relationship between transpiration rate and leaf water potential. *New Phytologist* **65**, 509.

Todd, G. W., Ingram, F. W., and Stutte, C. A. (1962). Relative turgidity as an indicator of drouth stress in cereal plants. *Proc. Oklahoma Acad. Sci.* **42**, 55.

Totsuka, T., and Monsi, M. (1959). Effect of water economy on plant growth. I. Influence of water level lowering on the growth of water-cultured tobacco plants. *Botan. Mag. (Tokyo)* **72**, 367.

Totsuka, T., and Monsi, M. (1960). Effect of water economy on plant growth. 2. An analysis of water economy of water-cultured tobacco plants. *Botan. Mag. (Tokyo)* **73**, 14.

Totsuka, T., Oshima, T., and Monsi, M. (1960). Effect of water economy on plant growth. 3. Effect of partial excision of root system on the dry matter production of sunflower plant. *Botan. Mag. (Tokyo)* **73**, 389.

Tranquillini, W. (1963). The dependence of carbon-dioxide assimilation by young larch, spruce and cembra pine trees on air humidity and soil moisture. Experiments in a climate-controlled wind tunnel. *Planta* **60**, 70.

Trickett, E. S., and Barrs, H. D. (1967). *Australia, CSIRO, Irrigation Res. Lab. Ann. Rept. 1966-1967*, 34.

Trip, P., Krotkov, G., and Nelson, C. D. (1964). Metabolism of mannitol in higher plants. *Am. J. Botany* **51**, 828.

Tukey, L. D. (1959). Periodicity in growth of fruits of apples, peaches and sour cherries, with some factors influencing this development. *Penn. State Univ. Agr. Expt. Sta. Bull.* **661**.

Tukey, L. D. (1963). Electronics record fruit growth. *Sci. Farmer* **11**, 3.

Tukey, L. D. (1964). A linear electronic device for continuous measurement and recording of fruit enlargement and contraction. *Proc. Am. Soc. Hort. Sci.* **84**, 653.

Tyurina, M. M. (1957). The effect of negative turgor pressure on the moisture retaining capacity of leaves. *Botan. Zh.* **42**, 1035.

Ulehla, J., Zichova, L., and Banoch, Z. (1965). Influence of soil heterogeneity on water regime and yields of lucerne, sugar beet and wheat. *Biol. Plantarum* **7**, 449.

Ursprung, A. (1915). Über die Kohäsion des Wassers im Farnannulus. *Ber. Deut. Botan. Ges.* **33**, 153.

Ursprung, A. (1923). Zur Kenntnis der Saugkraft. VII. Eine neue vereinfachte Methode zur Messung der Saugkraft. *Ber. Deut. Botan. Ges.* **41**, 338.

Ursprung, A. (1929). The osmotic quantities of the plant cell. *Proc. Intern. Congr. Plant Sci.* **2**, 1081.

Ursprung, A., and Blum, G. (1916). Zur methode der Sangkraftmessung. *Ber. Deut. Botan. Ges.* **34**, 525.

Ursprung, A., and Blum, G. (1927). Eine Methode zur Messung der Saugkraft von Hartlaub. *Jahrb. Wiss. Bot.* **67**, 334.

Ursprung, A., and Blum, G. (1930). Zwei neue Saugkraft-Messmethoden. I. Die Kapillar-methode zur Messung der statischen Saugkraft von Flussigkeiten, Quellkorpen und Böden. II. Die Hebelmethode zur Messung der Saugkraft von Hartlaub und anderen schweirigen Objeckten. *Jahrb. Wiss. Bot.* **72**, 254.

Vaadia, Y., Raney, F. C., and Hagan, R. M. (1961). Plant water deficits and physiological processes. *Ann. Rev. Plant. Physiol.* **12**, 265.

Vaclavik, J. (1964). Investigation of water supply conditions of plants using determination of cell sap osmotic pressure by means of refractometry. *Sb. Cesk. Akad. Zemedel. Ved, Rostlinna Vyroba* **12**, 1255-60.

van Andel, O. M. (1952). Determination of the osmotic value of exudation sap by means of the thermoelectric method of Baldes and Johnson. *Koninkl Ned. Akad. Wetenschap. Proc. Ser. C* **55**, 40.

van den Honert, T. H. (1935). Eine Methode zur Bestimmung von osmotischen Grössen mittels den Dampfspannung. *7th Ned-Indie Natuurw. Congr.* p. 482.

van Overbeek, J. (1942). Water uptake by excised root systems of the tomato due to non-osmotic forces. *Am. J. Botany* **31**, 265.

Virgin, H. I. (1955). A new method for the determination of the turgor of plant tissues. *Physiol. Plantarum* **8**, 954.

Virgin. H. I. (1965). Chlorophyll formation and water deficit. *Physiol. Plantarum* **18**, 994.

Wager, H. G. (1957). The effect of artificial wilting on the CO_2 production of developing pea seeds. *New Phytologist* **56**, 230.

Waggoner, P. E., and Zelitch, I. (1965). Transpiration and the stomata of leaves. *Science* **150**, 1413.

Waister, P. D. (1963). Equipment for measuring water stress in leaves. *Univ. Nottingham, Dept. Hort., Misc. Publ.* **15**.

Waister, P. D. (1964). An improved thermocouple for assessing leaf water potential by vapour pressure measurement. *Israel J. Botan.* **12**, 192.

Waister, P. D. (1965). Precision of thermocouple psychrometers for measuring leaf water potential. *Nature* **205**, 922.

Wallihan, E. F. (1964). Modification and use of an electric hygrometer for estimating relative stomatal apertures. *Plant Physiol.* **39**, 86.

Walter, H. (1931). " Die Hydratur der Pflanze. " Fisher, Jena.

Walter, H. (1963a). Zur Klärung des spezifischen Wasserzustandes im Plasma und in der Zellwand bei der höheren Pflanze und seine Bestimmung. Teil I. Allgemeines. *Ber. Deut. Botan. Ges.* **76**, 40.

Walter, H. (1963b). Zur Klärung des spezifischen Wasserzustandes im Plasma und in der Zellwand bei der höheren Pflanze und seine Bestimmung. Teil II. Methodisches. *Ber. Deut. Botan. Ges.* **76**, 54.

Walter, H. (1966). Remarks on the critique of the hydrature concept by E. Shmueli and O. P. Cohen. *Israel J. Botan.* **15**, 35.

Weatherley, P. E. (1947). Note on the diurnal fluctuations in water content of floating leaf disks. *New Phytologist* **46**, 276.

Weatherley, P. E. (1950). Studies in the water relations of the cotton plant. I. The field measurement of water deficits in leaves. *New Phytologist* **49**, 81.

Weatherley, P. E. (1951). Studies of the water relations of the cotton plant, II. Diurnal and seasonal variations in relative turgidity and environmental factors. *New Phytologist* **50**, 36.

Weatherley, P. E. (1954. Uptake of sugar by floating leaf discs. *New Phytologist* **53**, 204.

Weatherley, P. E. (1960). A new micro-osmometer. *J. Exptl. Botan.* **11**, 258.

Weatherley, P. E. (1965). The state and movement of water in the leaf. *Symp. Soc. Exptl. Biol.* **19**, 157.

Weatherley, P. E. (1966). A porometer for use in the field. *New Phytologist* **65**, 378.

Weatherley, P. E., and Slatyer, R. O. (1957). Relationship between relative turgidity and diffusion pressure deficit in leaves. *Nature* **179**, 1085.

Wecksler, O. S. (1963). Electric butt-welding of platinum wires. *J. Sci. Instr.* **40**, 543.

Werner, H. O. (1954). Influence of atmospheric and soil moisture conditions on diurnal variations in relative turgidity of potato leaves. *Univ. Nebraska Agr. Expt. Sta. Bull.* **176**.

Whiteman, P. C., and Koller, D. (1964). Saturation deficit of the mesophyll evaporating surface in a desert halophyte. *Science* **146**, 1320.

Whiteman, P. C., and Wilson, G. L. (1963). Estimation of diffusion pressure deficit by correlation with relative turgidity and beta-ray absorption. *Australian J. Biol. Sci.* **16**, 140.

Wiebe, H. H. (1966). Matric potential of several plant tissues and biocolloids. *Plant Physiol.* **41**, 1439.

Wiebe, H. H., and Wihrheim, S. E. (1962). The influence of internal moisture stress on translocation. *Proc. Symp. Use Radioisotopes Soil-Plant Nutrition Studies.* Intern. Atomic Energy Agency, Vienna. (Intern. Publ., New York.)

Wilkins, D. E., James, P. E., and Menear, J. R. (1964). Silage density measured by gamma energy attenuation. *Trans. Am. Soc. Agr. Engrs.* **7**, 213.

Wilson, A. M., and Huffaker, (1964). Effects of moisture stress on acid-soluble phosphorus compounds in *Trifolium subterraneum*. *Plant Physiol.* **39**, 555.

Wilson, C. C., Boggess, W. R., and Kramer, P. J. (1953). Diurnal fluctuations in the moisture content of some herbaceous plants. *Am. J. Botany* **40**, 97.

Woods, F. W., Hough, W. A., O'Neal, D., and Barnett, J. (1965). Gamma-ray attenuation by loblolly pine wood: an investigation of intergral counting. *Forest Sci.* **11**, 341.

Woolley, J. T. (1964). Water relations of soybean leaf hairs. *Agron. J.* **56**, 569.

Wormer, T. M., and Ochs, R. (1959). Soil moisture, opening of the stomata and transpiration of oil palm and groundnuts. *Oléagineux* **14**, 571.

Yamada, Y., Tamai, S., and Miyaguchi, T. (1961). The measurement of the thickness of leaves using S^{35}. *Proc. 2nd Japan. Conf. Radioisotopes*, 1958 (U.S. AEC-tr-44 82,), p. 1692.

Yemm, E. W., and Willis, A. J. (1954). Stomatal movements and changes of carbohydrate in leaves of *Chrysanthemum maximum*. *New Phytologist* **53**, 373.

Yoda, S. (1961). Effect of auxin and gibberellin on osmotic value of pea stem sections. *Plant Cell Physiol.* **2**, 435.

Zelitch, I. (1961). Biochemical control of stomatal opening in leaves. *Proc. Natl. Acad. Sci. U.S.* **47**, 1423.

Zemlyanukhin, A. A. (1964). Effect of ascorbic acid on water metabolism in plants. *Plant Physiol.* (*USSR*) (*Engl. Transl.*) **11**, 893.

Zholkevich, V. N., Xoller, V. A., and Kushirenko, S. V. (1962). After effect of cooling on the efficiency of respiration of cucumber leaves. *Plant Physiol.* (*USSR*) (*Engl. Transl.*) **9**, 278.

Zollinger, W. D., Campbell, G. S., and Taylor, S. A. (1966). A comparison of water potential measurements made using two types of themocouple psychrometer. *Soil Sci.* **102**, 231.

AUTHOR INDEX

Numbers in italics indicate the pages on which the complete references are cited.

Subject Index

A

Abscission of leaves, 209, 210
Absorption coefficient, 69
Absorption of water, 4, 129–131
Absorptivity, 69
Acceleration of gravity, 60, 76
Actinomycetes, 200
Active uptake
  ions, 334
  sucrose, 276
  water, 272, 273
Adiabatic profile, 87
ADP, 40
Adsorption, 30
Adsorption potential, 110
Advection, 89, 90, 186, 188
Aerial roots, 217
Aerodynamic formulas, 88
Air embolism, 152
Akinetes, 197
Albedo, 96
Alcohols, 16, 28, 214
Aldehydes, 16
Alkanes, 16
Alkenylsuccinic acid (ASA), 17, 18
Alkyl halides, 32
Aluminum, 227, 228
Amino acids, 29, 30, 32, 38, 228
Ammonia, 228
Ammonium chloride, 225
Anaerobiosis, 309
Anemometers, 79
Aneroid sphygmomanometer, 345
Annuli, 304, 307
Antitranspirants, 17, 18, 179, 228
Aphid-stylet technique, 332
Apoplast, 33, 34
Apparent free space (AFS), 330, 331
Argentol, 263
Ascent of sap, 151, 152
Ascospores, 200

Association-induction theory, 30
Atmometers, 74, 103
Atmosphere, 62
ATP, 40
Austrocknungsfähigkeit, 220
Austrocknungsresistenz, 220
Autofluorescence, 205
Auxograph, 255
Azide, 17

B

Backscattering, 261
Bacteria, 224
Bacteriophage, 29
Barger-Halket osmometer, 320
Bark transpiration, 219
Barometric pressure, 54
Beckman thermometer, 317
Bessel function, 127
Beta-ray gauging, 254, 255, 258–261
Beta radiation, 258
Biosphere, 68
Birefringence, 318
Bound water, 33, 44, 224, 225, 227
Bouyancy effects, 186
Bowen's ratio 76, 81, 85, 90, 91
Brownian movement, 26, 31, 32
Buffers, 156, 274
Bulbiform cells, 210
Bulk density, 162
Bulk flow, 141

C

Calcium, 31
Calorie, 63
Cambium, 15, 16, 216
Camera lucida, 265
Canopy resistance, 100